THE SURVIVAL OF THE

*The Highland Clearances
and the End of Isolation*

So long as there shall exist, by reason of law and custom, a social condemnation, which, in the face of civilization, artificially creates hells on earth, and complicates a destiny that is divine, with human fatality; so long as the three problems of the age – the degradation of man by poverty, the ruin of woman by starvation, and the dwarfing of childhood by physical and spiritual night – are not solved; so long as, in certain regions, social asphyxia shall be possible; so long as ignorance and misery remain on earth, books like this cannot be useless.

Victor Hugo, *Les Misérables*, Author's Preface.

THE SURVIVAL OF THE UNFITTEST

The Highland Clearances and the End of Isolation

Robert Mathieson

JOHN DONALD PUBLISHERS LTD
EDINBURGH

ISBN 0 85976 470 2

British Library Cataloguing in Publication Data

A catalogue record for this book is available
from the British Library.

Typesetting and origination by Brinnoven, Livingston
Printed and bound in Great Britain by Redwood Books, Trowbridge

Contents

Preface		ix
Acknowledgements		xiii
1	An Introduction to the 'Highland Problem'	1
2	The Making of A' Ghaidhealtachd	32
3	Am Fasgadh	48
4	Health	78
5	Nutrition	98
6	Ill-Health	124
7	The Most Prevalent Diseases	141
8	Eviction and Its Aftermath I	163
9	Eviction and Its Aftermath II	184
10	Gaeldom's Magna Carta	208
11	Legislated Health Care In the Highlands and Islands	225
12	The 'Thing' at Home	235
	Appendix A: *'The Dietaries of Scotch Agricultural Labourers', 1869*	244
	Appendix B: *Highlands and Islands Commission Report: Minutes of Evidence. [Vol I]*	247
	Appendix C: *Highlands and Islands Commission: Report by the Commissioners*	258
	Index of Subjects	263
	Index of Personal Names	267

Preface

Nullius addictus iurare in verba magistri
— Horace.[1]

(I am not bound to swear allegiance to the words of my master.)

This book was prompted by a friend in Cape Breton. She had just read an account of the Highland Clearances of the eighteenth and nineteenth centuries, from which she had concluded that the evictors must have been brutes.[2] Her judgement is understandable and ultimately it is not far wrong. But it does leave much unsaid. First, that the Clearances were not a time of outright war or bloody revolution. In fact, there is little evidence of violence during the whole of the century that they spanned. Moreover, many of the evictors were well-intentioned landlords who, in clearing their estates, sought simply to save themselves from financial ruin, or who in improving land management and agriculture believed the improvements to be beneficial to their tenant farmers no less than to themselves. Some landlords were indeed models of *noblesse oblige*, importing food for their tenants in times of want, financing parish charity, supporting health reform.

What is more, Highlanders themselves were not entirely blameless for the hardship that befell them. They resisted change, even when change was inevitable and might have profited them. They were passive, when participation might have influenced events or ameliorated their effects. And many Highland chiefs, seduced by the landowning elite they had joined, were as ruthless as any foreigner.

Yet an event can be brutal even when not violent and even though those it most harms bear some responsibility for it. The Clearances dispossessed a people, expelled them to wholly inadequate sites and condemned them to misery and disease. In that sense, my friend was right: the Clearances were brutal, and the evictors, though not sadistic, were in the main ruthless and rapacious. Beginning in the fourteenth century, ancestral clan lands in the Highlands and Islands of Scotland were granted to noblemen, Englishmen, Lowland Scots, even acculturated Highland chiefs, and to other friends of the English and Scottish courts. That feudal system of land ownership and the freehold ownership that evolved from it marked the demise of the ancient clan system: whereas Highlanders had once looked to their clan chiefs for protection, stability and egalitarian leadership, they had in the feudal and freehold systems nothing more than a tenant's tenuous claim to land.

The Clearances demonstrated just how tenuous that claim was. In that period, proprietors decided that their estates could turn more profit as sheep walks and deer preserves than as farms. To depopulate their estates would do more than make room for sheep and deer: it would relieve landowners of the burden of supporting their Highland tenants, their families always large and always poor. Highlanders were uprooted and relocated, at a pace and to sites determined solely by their landlords. The pace was too rapid, the new sites overcrowded, unsanitary and unsuitable even for subsistence farming. Destitution and disease were inevitable, as they were for evicted Highlanders who sought employment in the new manufacturing centres of Lowland Scotland and England. This book recounts the traumatic changes that the Clearances wrought, in lifestyle generally, and more particularly, in health and disease patterns, and it examines those movements, religious, medical and political, which from the early eighteenth century began to rally Highlanders in their own defence and effect land and health reforms.

To understand the effects of the Clearances, we must begin some distance back from the event. Thus Chapter 1 is an overview of the process and effects of acculturation in the Highlands and Islands. Chapter 2 examines in some detail the making of *A' Ghaidhealtachd* by those forces, geological, topographical, climatic and cultural, which shaped the Highland niche. Chapter 3 describes the two fundamentally different systems of land ownership we have mentioned, communal clan ownership and feudal tenure, and their implications for the social organization of the Highland household and community. Those topics, the ecology of the place and the politics of land ownership, are not the primary focus of this book: many others have written of them eloquently and in much greater detail. Yet I devote two chapters to them because they were, as I hope to show, instrumental in determining health and disease.

The next five chapters, 4 through 8, are the heart of this narrative: they discuss, respectively, nutrition, health and disease in the Highlands and Islands of the eighteenth and nineteenth centuries. More specifically, three of these chapters, 6 through 8, examine those diseases reported at the time as being most prevalent, as well as others that we now know were certain to have afflicted the area. Throughout, I have quoted first-hand accounts of illness and disease, the observations of parish ministers and other residents and travellers in the region. In fact, because those primary sources are not readily available to the general public, I quote many at considerable length and provide others in extensive end-notes. These chapters draw necessarily on two medical specialties, pathology and microbiology, though in language which I hope is sensible to lay readers.

Chapters 9, 10 and 11 discuss those reforms in religion, land tenure, and medicine and health care which, in the century after the Clearances, began to rectify the grossest injustices of that event. Chapter 12 describes the ideological conflict that raged during that century, the clash between socialist reformers and capitalist Establishmentarians, out of which came social and political reform, albeit reform delayed and hobbled by an entrenched and potent elite.

Notes

1 Epistles, I.i.14.
2 David Craig, *On the Crofters' Trail: In Search of the Clearance Highlanders*, London, Jonathan Cape, 1990.

ACKNOWLEDGEMENTS

For their contribution to the making of this book, I am indebted first to those who stimulated my interest in my homeland and its culture: the late Wing Commander D.D. MacSwein, *OBE*, a former Commanding Officer and Gaelic scholar, who excited my love for the Land of Lorn and its history; and Norman Macdonald, former Professor of Celtic Studies, UCCB, now with the BBC Gaelic Radio Service, Isle of Skye, and his wife, Kenna, both of whom taught me so much in Cape Breton and who in Portree continued their hospitality by introducing me to the culture and the people of the Islands.

I am especially grateful to the many Highlanders whom I met during three decades of studying the archaeological sites of mainland Scotland and the Inner and Outer Isles, men and women who gave time and talk freely. On the Isle of Skye, I am indebted particularly to Angus Lockhart, crofter of Earlish, for a practical introduction to the socio-economics of modern crofting; to Donald Stewart, formerly of Dunvegan Castle, whose family were crofters at Greep, for making the ruins of deserted communities come alive. Finally, to Dr James Hunter, I share the indebtedness of all interested in the Highland Problem, for his book, *The Making of the Crofting Community,* and for his friendship, advice and the hospitality of his croft at Borve. In the North West, my thanks go to John MacKenzie of Culkein, Drumbeg. A former vice president of the North Assynt Crofters Association and now secretary to the Board of the Assynt Crofters Trust, Mr Mackenzie took time out, invariably at lambing time, from his 'retirement' as a crofter, campaign leader and elder of the Free Church to discuss many facets of the Highland Problem. He also reviewed the sketch of religious history in Chapter 9. In Inverness, John A. MacKenzie, BVMS, MRCVS, Veterinary Officer, Animal Health Office, confirmed my interpretations of early descriptions of diseases and drew my attention to the emergence of new diseases occurring at the human/animal interface.

I am indebted also to those who supported my early determination to write: Allan E. Marble, Associate Professor of Surgery, Dalhousie University, Halifax, for encouraging me to continue my research and John Farley,

Professor of Biology, also at Dalhousie University, for convincing me of the logic of writing a book rather than a thesis. The book would not have been written, however, but for the encouragement given by John Norris, Professor Emeritus of the History of Medicine, University of British Columbia, whose patience, academic expertise and review of early manuscripts were invaluable.

My teachers at UCCB set the stage for the multidisciplinary approach in this account of the Highland Problem. The faculty of the Graduate School of History at Guelph patiently endured this 'mature' student's reluctant conversion to the tempo of a graduate department; in particular, Dr Ronald M. Sunter, my supervisor, gave advice, friendship and the hospitality of his home, and Edward J. Cowan, Professor of Scottish History, now Professor of Scottish History, Glasgow University, patiently guided my struggle to grasp the significance of *The People's Past*.

Two friends influenced the theme of this book. The late Professor Sir Alastair Currie suggested fruitful avenues of research and offered encouragement. The Sixth Baronet of Lochalsh, the late Major Sir Torquhil Matheson of Matheson, furnished unique insights into the Highland Problem and convinced me that possession and improvement of Highland land was possible only for those with access to wealth.

I am grateful also to others: librarians in Canada and the United Kingdom, especially Ms Laura R. Peverill MLS, of UCCB; Mr Russell Walker, Commissioning Editor of John Donald Publishers Ltd, for his guidance; Donald E. Tryon, whose expertise in computer technology eased my entry into the world of word processing; Ms Patricia Campbell MA, my editor, who introduced me to the world of true 'word processing'; Jessie MacLeod, DD, of Baddeck, Cape Breton, a descendant of emigrant Highland settlers and a friend; my parents, who struggled to make my odyssey possible, and my wife, Marion, for her constant support.

Robert Mathieson
Sydney, Nova Scotia

1

An Introduction to the 'Highland Problem'

Change is inevitable. In a progressive country change is constant.[1]

THE 'HIGHLAND PROBLEM' of the eighteenth and nineteenth centuries had its roots hundreds of years earlier when, at the end of the tenth century, the power base in Scotland, hitherto Celtic, was moved from Dunadd in the south-west Highland region to Scone in the south-east. The move was strategic, designed to escape the marauding Vikings then colonizing the islands and parts of the mainland.

Over the next few centuries, Norse colonization and English influence produced in the Islands and in Southern Scotland a cultural amalgam very different from the culture of Gaeldom in the West Highlands and Islands. The cultural differences among Gaeldom, England, and the newly formed Scotland gave rise over the next five centuries to mutual mistrust, with Gaeldom forging no permanent alliance with either Scotland or England.

In consequence, a succession of Scottish, English and United Kingdom monarchs and parliaments came to regard Scottish Gaeldom as a chink in the defensive armour of their respective national securities, one that had to be sealed at any cost and by any means, military, legislative or cultural. Gaeldom also represented a chink in the economic armour of the later English entrepreneur, bent as he was on making his Highland estate(s) profitable, whatever the cultural cost to his Highland tenants. The power of those political and commercial interests ensured the acculturation of Gaeldom, an acculturation often spurred by fiat from without, sometimes occurring as a voluntary response to internal influence.

Much ink has been used to denounce or justify the acculturated chiefs and landlords who propelled the assimilation of their people. Much ink has been spilled too in interpreting the effects of that acculturation. What is certain is that there is no 'winner' in the process of acculturation, unless the dominant culture practises outright genocide, an ethnic cleansing. Acculturation does not produce a country of clones. It is a dynamic process, a diffusion of cultures, a give-and-take in which both parties are changed, admittedly at different rates for different social strata, until, after centuries, an amalgam is formed in which the cultural characteristics of both can be identified. Thus Highland and Lowland Scotland, as well as England, show in their cultures evidence of their Celtic, Norse and Anglo-Saxon heritages. What is also certain is that acculturation changes a people irrevocably and that the change is invariably painful. The story of the Highlands demonstrates acculturation's dynamism as well as its pain.

Acculturation is that 'process of conditioning a member of an out-group for assimilation into, accommodation to, or imitation of the pattern of the in-group.'[2] Most out-groups see acculturating change as inevitable, voluntary and progressive. Furthermore, Alland, quoting Rosman, reminds us that individuals, not cultures are acculturated, that change is routed through particular status positions, and that individuals playing specific roles are likely to acculturate at different rates.[3] In the Highlands of Scotland, the Highland chiefs and the gentry were acculturated first.[4] Thus even early in the eighteenth century, a 'cultural lag' developed between the members of the Celtic 'out-group' and the Anglicized 'in-group.' That cultural lag represented a 'retardation in the rate of change of some one part of an interrelated cultural complex, the lack of synchronization producing maladjustment.'[5] With time, the lag became more marked, especially in remoter areas like the West Highlands and Islands.

In fact, the acculturation of Gaeldom was a cultural take-over of a region by peoples of a supposedly superior civilization. The agent of that take-over was what we now call the 'Establishment', that usually pejorative name for 'an ill-defined amalgam of those institutions, social classes, and forces which represent authority, legitimacy, tradition, and the *status quo*.'[6] Such take-overs were routine in the Western world, as Toynbee points out:

> On the north-western frontier of Christendom the same story repeats itself. The first chapter is the peaceful conversion of the English by a band of Roman missionaries, but this is followed by the coercion of the Far Western Christians by a series of turns of the screw which began with the decision of the Synod of Whitby AD 664 and culminated in the armed invasion of Ireland by Henry II of England, with Papal approval, in 1171. Nor is this the end of the story. Habits of 'frightfulness', acquired by the English in their prolonged aggression against the remnants of the Celtic Fringe in the Highlands of Scotland and the bogs of Ireland, were carried across the Atlantic and practised at the expense of the North American Indians.[7]

To the English and the Anglicised Lowland Scots, the Highlanders who lived in isolation to the north and west of the 'Highland Line' were a primitive society, cultural inferiors to be removed or assimilated. Their assimilation was accelerated by the agricultural and industrial revolutions which swept through England and into the Scottish Lowlands during the eighteenth and nineteenth centuries. Young Highlanders of both genders migrated seasonally in increasing numbers to the 'low countries' for employment. Most returned with winter, their savings helping to pay the land rent for another year. Their return brought more than money; it brought values and practices that hastened Gaeldom's acculturation.

Acculturation also progressed quietly and relentlessly among those who stayed at home. In his book, *A Summer in Skye*, Alexander Smith tells of a visit in the 1860s to an estate school in Skye. The landlord, Kenneth Macleod of Greshornish (1809–69), Smith regarded as a kindly and caring laird. The owner of several small estates, Macleod had returned to the Isle of Skye from India, where he had been a tea and indigo planter. In Macleod's estate school, Smith found that Gaelic-speaking children were taught in English, and made to fill their copy books with maxims like 'Emulation is a generous passion', and 'Emancipation does not make man.'[8] Elsewhere in Skye, the same insidious assimilation was underway. The parish minister of Strath commented on it:

> Gaelic is the language of the country, and that for the most part preached; but of late, in consequence of the constant intercourse held by the natives with the low country, it is very much corrupted with a mixture of English words and phrases.[9]

|

By far the most powerful propellant of acculturation is the relocation of communities. That movement can happen as part of a natural chain of events, a gradual movement of a people from an old ecological niche to a new habitat; or it may be precipitated by an unexpected natural crisis, an earthquake, volcanic eruption, or severe flooding.

In either case, the population is usually able to move to a new niche, resume its lifestyle, and so maintain its culture, though the culture may then reflect adaptive modifications engendered by the ecology of the new settlement. Such natural adaptation occurs, for instance, when people move from an internal upland area to a coastal lowland area within the same parish, or from an island to the mainland. Failure to adapt to the new circumstances inevitably leads to loss of the culture. In extreme cases, failure to adapt leads to loss of the individual, the species, or the race.

But the movement of communities may also be precipitated by human aggression, in which case the direction and speed of the exodus is usually dictated by the aggressor. The evicted normally have little say about the siting of their new home which, though it be only a few miles distant, may be less desirable than the traditional niche.[10] When people are relocated to a distant site, they can encounter radical differences in ecology and culture. Robert Redfield describes this kind of dislocation:

> The expanding civilization may in cases remove whole populations of folk people and set them down in some distant land. Occasionally the transplantation may be accomplished in such a way as to establish in the new home enough representatives of the folk society so that the indigenous culture may resume its life in the new land . . . When the folk are removed in such a way as to mingle in the new land with people of notably different languages and cultures, and are thrown down in conditions of isolation, they make a new folk life, but now chiefly out of elements of living provided by their conqueror.[11]

The Highland Clearances were one such wrenching movement of communities:

> The evictions of small tenantry from a habitat they had occupied for a very long period of time are a most unhappy episode in Highland history . . . some of [them] were of the order of brutality expected of a Norse raid a thousand years earlier, rather than the behaviour of richer and more powerful brother countrymen.[12]

II

The Clearances signalled a radical redefinition of land ownership, land laws and the clansman's relationship to ancestral land. That redefinition sparked revolution in social patterns and health. Indeed from as early as the fourteenth century, feudalism had spelled the death of the Celtic clan system and so bequeathed a major problem to the Highlands and Islands; namely, the dissonance between legal ownership of clan land, and its occupation and use. By the eighteenth century, two new classes of people occupied the old clan territories. The first included farmers or sub-tenants, as well as peasants, agricultural labourers and tradesmen, the latter three groups to become known as lotters, crofters or cottars, depending on their ties to the land.[13] The second class were the landowners, many of them acculturated clan leaders, freed from their traditional responsibility for the welfare of their clansmen. This class also contained landowners with no genealogical claim to former clan lands: they bought Highland real estate as a business venture or because it enabled them to become landed gentlemen, lairds known and addressed by the name of their estate. Many were not even Scots.

While some landlords were indeed interested in the welfare of the human stock that came with an estate, the business mores of the time did not dictate that 'improving' an estate meant caring for its inhabitants. From the perspective of most landlords, the surest way to improve an estate was to disperse the Highland population on it. The traditional freedom of Highlanders to make use of a given portion of ancestral land had been a fundamental code of Highland life. The new class of landlord put an end to that code. Under the new regime, use of land was to be determined solely by the landlord, and landlords were determined to make land use profitable. To do so, they remodelled the traditional pattern of agriculture. Their new model was a system of 'crofts', that term referring simply to a portion of land, not to a Highlander's home or family dwelling, which might not even be sited on the 'croft.'[14] Thus by the eighteenth century, a Highlander was no longer the 'proud clansman', part of a clan system which gave him ancient rights. He had become unwanted chattel, bought with an estate. Dependency and neglect fast made him a pauper as well. He had to live in 'a state of economic dependency on sources other than those recognized as normal in the mores' of his traditional society.[15]

The distribution, quality and ownership of land are vital components of the Highland Problem and will be discussed in more detail in Chapter 3. It is sufficient here to state that for generations of Highland tenants and landowners, the guiding principle of land ownership had been that land, no matter the cost or manner of its rental, would by its site, size and the quality of its soil, provide minimal sustenance to those who worked it. When the new landlords decided that their estates could be made more profitable only by clearing them of their occupants, that principle was abandoned; Highlanders were relocated without regard to the ability of their new sites to sustain them. The tragedy of the Clearances was the arbitrary eviction of a people, and the pauperism, malnutrition, ill-health and disease which followed that eviction.

III

In their remodelling of land ownership and use, landlords made two fatal mistakes. The first was their failure to furnish Highlanders with leadership and a sense of common cause. The traditional clan system had supplied both. For clansmen, both were vital if they were to accept 'improving' change. Richards identifies that vacuum as 'a fundamental lack of a rallying ideology.'[16] Highlanders' need for a 'rallying ideology' stemmed from their traditional bonding with a *chosen* leader and that leader's cause. The minister of Kilmalie, writing about the manner of living in his parish before 1764, commented on that traditional relationship:

They [the tenants] lived very comfortably. In return, they were always ready to perform for their landlords every kind of service. This was rarely an involuntary service. For, when they had the felicity to have a good master, their attachment to him was strong and ardent. Instances of such are fresh in the memory of many of the living: And there have been *proprietors, who never removed a tenant; and tenants who never fought a discharge for their rents* [italics are mine].

Landlords, when indulgent, actually possessed all the authority and love of a magistrate, of a protector and a father.[17]

This cultural characteristic to bond with a chosen leader had in turn enabled many Highlanders to inspire and lead others.[18] The same quality had enabled the British government to raise loyal and disciplined Highland troops for the British Army. Some idea of the power of this trait can be gleaned from the subsidy made to the Army by the Isle of Skye over the period 1797–1837. The population of this small area was estimated in 1801 (the first census year in Britain) to be 16,000; it peaked in 1841 at 23,000.[19] Nevertheless, Skye supplied men in considerable numbers for various ranks:

Lieutenant- or major-generals	21
Colonels	45
Commissioned officers	600
Other ranks	10,000
Pipers	120[20]

Yet the bonding so characteristic of Highlanders was ultimately part of their undoing, for when they were without the guidance of a chosen leader or 'ideology', they were incapable of being led, advised or 'improved' by an 'outsider.' Many would-be improvers soon learned that lesson, lost heart and left Highlanders to their own fate. More simply evicted them. The absence of a clan leader and a common ideology also prevented Highlanders from re-grouping to improve their lot. Thus they failed to reject or modify the forces of acculturation. Gaeldom crumbled, culturally and economically. Even the moral fibre of Highland life was put at risk, as was noted in reports by parish ministers.[21]

Much later, leadership was provided by a religious ideology, Evangelical Presbyterianism, itself ironically a product of acculturation. That conversion was a watershed in the social history of the modern Highlands; until the second half of the twentieth century, it supplied the mortar that held the remnants of Gaeldom together.

That Establishment landowners failed to appreciate the power of Highlanders' need for clan leadership was their first misjudgment. Their second had to do with the manner in which they announced and effected changes: improvements were often introduced unilaterally and precipitately.

In some cases, landlords were simply unaware of the effects on their tenants of their improvements, an ignorance often perpetuated by bad counsel from their managers. For example, it has been suggested that in the Sutherland estates, the root of the Highland Problem was the estate manager, out to impress his employer with his loyalty and efficiency:[22]

> On the larger estates, the agents might become, or be given the status of, minor squires in their own right; others had legal training, and the link with the legal profession was particularly close in Scotland . . . It was precisely because of the important share of estate administration handled by the legal profession in Scotland that accountancy itself became professionalized there long before it reached a similar stage south of the border.[23]

The affairs of the Sutherland estates illustrate the power of lay managers. From the 1770s to the death of the Duke in 1833, the major lay organizers of the huge Sutherland estates, William Young, Patrick Sellar and James Loch, were all Scots. Young was a capitalist and entrepreneur; Sellar and Loch were both lawyers. All three were educated, efficient managers. Unfortunately, educational superiority and efficiency may be undermined, in both Gael and *Sasunnach*, by an abrasive character, and those who might benefit from their methods are merely antagonized. The Countess of Sutherland's estate managers were known for their abrasiveness. In the Sutherland estates, therefore, the Countess kept the reins of her estates firmly in her own hands.[24]

In other estates, managers carried out evictions without consulting the proprietor, as was the case in the Isle of Lewis estate of Sir James Matheson:

> He left the management of the estate almost entirely to his Factor, who, in turn, listened only to the ground-officers and constables, who were themselves, 'frequently very tyrannical personages.'[25]

The 1874 evictions there were carried out by Matheson's Chamberlain, Mr Donald Munro, a Gael and a solicitor in Stornoway. In the trial which followed the evictions, Munro admitted to the court that he had operated independently:

> I did not consult Sir James Matheson about removing the people, and I issued all the summonses of removing against them without receiving instructions from him to do so. I am not in the habit of consulting Sir James about every little detail connected with the management of the estate.
>
> Question from the Court. — Oh! Then you considered the removing of 56 crofters and their families too small matter to trouble Sir James about?
>
> Answer from Chamberlain Munro. — I did.[26]

Such high-handedness ensured Matheson's tenants' hatred of his Chamberlain. The depth of their hatred is depicted in the poems of Iain Mac a'Ghobhainn (John Smith of Iarsiadar, 1848–1881). His poem, 'Spiorad a' Charthannais' (The Spirit of Kindness), denounces Chamberlain Donald Munro:

> The wriggling worm will praise you then
> for your flesh's enticing taste,
> when it finds you placed before it
> on its table, silent now,
> saying 'This one's juicy flesh
> is good for earthy worms,
> since he made many hundreds thin
> to feed himself for me.'[27]

Munro's management tactics were the model for others:

> [He was] the godfather of a little legal maffia of cousins, operating together in the law courts in Lewis and Edinburgh, who held a community of more than twenty thousand people in thrall for a generation.[28]
>
> This little mafia acted as if they were prime movers, '. . . disposing of others like pawns on the board.'[29]

Adding insult to injury, many estate managers and supervisors, especially in the West Highland estates, were themselves Highlanders who, acculturated and better educated, often acted as they did in order to distance themselves from their roots.

In other estates, landlords acted as ruthlessly as the most maligned agents. In those estates, the landlord himself, not merely his manager or chamberlain, incurred Highlanders' hatred. This was especially true if the landowner was Scottish by birth but English 'by conversion' and thus, as was usually the case, contemptuous of Highlanders. More especially was the landlord hated if he was absentee, and many were.[30] In 1842, a parish minister remonstrated:

> Perhaps there is no part of the Highlands where nature has done more, and the landlords so little, for the benefit of the inhabitants, as some parts of the parish of Kilmonivaig . . . Ireland is not the only country that suffers from the system of middlemen and absenteeism.[31]

In the main, Highlanders felt displaced and betrayed by their landlords, and in a few instances, landlords' unilateral action led to physical violence over the use of land, violence in which, interestingly, 'women took an extraordinarily prominent, often a dominant, role.'[32] This physical violence, unlike that seen in Ireland, was not politically engineered, nor was it organized, largely because the most vocal and peripatetic of the Scottish

Land Reformers, John Murdoch, was a confirmed pacifist.[33] That Highland unrest was not organized and thus less worrisome meant that the rulers of Scotland, England and, from 1707, of the United Kingdom, largely ignored the Highland problem. By the time they did concern themselves with it, the cultural lag between ruler and subjects was immense. It had not become so in the United Kingdom's other troublesome 'Celtic Realm', Ireland. In Ireland, the problem had been solved, despite the criminal actions of constituents, by an able, dedicated and duly elected group of Irish parliamentary members of the British House of Commons. More politically astute, the Irish had won their land war. Leaders with similar finesse and political acumen were not available to the Highlanders and Islanders of Scotland.

Indeed, Lenman locates the root of Scotland's problem in the union of the Scottish and English parliaments in 1707. The United Kingdom was, he charges, 'a state whose masters regarded Scottish politics as an exercise in buying individuals to ensure that Scottish problems were not even raised . . .'[34]

The union of the two parliaments should have guaranteed Scotland locally-elected proportional representation. It did not. In fact, union meant that the sovereign nation of Scotland lost effective parliamentary representation. When Lowland Scotland could be so subjugated, voices crying in the remoteness of a disorganised Gaeldom would certainly go unheard. Absentee Highland landowners and distant government officials, ignorant or intolerant of cultural differences, did by their actions or indifference misjudge the impact of the Clearances.

It must in fairness be acknowledged, however, that it was ultimately the government, more precisely the embryonic permanent Civil Service, that finally realised the full extent of the Highland Problem. Furthermore, within the restrictions imposed by a parliamentary system, the Civil Service also commenced the slow process of rectifying past wrongs. In fact, as we have said, a few Highland landowners must be credited with a genuine attempt to help their people, sometimes at the cost of their personal fortunes. A prime example was the chief of the historically powerful Jacobite family, Mackenzie of Seaforth, who resisted the new economics of estate management:

> The height of the parish is believed to be much calculated for rearing sheep; and, in the year 1786, triple rent was offered for that district by sheep-farmers, (it being then out of lease), which the proprietor [Seaforth] absolutely refused, declaring, that he would *never prefer sheep to men*, at the same time he set the lands to the old inhabitants (who were not over fond of sheep) on their paying a pretty moderate augmentation.[35]

Not surprisingly, the Seaforth estates were the first to declare bankruptcy in the second quarter of the nineteenth century.

Some landowners attempted to compensate for relocation by introducing local industries or technologies, though most soon had to withdraw in the face of financial ruin. Others used the profit from various business enterprises to subsidize their estates. The Matheson family of Lochalsh was one such:

> Matheson was the apotheosis of one type of the new landowner in the Highlands, an individual of colossal wealth who lavished expenditure on his estates and in the process helped to subsidise the local economy from the profits of trade earned in distant and exotic parts of the world. The activities of men like him ensured that the drain of rental income from the Highlands, which had occurred when the old elite expended much of the surplus of their estates in the fashionable capitals of the south, was now reversed. Instead, the new landed class spent much of the profit derived from their commercial and professional success outside the Highlands in the north and west.[36]

James Sutherland Matheson had wealth enough not only to reclaim traditional family and clan lands, but also to purchase other Highland estates. In 1844, he bought the Lewis holdings from the then-bankrupt Seaforth estate. For his charity to the people of Lewis during the famine of 1845–46, Matheson was created a Baronet in 1851.

But the good intentions of a few successful, native-born Highlanders could not neutralize the bitterness that attended the wholesale eviction from ancestral land. The effect of the cultural threat that the Clearances represented was predictable. Contemporary social commentators instruct us about the impact on any people of such a threat:

> Implicit in each culture is a vision of human fulfilment, a set of standards of a desired personal identity which it exists to uphold. Cultures get out of phase (when discordant influences impede performance of this task) when under attack . . . The ideal identity then becomes indistinct, and the resulting emotional insecurity produces social breakdown, political reaction, conflict.[37]

By the middle of the nineteenth century, Highlanders were resisting passively. That they did not receive the advances of their improvers enthusiastically the Establishment took as proof that they could not provide a reliable workforce. That view was rooted in a long-standing perception that Highlanders were indolent and resistant to change. Indeed, Highlanders were 'people who are tenacious of old customs and averse to deviate from the practice of their ancestors.'[38] Their critics forgot, however, that the majority of the rapidly increasing Highland population was composed of unemployed Highlanders whose grandparents had hitherto been self-employed cattlemen. That independent lifestyle had suddenly disintegrated; long-valued skills had become redundant; freedom to move to more productive niches was curtailed. Highlanders were reduced to the level of agricultural labourers and minor tradesmen grasping at any job. Immediate amelioration of their plight meant having to move to an urban centre, to be retrained in an industrial trade, or to go as unskilled labourers competing with the ever-increasing influx of even cheaper manual labour from Ireland. Both options were anathema to a proud and self-reliant Gael.

The Establishment failed utterly to see the connection between dispossession and passivity. Their faulty assessment of Highland character was 'the giving of a dog a bad name.' A parish minister of the late eighteenth century recognized this fallacy:

> . . . people who are not well acquainted with their [Highlanders'] peculiar situation, and who form an opinion of their character in this respect, by a comparison with the inhabitants of the Low Country, may rashly conclude, that it is natural for them to be lazy and indolent. But nothing can be more unfair than to judge them in this way . . . the reasons commonly assigned for their inactivity are quite erroneous. It is not a natural disposition to be idle, but the want of encouragement and regular employment, that checks the industry of the Highlanders. It is well known, that, when habituated to any line of life, they are found careful, active and enterprising.[39]

Another observer, Captain Edward Burt, an English Engineer officer stationed in Inverness, had also refuted the allegation that Highlanders had a 'natural disposition to be idle':

> It is a received Notion (but nothing can be more unjust) that the ordinary Highlanders are an indolent lazy People; I know the Contrary by troublesome Experience; I say troublesome, because, in a certain Affair wherein I had Occasion to employ great numbers of them, and gave them good Wages, the Solicitations of others for Employment were very earnest, and would hardly admit of a Denial; they are as willing as other People to mend their Way of Living, and when they have *gained strength from substantial Food* [italics are mine], they work as well as others; but why should a People be branded with the Name of Idles in a Country where there is generally no profitable Business for them to do? . . . I never had the least Reason to complain of the Behaviour towards me of any of the ordinary Highlanders, or the *Irish* [the Gaelic speakers]; but it wants a great deal that I could truly say as much of the Englishmen and lowland Scots that were employed in the same business.[40]

Yet the Establishment blamed Highlanders for their own misfortune after the Clearances; they pointed to the failure of successive attempts to introduce local industries as a case in point. Industry, it was thought, would employ people, relieve destitution and poor nutrition, and remedy immorality. That it failed was generally attributed to Highlanders' laziness. In fact, location was the real reason for its downfall. A capitalist from the south might speculate about the possibility for local industry and point to the abundant supply of cheap labour in Highland communities, but the remoteness of these sites from main factories, already supplied with cheap local labour, home markets and international seaports, precluded any serious chance for development and profit. For example, many parishes in the Highlands were suitable for the growing of flax, but all that they could hope to obtain was a minor role in that industry, such as spinning imported flax. This task, while labour-intensive, was poorly paid; moreover, it diverted people, especially women, from farming at home. Even the finished yarn was sent to a factory in the south for final processing into linen goods, the only profitable stage.[41] A similar situation existed in sheep farming: a few Lowland shepherds produced all of the raw wool, which was then shipped to the Lowlands or to England, to be manufactured there into woollen goods which were then sold to Highlanders.[42]

IV

The death of the clan system had left Highlanders leaderless and demoralized and their new landlords' changes had dismantled their lifestyle. In the face of that disruption, Highlanders had only three options, the first of which was 'If you can't beat them, join them.' Many chiefs and their followers did just that. The conviction that the high road to success was the highway to England became an established part of Scottish culture in both the Highlands and Lowlands:

> The great bulk of the nobility had effectively abandoned the country to pursue social, political, military, or naval careers which required the systematic cultivation of metropolitan society in the south of England.[43]

Burt made the same point about the emigration of Highland tradesmen:

> Here I may observe, that when a young Fellow finds he has a Genius for his Trade or Business, and has any Thing of Spirit, he generally lays hold of the first Occasion to remove to *England*, or some other country, where he hopes for better Encouragement. Hence, I take it arose a Kind of Proverb, That there never came a Fool out of *Scotland*. Some perhaps would be giving this a different Interpretation, but what I mean is, that the cleverest and the most sprightly among them leave the narrow Way of their own Country: And from this may come, for ought I know, another saying, That they seldom desire to return Home.[44]

Highlanders, therefore, 'joined' England for material advancement.[45] They joined too for education. The traditional Celtic respect, amounting almost to adoration, for education and the educated was traceable to the cult of the Druids.[46] From the sixteenth century onwards, this respect produced an assiduous attempt by the Church to achieve John Knox's promise of 'a school in every parish.'

Other Highlanders found a second alternative to encroachment and acculturation. Equally logical and tactically sound to those in a position to act on it was the proposition that 'If you can't beat them, run away from them.' In fact, this philosophy had generated the traditional 'westward drifts' of the Celtic peoples throughout the millennia. A writer on tour in the Western Islands of Scotland in the last decade of the seventeenth century noted that the natives of Skye found elsewhere what they could not create at home. They were, he wrote, 'a very prolifick People, so that many of their numerous Issue must seek their Fortune on the Continent, and not a few in Foreign Countries, for want of Imployment at home.'[47] And by the end of the seventeenth century, the minister of Jura and Colonsay was urging his parishioners to learn English so that their relocation elsewhere would be eased:

> The language universally spoken in the parish is Gaelic. Very few old people understand English. But from the laudable endeavours of the schoolmasters to teach their scholars the vocabulary, and use of that language, and from a general opinion gaining ground, that it will be of great service in life, it is hoped that the rising generation will make considerable progress in acquiring the English language . . . [since] they foster the notion of getting at once into a state of ease and opulence, with their relations beyond the Atlantic.[48]

In 1841, the minister of Duirinish on Skye noted that the best educated were those most apt to emigrate:

> It is well known to those who are acquainted with Skye, that the best educated among its common people generally, almost universally, have sought a foreign country where to advance their fortunes.[49]

In the eighteenth century, it was the tacksmen who 'ran away' in the greatest numbers. Tacksmen leased large 'tacks' of land from a chief to whom they were usually related. These tacksmen in turn divided some of their tack among sub-tenants and so acted as middlemen between chief and clansmen. They had been the middle class and the military officers of the clan, but by the end of the seventeenth century, this role had all but disappeared. Sensing the imminence of social disruption in a rapidly changing Gaeldom, many tacksmen decided to emigrate to America, taking most of their sub-tenants and followers with them.[50]

This voluntary emigration gathered momentum in the second half of the eighteenth century, and by that time included even the poorer independent class of tenants. The exodus from the Highlands to new homes overseas brought an emotional outpouring of Celtic poetry, song and art. This surge of emotion was often the product of nostalgia, never in short supply in the Celtic realms. Often it came from those not themselves evicted and therefore in no position to evaluate. Many were merely advancing personal or political biases. This is not to suggest that expressions of grief were not genuine or appropriate. Nonetheless, those outpourings did not represent the prevailing Highland reaction to the evictions. The fact is that a great many poorer Highlanders, once they had accepted the inevitability of eviction and the futility of resistance, were as willing to emigrate overseas as to resettle elsewhere in Scotland:

> If a Highlander is forced or induced to leave the small circle which occupies his first affection, he cares not how far he goes from home. Going to another parish, or to the district of another clan, is to him entire banishment; and when he has resolved to set out, whether from necessity or choice, he would as soon cross the Atlantic as he would cross the arm of the sea.[51]

The minister of Applecross attested to the readiness of many Highlanders to leave a homeland that could no longer support them:

> The local attachment of the Highlanders, hath, for some time back, been gradually abating. The influx of money, and their communication with other countries, hath introduced a desire for better living; and the rapacity of the superiors, in applying all the advantages of the times to their own private interest, hath effectually relaxed those attachments.[52]

Those who did not join the enemy, or run away from him, stayed on in the hope that conditions would improve or revert to the 'old ways'. This was the option of those unable to sever the emotional ties to the lands of their ancestors, and of those who could not afford to go. For them, freedom of choice was empty rhetoric. In fact, they had become almost completely dependent on private and government assistance:

> In a year of scarcity . . . the session [the church session] make a shift to buy 20 bolls of meal for their relief. In summer of 1773, Government generously sent a cargo of meal to the Western Islands, of which this parish got 44 bolls and 3 firlots, which was a most seasonable relief to the poorer sort of people.[53]

They had been legally evicted from their ancestral land by the simple expedient of not being granted renewal of their leases, and relocated to pitiably inadequate lots elsewhere in the Highlands. Some believed that those who resisted acculturation by staying embodied an ideological principle:

> . . . that the possession of land – the tenure (not the ownership) of a croft – was the highest good a man could desire. Other forms of earning a living were possible but less desirable than crofting; a man should only take to them in an emergency, to pay the rent, but not as a lifestyle to help him enrich himself to the maximum extent possible.[54]

And indeed, the Highland paupers' resistance to improvement was rejection of the pursuit of wealth for wealth's sake, a rejection which widened the gap between Highland culture and Establishment ideology and hence hastened the demise of Gaeldom. The only course left open to the resisters was to accept their fate. They had reached the nadir of their struggle. In truth, their plight was grave, as Dr Johnson observed:

> In pastoral countries the condition of the lowest rank of people is sufficiently wretched. Among manufacturers, men that have no property may have art and industry, which makes them necessary, and therefore valuable. But where flocks and corn are the only wealth, there are always more hands than work, and of that work there is little in which skill and dexterity can be much distinguished. He therefore who is born poor never can be rich. The son merely occupies the place of the father, and life knows nothing of progression or advancement.[55]

With no goods or money to buy the basic requirements for even a modest lifestyle, the poor in their wretchedness became, to Establishment spectators, a blight on the landscape, an irritant to conscience and a source of pestilence to be got rid of. The same spectators believed that the poor lacked more than income and sustenance, that their very lifestyle, religion, mores, home environment and dress were depraved.[56]

By the early nineteenth century, the Highlands and Islands had become untenable for its destitute population. The parish minister of Morvern, one of the Duke of Argyll's estates, described the plight of his population:

> Accordingly, on the sale of the Argyle estates, and the breaking up of the old tack leases, the sheep system came into more general operation. The people, though in some cases partially continued, from motives of compassion, have but slender holdings. In other cases, they have been wholly removed. This process has again facilitated the introduction of another, in one point of view, certainly the most commendable, but, on the whole, perhaps not the least pernicious in its effects; for, in place of repairing to the south, in search of steady employment, or taking the more decided and advisable step of emigrating, the dispossessed tenantry have here and elsewhere become the occupants of small allotments in wretched villages, where idleness exercises its unhappy influence over them, and lands them in penury and wretchedness.[57]

The fact is that by the nineteenth century, ordinary Highlanders who had stayed at home had 'lost their vision of human fulfilment . . . [and their] standards of . . . personal identity.'

V

The misery of those who stayed was at no time deeper than during the potato famines of the 1840s. By that time, most proprietors had all but abdicated responsibility for their people. Relief was neither timely nor adequate.[58] In fact, the psychological trauma of the potato famines overshadowed that of Glencoe and Culloden and severed any remaining cultural bonds between Highlanders and their landlords.[59]

At the time of the famines, many landowners, and later their factors, were members of the House of Commons or the House of Lords. They were, by our definition, part of the Highland Establishment. Thus they were able to influence government policy. To them, resolution of the problems the Clearances entailed was simple, swift and one to the people's own advantage: the population had to be carefully culled by emigration.[60] But their scheme met opposition from the intelligentsia in Britain and in Europe. A lecturer at the University of Oxford noted that some members of the British Establishment disapproved of forced emigration on pragmatic grounds. They were concerned about

> the effects of emigration, real or supposed, on the proportion between the supply and demand of labour at home; the effects of the export of capital which accompanies emigration on national wealth; and the character of the commerce which takes place between the colonies and the mother country, with special reference to the history and results of that series of protections and restrictions which constitutes our so-called colonial system.[61]

In that Age of Revolution, Europeans in particular showed great interest in the socio-political welfare of the Celtic Fringe. Europeans recognized Celts as part of their own cultural heritage, given Celts' westward movement across Europe centuries before. European interest was stirred by reports of Glencoe and Culloden and by a Celtic revival following James MacPherson's (1736–96) discovery of 'hitherto unknown' Ossianic poetry. Observers mused about a primitive Celtic people still living in a golden age. A British writer in the second decade of the nineteenth century articulated Europe's condemnation of the wholesale uprooting of Highland populations, whether to new sites in Scotland or overseas:

To excuse the conduct of proprietors and agents in the Highlands, it is said Scotland was overpeopled by clanship; that a greater population should not be reserved in a country than can be profitably employed; that we are to look to the surplus produce only; that what is more productive should be preserved – pasture to agriculture, beasts to mankind: – therefore it is fitting that the sons of those who redeem the wilderness from nought should be expelled, and that sheep should be substituted for men . . . This proposal many Highland proprietors have effected in their own country against their own countrymen . . . the rich have banished their poorer countrymen by families, by hundreds, by districts, and they have been exchanged for herds . . . The Scotch resorted to towns, there to contend for life with men who were inured to city-labour; for, when the proprietors dispossessed them for sheep, they obtained a law to prevent emigration to America. Some, however, were forced abroad and vagabond, some to St John's Island [Prince Edward's Island], some to Canada, and to places which, compared with Botany Bay, are as hell to heaven. Yet happier were they in these ruthless regions than their friends who lingered at home.[62]

Yet some of those most critical of the Clearances were themselves residents of countries whose policies mirrored those at work in the Highlands. In fact, all nations faced the problem of redundant populations, and all solved it in like manner:

Moreover, at the same time, Europe was sustaining huge emigration of her stocks. In the 1830's European emigration overseas first passed the figure of 100,000 a year; in 1913 it was over a million and a half.[63]

Eric Richards describes the economic pressures operating everywhere in Europe and he lists the measures adopted almost universally to deal with those pressures:

In particular it is undeniable that the combined pressures of agricultural re-organisation and unprecedented population growth altered the relationship of people to the land almost everywhere. Dislodgement, sub-division, enclosure, clearance, resettlement, internal colonisation and emigration were all marks of the pressures.[64]

Moreover, the treatment of Highland peasants was no different from that meted out by the Establishment to natives across the world. What is more, the hunger for productive land drove the Highland emigrant himself to treat his 'cultural inferiors' as well as his own countrymen as ruthlessly as he himself had been dealt with.

Destitution, despair and disease made Highlanders who stayed at home during the Clearances and famines of the 1840s passive and powerless. In the post-Culloden world, however, Highlanders who had served with the

British army or navy in other parts of the world returned home.[65] These men and their relatives had not forgotten the malfeasance of many landowners, and the apathy and broken promises of the British government. They began to resist and to undermine landowners' unilateral actions. In one of his 'Rambles' in the Glendale district of Skye in the 1880s, Malcolm Ferguson noted one effect of that resistance:

> The Glendale shootings which are rented, are unlet this season, incurring a considerable loss to the proprietor. I believe that owing to the crofters' ill-advised squabbles with their landlords, parties in the south did not care to venture amongst them.[66]

The squabbles Ferguson referred to were the outcome of the refusal by the proprietor of the Waterstein estate to let grazing rights to the Crofters of Milovaig and Glendale. That rebuff was worsened when the farm was eventually handed over to the estate factor, himself a farmer. The Crofters declared that they would occupy Waterstein with or without permission. This they did, violating the most sacred of Establishment rights, the security of property. Warrants were issued for the arrest of twenty-five men, though no arrests were actually made. Justice appeared to have been done and a potentially explosive situation was thus defused.[67]

Nonetheless, that and similar uprisings forced the government to acknowledge that there was a problem in the 'crofting counties.'[68] By 1883, a Royal Commission, chaired by Lord Napier, was appointed to look into the Highland Problem. Highlanders had their day in court, where they proved convincingly that the deer forests that stretched across the Highlands endangered their lifestyle, and in some areas, their very lives, and that remedy required immediate government intervention.[69] But Royal Commissions are seldom powerful enough to break the hold of a powerful Establishment, however unbiased their inquiries or brilliant their reports: the Commission did not restore to crofters the pasture land that had made their ecological niche viable. Nor have they regained it to this day.

VI

The powerful cultural and social tensions which the Clearances set in train affected health profoundly. Knowing what we do today about the relationship between social conditions and physical and emotional health, we know that it could not have been otherwise:

> man is . . . a psychobiological system comprised of an internal natural system of biochemical, physiological, psychological, and other organic and sensing subsystems. This internal system interacts with the external natural and social

systems by receiving and seeking influences and information from them and emitting influences and information to them . . .

The major processes of health, illness, and care are, therefore, to be seen as essentially adaptive and regulatory, and the corresponding behaviour is directed either towards the psychobiological system through the seeking of treatment, or toward altering the system of social connections, or toward some combination of these.[70]

In the context of this book, the 'Natural System' shown in Figure I was a Highlander's freely chosen ecological niche, a niche that had permitted him time and space to adapt. His 'Social System' was the small, closely knit traditional Highland township, community or social group with its associated local Celtic *céilidh*, the focus for 'Gossiping, visiting, sojourning and pilgrimage.'[71] As early as 1785, James Anderson had drawn the attention of the Government to the connection between health and social relationships:

Man owes his superiority over other animals entirely to society. To the united efforts alone of many individuals, exerted to produce one effect, he owes his power — To the accumulated store of facts collected by the attention of many observers, he owes his knowledge. When detached from all others, his mind, like his body is weak; and it is made to bend, without effort, to every superior power that is calculated to overawe the individual. Hence it is found, that degree of personal independence which constitutes what is generally called *political-freedom*, can be found only in those places where men mingle in society; and where the minds of men exalted by communicating with others, come to be gradually expanded, till they acquire an idea of their own united power and importance. — Slavery, on the other hand, is found only to prevail (without the perpetual exertions of constraining power) where the people are divided into scattered families, that do not admit of social intercourse.[72]

For a Highlander, his niche was the essence of his 'social group', that group being

A number of persons between whom exists a psychic interaction and who are set apart by that interaction in their own minds and in those of others as a recognized entity. The social group requires for its existence a durable contact between persons out of which continuous interaction may arise, a consciousness of sufficient likeness or common interest to establish some degree of identification of each with the group and some structure recognized by the members as essential to achieve its continued existence as an entity.[73]

By uprooting Highlanders from their traditional niches, the Clearances had dismantled their social and natural systems simultaneously.

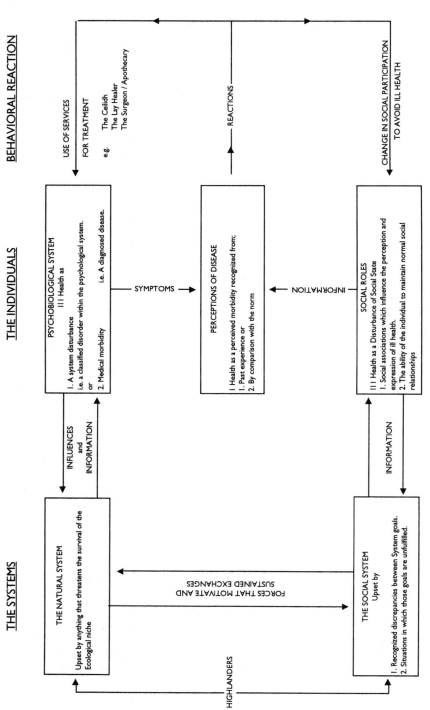

Figure 1. Model of relationships between the individual and social systems, modified from Kohn and White 1976.

VII

In summary, all cultural adaptations are responses to geography, climate and resources. The differences in adaptive response distinguish one culture and lifestyle from others. Moreover, the potential of a region's economic resources attracts the interest of 'advanced', often rapacious societies who justify their development of those resources as being for the good of all. Such was the exploitation that created the Highland Problem. Smout explains:

> . . . the language of patriotism was nowhere used more persistently than by the improvers in describing and legitimating their own pursuit of opulence. Their occupation of this lofty ground was one of several reasons why it was so hard to overturn the hegemony of the twin ideas that national enrichment was synonymous with patriotism, and that national enrichment was best attained by allowing the upper classes a free hand in the pursuit of wealth. It was as though the Invisible Hand belonged to an Englishman with a sharp set of Scottish fingernails.[74]

Such acculturation polarizes populations and subjects common people to poverty and drastic modification or loss of their culture. No amount of *a posteriori* improvements can reverse those losses. In fact, the process becomes deculturation, 'the weakening of traditional norms and sanctions without replacement with other forms of social and psychological control.'[75] Those who resist are at peril, as researchers have warned:

> . . . any attempt to hold rigidly onto old cultural patterns in the midst of a disintegrating social environment becomes very destructive to the individuals involved.[76]

The hope of many people now studying cultural change is the hope of the social reformers of the nineteenth century; namely, that the future will deliver to people thus wronged a quality of life and a cultural identity, if not equivalent to what they lost, then at least somewhat better than that to which they were abandoned.

Notes

1. From a speech delivered in Edinburgh 1867 by Benjamin Disraeli, Earl of Beaconsfield (1804–1881). He was Prime Minister 1868, 1874–1880 and, as a Conservative, claimed that as such he would ' preserve all that is good in our constitutions' and as a Radical ' remove all that is bad.'

2. *Dictionary of Sociology and Related Sciences*, Ed. Henry Pratt Fairchild, New Jersey, Rowman & Allanhead, 1970.

3. Alexander Alland, Jr., *Adaptation in Cultural Evolution: an Approach to Medical Anthropology*. N.Y., Columbia University Press, 1970, 159.

4. James Hunter, *The Making of the Crofting Community*, Edinburgh, John Donald, 1976, 7.
   For a further discussion on the cultural changes in Gaelic Scotland resulting from the Anglo-Saxon acculturation of Lowland Scotland see Malcolm Chapman, *The Gaelic Vision in Scottish Culture*. London, Croom Helm, 1978, Introduction: 'History and the Highlands'. 9-28.
   Chapman also notes:
   > Gaelic culture has been subject to what I term 'symbolic appropriation' at the hands of the majority and dominant culture. At the same time, the face that Gaelic culture is given within this appropriation is often persuasively apt, even for those within that culture. I would risk the assertion that Gaelic culture has to a considerable extent become, particularly in its more self-conscious moments, the literary interpretation to which it was initially subjected by an alien tradition [page 28].

5. *Dictionary of Sociology*, Ed., Henry Pratt Fairchild, Totowa, New Jersey, Rowman & Allanhead, 1970.
   The influence of the lag has been further explained:
   > The hypothesis of culture lag holds in particular that in modern societies there has been a tendency for changes in the political, educational, family, and religious institutions not to keep pace with technological changes.

   G.A. Theodorson and Achilles G. Theodorson, *A Modern Dictionary of Sociology*, New York, Thomas Y. Crowell Co., Apollo Edit., 1970.
   For further discussion of this facet of the Highland Problem see:
   William Fielding Ogburn, *Social Change*, New York, A Delta Book, Dell Pub. Co. Inc., 1966, 'The Hypothesis of Culture Lag', 200–213.

6. *The Fontana Dictionary of Modern Thought*, 2nd edn., Eds., Alan Bullock, Oliver Stallbrass and Stephen Trombley, London, Fontana Paperbacks, 1977, 284.
   It is of interest to note that the word 'Thing', introduced by the Vikings, was the name for a system of government by means of council meetings which dealt with affairs both great and small. The Al-Thing, for example, dealt with many matters and was equivalent to a House of Commons.

7. Arnold J. Toynbee, *A Study of History*, Abridgement of Volumes I–VI, by D.C. Sumervell, London, Oxford University Press. 413.
   A similar acculturation took place in French equatorial Africa. See:
   Jan Vansina, *Paths in the Rainforests*: Towards a History of Political Tradition in Equatorial Africa. Wisconsin, University of Wisconsin Press, 1990. 247–8.

8. Alexander Smith, *A Summer in Skye*,(1865) reprint, Hawick Scotland, Byway Books, 1983, 131.

9. N.S.A., XIV (Strath), 308.

10. Hunter (1976), Op cit., 19.

11. Robert Redfield, *The Primitive World and its Transformations*, Ithaca, N.Y., Cornell University Press, 1953, 47.

12. F. Fraser Darling, Ed., *West Highland Survey: An Essay in Human Ecology*, Oxford Univ. Press, 1955, 5–6.

13. See: Lord Napier, *Report of the Commissioners of Inquiry into the Condition of the Crofters and Cottars in the Highlands of Scotland. 1884. British Parliamentary Papers (Hereafter B.P.P.).*

    The word crofter was rarely used before this *Report*. Those people were previously identified as sub-tenants or tenants who were pastoral farmers and as such were able to subsist, raise a family and pay their rent in cash or kind. As a result of socio-economic changes in the eighteenth century, this economically independent lifestyle began to disappear rapidly, particularly in the decades that followed Culloden. The traditionally proud and self-reliant Highlander (clansman) now found himself reduced to the level of a redundant pauper and regarded as lazy and unambitious.

14. By the twentieth century, as a result of protective legislation that many would call Establishment 'loaded', the modern croft can be defined as 'a small portion of land surrounded by legislation.'

15. *Dictionary of Sociology*, Op cit,.

16. Eric Richards, 'How Tame were the Highlanders during the Clearances', Scottish Studies, XVII, Part I, 1993, 41.

17. O.S.A.,VIII (Kilmalie), 443–4.

    Reflecting no doubt on changes during the ensuing thirty years, the minister added, 'In those days, however, the tenants were ill lodged, and as ill clothed.' The importance of this afterthought becomes apparent when one remembers that the parish was situated at the southern end of the Great Glen, a natural gateway into the Highlands and Islands. That gateway was controlled by the important British garrison at Fort William and consequently the parish was exposed early to intense acculturation.

    See also Ibid., III (Luggan), 150.

18. This 'rallying ideology' had serious disadvantages.

    The full members of a Celtic clan, virtually classless, enjoyed from their leaders a respect unknown to the men of most other countries, where peasants were dealt with as livestock attached to the land. The clansman followed his chief by choice, not compulsion, and could feel himself to be of consequence in a society whose every commitment was his, and on which he could speak his mind without his loyalty being questioned. One product of the system had potential danger. Tacitus remarks that the Celt adopted all enmities as well as friendships. This meant that an injury suffered by one man was an injury to a whole clan, and that could lead to endless feuding unless the chiefs had commonsense.

W.H. Murray, *The Islands of Western Scotland*. London, Eyre Methuen, 1973, 151.

19. Alexander Nicolson, M.A., *History of Skye*, (1930), Second Edition (revised and enlarged), Ed., Dr Alasdair Maclean, Portree, Maclean Press, 1994, 269.

20. Ibid., 274.

Without wishing to denigrate this or other contributions made by the Highlands and Islands in time of war, the interpretation of biological statistics must be viewed with caution. Dr Johnson remarked that

> The religion of the North was military; if they could not find enemies, it was their duty to make them; they travelled in quest of danger, and willingly took the chance of Empire or Death. If their troops were numerous, the countries from which they were collected are of vast extent, and without much exuberance of people great armies may be raised where every man is a soldier. But their true numbers were never known. Those who were conquered by them are their historians, and shame may have excited them to say, that they were overwhelmed with multitudes. To count is a modern practice, the ancient method was to guess; and when numbers are guessed they are always magnified.
>
> Thus England has for several years been filled with the achievements of seventy thousand Highlanders employed in America. I have heard from an English officer, not much inclined to favour them, that their behaviour deserved a very high degree of military praise; but their number has been much exaggerated. One of the ministers told me, that seventy thousand men could not have been found in all the Highlands, and that more than twelve thousand never took the field. Those that went to the American war, went to destruction. Of the old Highland regiment, consisting of twelve hundred, only seventy-six survived to see their country again.

Samuel Johnson, *A Journey to the Western Islands of Scotland*, in *A Tour to the Hebrides* Johnson & Boswell, Ed., R.W. Chapman, London, Oxford Univ., Press, 1933. 89.

The actual composition of General James Wolfe's army at Quebec in 1759 was also suitably slanted by nationalistic historians. The Scottish contribution was minor, about the same size as that of the English:

American 33%; Scottish 15%;

Irish 25%; German/Swiss 4%; English 23%

It is also interesting to note that most of the American, Scottish and Irish soldiers who served Wolfe so diligently at Quebec and then retired to North America after the war almost invariably reappeared as high ranking officers and generals in George Washington's Continental Army some years later.

Major Ian McCulloch, 'With Wolfe at Quebec', *The Beaver*, Winnipeg, Manitoba, April–May, 1992, 25.

Wolfe (a major at Culloden) was reputed, when asked where were good sturdy men for recruiting into the forces, to have answered: 'The Highlanders. They are a hardy and intrepid race, and no great mischief if they fall.'

John Macleod, *No Great Mischief if You Fall: The Highland Experience*, Edinburgh, Mainstream Publishing, 1993, 15.

Yet another side of the above numbers game is one with which this book is primarily concerned. How many Scottish Highlanders, during the late eighteenth and first half of the nineteenth centuries, were medically fit for active service? Johnson's remarks on the warlike nature of the clansmen, like those of the romantic historians and novelists, do not stand scrutiny. Certainly the Celts engaged in tribal and clan warfare, but no more than any other people. In times of famine, and those were numerous in the Highlands and Islands, hunger drove starving clansmen to raid adjacent richer clan lands and Lowland areas in search of cattle and corn. In later chapters we shall show that well fed Highlanders were not easily induced to join the army or navy. Furthermore, in the pre-Culloden decades, most clansmen were primarily small tenant farmers, paying rent from the product of their own labour. They were tied to their land and lifestyle by the vagaries of the climate and the limited natural resources of the Highlands and Islands. Prince Charles, during his ill-fated rebellion, was to discover the closeness of this bond between his clansmen and their land when the desertion rate of his Highland troops climbed at harvest time. For the clansmen, as for their chiefs, the rebellion offered a chance for quick booty but unlike their leaders, most clansmen had to return to their land before winter set in if they hoped to feed their families in the coming year. This statement does not malign the intense loyalty that Highlanders were capable of conferring on a chosen leader. But even that had limits, as the British Government soon found when it attempted to harness directly that loyalty and hardiness. The radicalism of the French Revolution, the territorial ambitions of Napoleon and the subsequent Napoleonic wars and the fear of a French invasion, aggravated by a growing internal social unrest, had galvanised the Establishment into implementing a series of emergency measures. One such measure in Scotland was the Militia Act of 1797. This Act conscripted, by ballot, young males between the ages of 18 and 23. The list of names for the ballot was to be drawn up by local school masters but most importantly, the militia could be drafted overseas. The Volunteer companies raised by the Establishment, on the other hand, were not eligible for conscription and therefore were not available for overseas service. Furthermore, the Volunteer officers consisted mainly of the middle and upper classes, who could also afford when necessary to buy themselves out of the service. The iniquitous Militia Act led to widespread rioting throughout Scotland and resulted in several deaths.

For Highland opposition to the Militia Act see:

John Prebble, *Mutiny: Highland Regiments in Revolt 1743–1804*, Harmondsworth, Middlesex, England, Penguin Books, 1977, 402–3, 426, 429.

Kenneth J. Logue, *Popular Disturbances In Scotland* 1780–1815, Edinburgh, John Donald, 1979, 'The Militia Riots', 75–115.

21. The effect of this deculturation was not confined to the people of the Highlands and Islands of Scotland. It followed them to Atlantic Canada.

22. Eric Richards, 'The mind of Patrick Sellar (1780–1851)', Scottish Studies, XV, 1, 1971, 1–20.

Idem., *The Leviathan of Wealth: The Sutherland Fortune in the Industrial Revolution*, London, Routledge & Kegan Paul, 1973, 25–34.

23. Sidney Pollard, *The Genesis of Modern Management: A Study of the Industrial Revolution in Great Britain*, London, Edward Arnold Ltd., 1965, 28–9.

24. To her alone fell the responsibility of the evictions from her estate for 'it was she who brought such enduring infamy upon her house by presiding over the Sutherland clearances.'

Ian Grimble, *Clans and Chiefs*, London, Blond & Briggs, 1980, 147.

25. James Shaw Grant, *A Shilling For Your Scowl: The History of a Scottish Legal Maffia*, Stornoway, Isle of Lewis, Acair Ltd., 1992, 198.

James Matheson was born in 1796 and died aged 82. He purchased the Lewis estate in 1844 and Munro's trial was in 1874 – four years before Matheson's death.

26. Evidence given in the trial of three men being tried for assaulting the law officer who had served the eviction notice to the 56 crofters on the Island of Bernera. The jury unanimously found the accused not guilty. The Chamberlain soon resigned his position.

Report to the Secretary For Scotland by the Crofters Commission on the Social Conditions of the People of Lewis in 1901, As Compared with Twenty Years Ago, 1902, B.P.P. LXXXIII, lxxi.

27. Iain Mac a' Ghobhainn, 'Spiorad a' Charthannais', in Bardachd Leodhais, Ed., Iain N. MacLeoid, Glasgow, A. MacLaren and Sons, 1924, 76–84.

For more details of Smith's works translated into English see:

Derick Thomson, *An Introduction to Gaelic Poetry*, London, Victor Gollancz Ltd., 1977, 237–245.

28. Shaw Grant, Op cit., 9.

29. Ibid., 35.

30. *The Statistical Accounts* record that a high percentage of the heritors of Highland estates were non-resident. *The Statistical Account of Scotland* (1791–1799) [hereafter O.S.A.] was compiled by Sir John Sinclair of Ulbster (1754–1835) from replies obtained from parish ministers throughout Scotland in

answer to a set of questions pertaining to all facets of parish life. It was, therefore, a major socio-economic survey of the Highlands and Islands of the eighteenth century. In 1825, Sinclair published his *Analysis of the Statistical Account of Scotland*, which reviewed and updated the O.S.A.. A second survey, not compiled by Sinclair, *The New Statistical Account* (1830s–1840s) [hereafter N.S.A.], provides a useful comparison and update.

31. N.S.A., XIV (Kilmonivaig), 504–5.

32. Richards, Op cit., 1973, 39–40.

33. For a detailed insight into this problem and the opinions of Murdoch see:

James Hunter, *For the People's Cause: From the Writings of John Murdoch*, Edinburgh, H.M.S.O. 1986.

See also a series of letters and articles written by Murdoch on 'Highland Estate Management' in the *Paisley and Renfrewshire Gazette* over the period 27 Mar, 1886 to 4 Dec, 1886. In these articles, the 8th Duke of Argyll was his main target.

34. Bruce Lenman, *Integration, Enlightenment, and Industrialization, Scotland 1746–1832* (The new History of Scotland No. 6.), London, Edward Arnold, 1981, 148.

For an exposé of the mechanism of this 'internal colonialism' see:
Michael Hechter, *Internal Colonialism: The Celtic Fringe in British National Development, 1536–1966*, London, Routledge & Kegan Paul, 1975.

35. O.S.A.,VII (Glensheil), 128. : III (Luggan), 150.

Hunter (1976), Op cit., 58–59, discusses this point with regard to the actions taken by some proprietors during the famines of the mid 19th century.

A renowned twentieth-century ecologist also defends the actions of many landlords:
The solicitude of some of the lairds of this period should be more generally known and it should be realised how they were compelled to work out entirely for themselves what was the problem of a people, namely an unprecedented rate of survival without the natural resources to cope with such an increase of births over deaths.
F. Fraser Darling, Ed., *West Highland Survey: An Essay in Human Ecology*, Op cit., 8.

36. T.M. Devine, 'The Emergence of the New Elite in the Western Highlands and Islands, 1800–60' in *Improvement and Enlightenment*, Proceedings of the Scottish Historical Studies Seminar University of Strathclyde 1987–88, Ed., T.M. Devine, Edinburgh, John Donald, 1989, 130. See also:
'Lord Leverhulme', in Hunter,(1976), Op cit., 197–201, 204.

37. Ralph Glasser, 'Perspectives of Fulfilment', in his book *Gorbals Voices, Siren Songs*, London, Pan Books, 1990, 197.

38. O.S.A.,VIII (Gigha and Cara), 40.

39. Ibid., 68–9.

40. Edward Burt, *Letters from a Gentleman in the North of Scotland to His Friend in London*, (c 1720–30), 2 vols., 2nd edn., London, II, 113–4.
    Burt's duties were concerned with the surveying and building of the 'new roads' that would link the various garrisons in the Highlands. His duties not only took him into the West Highlands but brought him into personal contact with several chiefs, chieftains, tacksmen and clansmen. From the latter group he obtained his guides and interpreters and as a result of this association he formed a high opinion of the character of many of the common Highlanders.

41. O.S.A., XX (Thurso), 517.

42. S.A.,VIII, (Kilmalie), 442.; XX (Thurso), 517.

43. Lenman, Op cit., 58.

44. Burt, Op cit., I, 129.
    As an English officer in the British army, stationed in Inverness and considered by the locals to be depriving a 'native' of employment, Burt was to find himself the target of such remarks as ' . . . it would have been but just that some Native had my Appointment', to which he gave the now standard reply: ' . . . that he would chearfully resign . . . provided no Scotsman had any Government Employment be-south the Tweed; and then I doubted not, but their would be ample room at Home for us all.'
    Ibid., I, 120–1.

45. A professor of History in a Scottish University demonstrates that this option is still exercised today:
    In material terms it paid Scotland 200 years ago to be in full political and economic association with England because of the opportunities provided by the association. And – though I am a simple historian and not involved in political debate – I would have thought that the key question today is the same: what system offers not simply another 20p a week off the rates but what offers the best opportunity for the school leavers and graduates of 1976 to achieve their fullest potential in the remaining 24 years of this century.
    'The Anglo-Scottish Unions', an address given by Prof. S.G.E. Lythe,Vice-Principal and Head of the Dept. of History, University of Strathclyde, to the A.G.M. of the Graduates Association, 1976, Univ. of Strathclyde Newsletter, No.3, Summer 1976, 5–6.

46. Nora Chadwick, *The Celts*, Harmondsworth, Middlesex, Penguin Books, 1970, 47–8.

47. Martin, *A Description of the Western Islands of Scotland* (circa 1695), 2nd edn., Edinburgh, Reprint James Thin, 1970, 195.

48. S.A., XII (Jura and Colonsay), 332.

    A minister on the Isle of Mull also hoped for a more rapid introduction of English and encouraged the introduction of more schools.

    Idem, XIV (Kilninian), 155.

    A modern observer of this scene, Donald MacDonald, a native of Lewis and a school master, has in the last paragraph of his authoritative book on the history of Lewis, the old Lewis proverb:' An diugh anns a'bhuntat, agus a maireach ann an Lunnainn.' [Today in the potatoes and tomorrow in London].

    Donald MacDonald, *Lewis A History of ohe Island*, Edinburgh, Gordon Wright, 1970, 198.

49. N.S.A., XIV (Duirinish), 345.

    In the first half of the eighteenth century, the relationship among education, 'brain drain' and emigration was lamented:

    As manufacture was in no Esteem, men of Fortune thought it beneath them to breed their Children to any Business of that Sort; and therefore, since War ceased to be our chief Trade, the professions of Law, Physick, the Business of a foreign Merchant, and Shop-keeper, reckoned the only suitable Imployments for Persons of Birth and Fortune, have been greatly overstockt. Many Gentlemen, after an expensive Education, are obliged to betake themselves to another Way of Life, or, if they want Spirit and Discretion, to continue in an idle and fruitless Attendance, a Burden upon their Friends and Country. Some young Physicians go abroad, and in these scarcely one in Ten returns: For few Men of Genius, are sufficient to serve the Country in these Professions of Law and Physic, etc.

    Patrick Lindsay, *The Interest of Scotland Considered*, Edinburgh, 1733, 121–2.

50. Margaret Adam, 'The Highland Emigration of 1770', *Scottish Historical Review*, 63, April 1919, 280–293.

    Eric Richards, *A History of the Highland Clearances*, 2 Vols., London, Croom Helm, 1985, II, 46–7, 182–4.

51. O.S.A., IV (Strachur and Stralachlan), 577.

52. O.S.A., III (Applecross), 377.

53. O.S.A., IV (Duirinish), 134–5.

    One boll was the equivalent of 140 pounds. Four firlots equalled one boll. Dry measures varied according to the district and the nature of the weighed crop.

    See also; Logue, Op cit., Meal Mobs, 18–53.

54. T.C. Smout, *A Century of the Scottish People* 1830–1950, London, William Collins, 1987, 67.

55. Johnson, Op cit., 92.

56. The principle of cultural relativism cannot be forgotten when attempting to analyse the ideas, ideals and actions of the past, for, according to Boas,
    The value systems of different cultures are equal: customs, therefore, must be judged in terms of the culture to which they belong, and not by the cultural standards of the anthropologist [or the Establishment].
    Ino Rossi, Ed., *People in Culture*, New York, J.F. Bergin, 1980, 48.

57. N.S.A., VII (Morvern), 186.

58. For a more detailed account of this episode of Highland history see;
    T.M. Devine, *The Great Highland Famine*, Edinburgh, John Donald, 1988.
    Hunter (1976), Op cit., 50–106.

59. The potato famines had two separate effects: an increase in antilandlordism, which polarized the Highlands and further delayed normal acculturation; and the emergence of a modern cultural identity for Gaeldom. Famine also had a significant effect on Highlanders' nutrition, health and disease. Both effects will be discussed in later chapters.

60. It will be subsequently shown that government policy changed arbitrarily to adopt a solution favourable to them. An Act was revoked or amended very rapidly if it impeded other Establishment strategies.

61. Herman Merivale, *Lectures on Colonization and Colonies*, London, 1861, Reprints of Economic Classics, New York, Augustus M. Kelley, 1967, Intro., 1st edn., xii–xiii.

62. George Ensor, *An Inquiry Concerning the Population of Nations*, (1818) N.Y. Reprints of Economic Classics, Augustus M. Kelley, 1967, 214–217.

63. J. M. Roberts, *The Pelican History of the World*, Harmondsworth, Middlesex, Penguin Books, 1983, 660.

64. Eric Richards, *A History of the Highland Clearances*, 2 Vols., London, Croom Helm, 1982, 1985, I, 32.

65. D.M. Sinclair, 'Highland Emigration to Nova Scotia', *The Dalhousie Review*, 28, 1943–44, 212.

66. Malcolm Ferguson, *Rambles in Skye*, Irvine, Chas. Murchland, 1885, 36.

67. Hunter (1976), Op cit., 138–9.

68. J.A. Cameron, 'Storm-Clouds in the Highlands', *The Nineteenth Century, XIV*, No. 91, 379–395.

69. Hunter (1976), Op cit., 138–9, 172, 181.
    A.D. Cameron, *Go Listen to the Crofters*, Stornoway, Acair Ltd., 1986, 49–52.

70. *Health Care: An International Study* Report of the W.H.O./International Collaborative Study of Medical Care Utilization, Eds., Robert Kohn and Kerr L. White, London, Oxford Univ. Press, 1976, 10–11.

71. Edward Dwelly, *The Illustrated Gaelic-English Dictionary,* 8th edn., Glasgow, Gairm, 1973.

72. James Anderson, *An Account of the Present State of the Hebrides and West Coasts of Scotland* etc., *A Report to the Lords of the Treasury,* Edinburgh, 1785, Intro., xxxiv–xxxv.

73. The *Dictionary of Sociology,* Op cit,.
      This definition of a modern social group is akin to the traditional clan parliament, the Norse thing, the Anglo-Norman motte and later the céilidh.

74. T.C. Smout, 'Problems of Nationalism, Identity and Improvement in later Eighteenth-Century Scotland', in *Improvement and Enlightenment,* Ed., T.M. Devine, Edinburgh, John Donald, 1989, 19.

75. Rossi, Op Cit., 238.

76. Ibid., 238.

2

The Making of A'Ghaidhealtachd

this wide extent of hopeless sterility.[1]

POWERFUL PRIMEVAL FORCES had created in Gaeldom a distinctive ecological niche. The Caledonian orogenesis which occurred approximately 400 million years ago brought with it granitic intrusions and further contortion of the ancient sedimentary rocks into folds, overthrusts and metamorphic rock. The faulting associated with this orogeny also produced the thrust-planes that gave rise to the complex geology of the Highlands.

Three of these major faults, which run in an approximate north–north-east to south–south-west direction, are of great significance to the history of the Highlands. The first fault is the Great Glen, which runs from Loch Linnhe to the Moray Firth, effectively separating the Northwest Highlands from the Grampian Mountains. The second, the Highland Boundary fault, extends from Helensburgh on the Firth of Clyde to Stonehaven on the Northeast coast, physically separating the 'Highlands' from the 'Lowlands.' Finally, to the south lies the Southern Uplands fault, running from Loch Ryan in the south-west to Dunbar on the east coast (See Fig. 2).

The same Caledonian upheaval produced an east–west difference: to the east stretches of sedimentary rocks, boulder-clay and outwash material; to the north and west, primary sedimentary rock, with outcrops of older and younger rocks, the features which gave this region its characteristic topgraphy. Furthermore, the tilting of the Highland massif resulted in a long, gentle slope to the east, giving rise to longer river courses there. The pluvial periods of heavy rainfall and the action of the glaciers had also ensured a greater degree of erosion in the wetter west. As a consequence,

> Zones of weakness, lithological or tectonic, were exploited by both main and tributary streams, so that to the basic west-east drainage direction (of the massif) was added another orientation parallel to the strike of the Caledonian folding. River capture on a large scale also dismembered certain sections of former consequent streams to give the aligned, but disconnected, series of east-west valleys which make such a prominent feature of the Highlands at both high

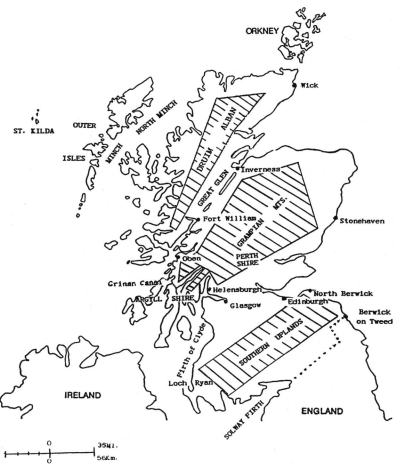

Figure 2. Map of Scotland showing site of natural defences.

and low levels and give a sound geographical basis to the directions followed in the song 'Road to the Isles' although there is no trunk road.[2]

An even more striking geological formation, the profusion of islands lying off the coast, distinguishes Gaeldom's west. These islands can be separated, geologically, historically and culturally, into an outer and an inner group.

In the outer islands, or Hebrides, the geological formations are similar to those found in the north-west Highlands. Their eastern aspects are composed of rock outcrops sparsely covered with bogs and peat; the coast is heavily indented with small, deep inlets. On their west coasts, the pounding Atlantic has produced miles of beautiful beaches. Beyond the sand dunes of the beaches lies the machair, an extensive low-lying plain consisting of a thin layer of topsoil covered with wind-blown sand, sea shells and sea weed.

By contrast, the Inner Hebrides are the product of the Alpine Orogenesis of the Tertiary period and are composed of basaltic volcanic rocks, sills and dykes typified by the basaltic structures of 'Fingal's Cave' on the island of Staffa, near Iona. This formation is linked geologically to the 'Giant's Causeway' in Ulster.

Separating those two island groups is a particularly rough stretch of water, the Minch. While the inshore waters of the inner islands are blessed with the warm Gulf Stream, they are also notorious for swift currents, tidal races and other dangers to navigation.

The topography of the region was further modified by long periods of erosion under climatic conditions as varied as desert and ice field. Indeed, the melting and movement of Ice Age glaciers fashioned the region's environment and permitted the growth of higher forms of life.

On the upper slopes of the glens, the glaciers influenced the topography, the composition of the soil, and the permeability of the ground. The soil of the flats along the river, being either sand or gravel, was liable to excessive drainage and drying out. Nearer the river, the ground of the flood plain was subject to frequent flooding from heavy rainfall carried by the short, steep, swift rivers of the west. Higher up on the valley sides, the soil of the terraces (kames) was laid down by the deposition of sediment from streams that ran beneath the glaciers. O'Dell and Walton accent the importance of glacial action to shaping the Highland ecology:

> From the human point of view, the values of the landscape were profoundly changed. The mantle of débris on the mature valley slopes was frequently swept away and deposited in a less valuable and attractive form at localities on valley floors, which themselves were deepened and widened . . . If the action of the

pre-glacial rivers created the valleys and lowlands which, because of the altitude of the Highlands, were to become permanently settled areas, it was the glaciers which modified them by erosion.[3]

The routeways formed by glacial action later permitted easier social contact among the ecological niches and so expedited the process of acculturation.

I

The flora of the Highland region ranged from Alpine plants above the 3000-foot contour, to stands of hardy sub-Alpine birch trees near the 2000 foot level. Below this elevation and depending on the particularities of topography and climate, there appeared pine and oak forests, heather moors and dry grasslands. At a lower altitude, settlers in some areas would much later manage to grow oats, and in the even lower land of the east and the south, wheat.

Beneath the 2000-foot contour, two forest types developed, pinewood with birch, and the broad-leaved deciduous forest of oak with birch and alder.[4] O'Dell and Walton note that forest cover was not continuous: its presence was influenced by altitude and climatic change.

The passing of the Ice Age, *c.* 10,000 BC, gave rise to several important climatic sub-stages. The first of these was the Pre-Boreal or Subarctic (*c.* 8300–7700 BC). This was followed by the Boreal (*c.* 7700–5550 BC), with its drier, warmer climate. As a result of 3000 years of Boreal climate, the hillsides of the mainland and the eastern side of the inner islands were covered with birch, hazel and alder. In contrast, the western side of the inner islands, as well as the outer islands, were only sparsely covered.

In the next, Atlantic sub-stage (5550–3000 BC), the climate became wet and warmer, and on the mainland's western seaboard the acid soil stimulated the growth of pine and birch. In the outer islands, strong winds restricted tree cover to a lower altitude. Early in this sub-stage, the first mesolithic men arrived. By the end of the period, Neolithic man had appeared.

By the Sub-Boreal (3800–1200 BC) stage, rainfall had eased off. Thus for the next 1500 years, tree growth once more reached the 3000 foot level, and on the inner islands, stands of alder, oak, pine, and ash appeared. On the outer islands, the same trees presented only as scrub. In the next sub-stage, the Sub-Atlantic, from about 1200 BC to the present, the climate has become cooler and wetter; in consequence, the distribution and composition of forests has again changed. In most areas, the forests have retreated, their remains leaving behind thick deposits of peat.

Like the flora, the fauna of the Highlands reflected climatic changes. The ancient animals of the Ice Age adapted to a warmer climate, or became extinct. As the climate improved, the forests maintained a population of elk, deer, boar and beaver. Grasslands provided nourishment for reindeer, Irish elk, wild horse, wild ox, hares and lemmings. Vegetation supported other animals, among them European lynx, brown bear, wolf, fox, stoat and weasel. The seashore abounded with birds, and the seas were rich with seals, dolphins, fish, crabs and shellfish. Whale and walrus were frequent visitors.[5]

Topography and climate dictated which land was suitable for permanent human settlement. The land had to provide protection from the strong forces of nature and later from human encroachment. It had also to support the primitive agriculture of the period. Such land was at a premium, virtually limited to well-drained river deltas and old lake flats, although in areas with drainage, terraces could be reclaimed for human settlement. In short, it was the holding capacity of the land that dictated the eventual demography of the Highlands and Islands, that, in other words, limited its population.

II

This mix of geomorphology, topography, climate, soils and vegetation wove the fabric of Highland life and culture. It made life arduous: survival was vulnerable to any irregularity in the normal rhythm of the seasons and, later, to strangers' misjudgments of its fragility.[6] O'Dell and Walton's description of the extremes of climatic variability of the Highlands and Islands suggests why the Clearances were to cause such misery:

> There are comparatively few regions of the British Isles where, in only a few miles, one may pass from an almost unbelievable luxuriance of vegetation to tundra; from mild oceanic conditions to the rigours of a sub-Arctic climate, from forested valleys and lowlands to a tree-line at less than 1,000 feet above sea level. In addition, the high dissected tableland, straddling the region between the Atlantic and the North Sea, offers similar contrasts in rainfall.[7]

Such profound differences in geology and climate made each area of the Highlands and Islands distinct topographically, which in turn dictated differences in development and settlement. In this discussion we will consider three distinct areas: the Outer Islands, the Inner Islands and the Mainland.

In the Outer Islands, beyond the beaches of the western coast, lies the machair, the 'tangle of the Isles.' In this windswept land (in modern geological times, treeless as well), the machair, especially when manured with sea weed or dung, has been the site of agriculture since prehistoric times. To the east of the machair, the surface of the Outer Isles becomes wet, boggy and covered with numerous lochans. While it is agriculturally useless, this area does supply peat, the only local source of fuel. Further east, however, the land rises, and in this hill country, sheltered, shallow valleys are covered in summer with the rich grazing verdure of the shielings. The eastern coastline of the Outer Islands is indented by small, deep and sheltered harbours, out of which the Islanders fished. When they found it necessary, Islanders engaged also in piracy or, in the eighteenth and nineteenth centuries, in the lucrative and locally respectable vocation of smuggling. In the Outer Isles, then, geology spelled isolation, which in turn fashioned the distinctive culture and history of the area: one of superstition, maritime mythology and tales of sea warriors, pirates and smugglers.

The Inner Islands lacked even the agricultural potential of a machair. On the low flat island of Tiree, the topsoil was unusually thin and always at the mercy of the wind, as a parish minister in the late eighteenth century reported:

> The soil of Tiry is various; sandy, mossy, clay, and black earth, with their different compositions. The sandy soil prevails, and produces very poor crops, except when very well manured. If sown early, there is danger of blowing; if late, of summer drought. The country being flat, even a short continuance of rain endangers the vegetation in the lower grounds. Two-thirds of the whole arable ground are either too wet or too dry; and almost the whole surface is exposed to storms.[8]

Yet though the land was not fertile, it was in many areas dry enough to graze animals. Again, geology determined occupation and therefore a cultural characteristic, in this instance the predominantly pastoral character of the Inner Islanders.

In the third area, the Highland Mainland, early hunter–gatherers had colonised the narrow strips of agricultural land along the western seaboard, as well as the fertile plains and valleys of the eastern lowlands. They had travelled up the eastern and western coasts of Britain, never venturing far from land in their primitive log boats. The decay of the glaciers caused the land to rise and lowered the level of the sea at many points, thus making raised beaches a geological feature of the Highland Mainland. Evidence of the presence of prehistoric man is still being found at the sites of their middens and caves on these raised beaches:

> The raised beaches of the coastal fringe of the Highlands have been of great importance, since apart from providing a habitat with shellfish food supply for

the earliest inhabitants, they frequently afford a belt of fertile flat ground along the otherwise inhospitable glaciated and drowned valley sides of the west Highlands and Islands. They usually form the basis of crofting activity and [trade] routes, while the indentations in the edge of the raised beach themselves are frequently used for small-boat harbours.[9]

In fact, the 'coastal fringe' and 'inhospitable valleys' of the Mainland, no less than the tortured approaches to the Inner and Outer Isles, deterred all but the most determined invaders. A physical map of Scotland (Fig.2) demonstrates the near impregnability of the central and western Mainland. Those who attempted invasion by land were channelled into and along easily-defended natural passes, while those who, like the Vikings, used the sea route to the Highlands and Islands, had not only to be seamen of the highest calibre, but their ships had also to be superbly seaworthy. While it is true that for seamen of a lesser breed, the proximity of Northern Ireland to south-west Scotland made invasion and subsequent settlement by this route relatively simple, history reveals that until the eighteenth century, the topography of *A'Ghaidhealtachd* had discouraged all would-be invaders, at least from the south and the east. In the early period of Highland history, then, the few choice agricultural lands could be won only by force of arms. Later, land would be won by guile and legalities.

In Mainland Scotland, the lifestyle of the early colonists developed differently from that of the Islanders. Here, lifestyle was influenced not so much by the sea as by the dense forests that provided fuel and food. From Mainland Scotland, therefore, came another major influence on Highland culture and folklore, the flora and fauna of the forests, an influence that is evident in the mythology and early histories of many clans. For example, the founder of Clan Matheson (Mathieson); that is, Clann Mhthain, was MacMhathain, the 'son of the bear', and the clan plant badge was the Broom.

The earliest Mainland settlers had started to clear the forests, not only for cultivation, fuel, and building material, but also to create open defensive perimeters to protect their settlements and their domestic animals against surprise attack from man and beast. In the Early Iron Age (*c.* 450 BC to 400 AD), more efficient weapons and tools enabled settlers to increase the clearings; in fact, Iron Age settlement heralded the destruction of most of the original Mainland and Island forests. That critical observer of the late eighteenth-century Highlands and Islands, Dr Samuel Johnson, noted mankind's effect on landscape there:

> The country is totally denuded of its wood, but the stumps both of oaks and firs, which are still found, shew that it has been once a forest of large timber.[10]

Peat, the organic remains of trees and an important source of fuel, was abundant in the cool, wet and poorly drained sites of these ancient forests, and was to become of great economic significance to the Highlanders.

Another set of geological features, the faults, was also significant to the evolution of Gaeldom. The Great Glen fault would become, within the time-frame of this book, the site of the Caledonian canal. Approved for construction in 1802, the canal linked several lochs lying in the fault, and so provided quick and safe boat passage between the east and west coasts. The much smaller Crinan canal, running across the narrow neck of Kintyre, was of more cultural significance since it provided a quicker and safer entrance to the industrial heartland of the West Highlands and Islands, Glasgow and its ports.

Two other faults, the Highland Boundary in the north and the Southern Uplands in the south, demarcated the central lowlands. Between these two faults the nation of Scotland would emerge, and at that border the seeds of cultural disparity would be sown. In recent times, the Highland Boundary fault has been regarded as the 'Highland Line': to the north, Highlanders; to the south, Lowlanders. Yet we do well to remember that the term Highland was not always used to identify a specific territory:

> The commonly reiterated division within Scotland between Highlands and Lowlands is not an immutable fact of geography. It is a cultural creation with precise chronology and known causes: 'Neither in the chronicle nor in the record of the twelfth and thirteenth centuries do we hear of anything equivalent to the 'Highland Line' of later time. Indeed, the very terms 'Highlands' and 'Lowlands' have no place in the considerable body of written evidence surviving before 1300.'[11]

III

The culture of *A'Ghaidhealtachd* was shaped as certainly by its political history as by its physical geography. The initial inhabitants of the Highlands and Islands were Stone Age hunter-gatherers. Their middens and the remains of their fires have been found in the caves of the raised beaches of the area. Those earliest settlers presumably entered the British Isles from Europe before the English Channel was formed; that is, approximately 7000 years ago. Stone Age people were followed by Celts from the Russian steppes. The Celts drifted thus westward across Europe, fleeing successive waves of invaders from the east and south.

While the Celtic peoples did not invade Britain *en masse* between 2000 and 600 BC, they did gradually colonise Britain and Ireland during the next few centuries. From the western seaboard of Europe, the Brythonic Celts migrated to England, the Goidelic Celts to Ireland. The Goidelic Celts who later emigrated to the west Highlands and Islands of Scotland, *c*. 500 AD, were Goidelic Celts from Ulster.[12]

The Brythonic Celtic tribes of Briton were eventually conquered by the Romans and endowed with the distinctive culture of the Roman Empire. The Romans did not invade Ireland, nor did they manage to permanently colonise the lowland areas of Scotland. In the Highlands and Islands of Scotland, cultural infusion came only through colonists from Northern Ireland. Though Irish culture had experienced no direct acculturation by the Roman Empire, it nevertheless bore the signs of Roman Christianity, brought to Ulster from the south-west of Scotland by the Romano-Briton Saint Patrick in *c*. 432. Indeed, Christianity was already present in Ireland before the arrival of Saint Patrick, but the early Christian Church he founded there practised a Christianity heavily influenced by Druidism. When Saint Patrick died and his influence declined, the religion of the people reverted to the Druid-Christianity amalgam:

> People who had believed that their gods and goddesses consorted with them on earth had no difficulty in accepting that Christ had done the same. Saint Columba [521–597], a prince of the royal house of O'Neil, prayed to 'my Druid, Son of God.'[13]

By *c*. 500 AD, the Scotti of Northern Ireland had crossed the narrow sea channel that separated Ireland from Scotland and founded the kingdom of Dalriada in a location that became known as Argyll (*Earraghàideal* – the coastland of the Gael). Christian missionaries such as St Columba (who in 563 founded a monastery on Iona), St Brendan, St Moluag, St Comgall and many other 'lesser saints' brought this Early Christian Church to the Highlands and Islands.[14] In many respects, the Celtic component of the Druid-Christian amalgam practised in Ireland was representative of the original Celtic culture of prehistoric Europe: many of its features were those of its founding Indo-European culture. This mix of European and Celtic culture was common to both Goidelic and Brythonic Celtic peoples, between whom there existed only minor linguistic differences. Yet the Indo-European roots of Celtic culture were preserved only in the remote highlands of Wales. Elsewhere in 'Britain', especially in the more fertile and therefore more populated lands to the south, lands occupied by the then-Romanized Brythonic Celtic tribes, this fundamental Celtic culture survived with less integrity.

The conversion of the Roman Empire to Christianity ensured the introduction of Roman Christian dogma into British Christianity. Differences between Roman Christianity and the earlier Celtic-Christian Church would lead eventually to considerable discord.

The subsequent decline of the Roman Empire ensured the invasion of Britain by Jutes, Angles and Saxons; thus was the Celtic culture compromised further by this second dominant culture, the Anglo-Saxon. The clash of Celtic Goidels and Anglo-Saxons went on for centuries, but the Anglo-Saxon invaders never penetrated Ireland or the Scottish Highlands. On the contrary, the Scottish Picts and the Irish Celts, the Scotti, acting as allies, had themselves raided Roman Britain, *c.* 360–65 BC. In fact, these raids marked the beginning of what became continuous border warfare among the emerging Scottish nation, England to the south, and the Highlands and Islands to the north and the west (the Islesmen at times acting as allies of England). Thus very early were the seeds of cultural turmoil sown among English, Scots and Highlanders.

A significant ecclesiastical event, the 664 Synod of Whitby, also had far-reaching effects on the political history and thereby on the culture of the Gaels. The initial isolation of the Goidellic Celts from the strict influence of Rome meant that this early and isolated Christian Celtic Church still retained, as we have said, many pre-Christian and early Christian traditions and social practices, a heritage unacceptable to the Roman Church.

King Oswiu of Northumbria in northern England decided at the 664 Synod to adopt Roman Christianity. The Celtic monks in the monasteries of Northumbria, lacking charismatic leadership such as might once have been provided by Saint Columba, could only withdraw in protest. During the next few centuries, a discord amounting to schism developed in the Christian Church. In the end, however, the monastic extremism of the Celtic church, coupled with the powerful episcopal control of Rome, guaranteed the decline of the native church, as Berresford Ellis explains:

> . . . its asceticism, monastic extremism and, indeed, fanaticism, its attitudes to social order, views on land tenure, contrary philosophies towards feudal and hereditary rights, brought it into early conflict with Rome. Absorption was inevitable; inevitable because of its very individualism, its lack of cohesion and centralism.[15]

Rome's success notwithstanding, many semi-pagan, Druid-inspired Celtic characteristics survived in remote Gaeldom until the nineteenth century, though they were thinly disguised by the new Roman doctrines and rituals. Many knew that 'The Druids are said to have had a temple at the head of Loch Scridain, in a farm called Rossal, which in Gaelic signifies Judgement or Justice, and here they held their courts.'[16]

Two other events figured significantly in the political history of Gaeldom. Both aggravated the tension between Gaels and their southern neighbours; both mark the gradual erosion and displacement of Celtic culture by the dominant culture to the south. Late in the eighth century came Norse settlement of the Western Isles. The initial Norse invaders, fleeing their own country in search of land and an alternative to feudal despotism, reached Scotland by sea, either as raiders or as refugees. They remained, intermarried, and bequeathed to the West Highlands and in particular to the Islands, a rich cultural legacy. The new Norse-Highland culture conflicted at many points with the Roman-enriched culture of the south, specifically in respect to the tenure of land. Norse law, that is, *Udal* law, asserted that land was held in absolute proprietorship and not as a fief, the possession of which depended on a feudal lord. This *Alloidal* system held further that land was not subject to any burden other than the call to national defence and that on the death of the proprietor, it passed equally to all children or, failing issue, to the next of kin. This law was widespread in northern Europe until the twelfth century, when various monarchies reasserted their authority. In twentieth-century Scotland, certain land is still held alloidally, 'That is to say, of no superior. Church land is of this kind. So is the land (except where feudalised) in Orkney and Shetland Islands whose history and customs are so interestingly foreign.'[17]

Shortly after the first Norse invasion, in the first half of the ninth century, the Kingdoms of the Picts and Scotii were united, creating the new Kingdom of Scotland. Three years after the Norman Conquest of England, the new Scottish Kingdom arranged the marriage of Margaret (two centuries later to become Saint Margaret) to Malcolm III (Malcolm Canmore) of Scotland. That marriage was to seriously erode Celtic customs and the Celtic clan system itself. Queen Margaret, a Saxon brought up in the English court, found Scottish society crude and uncivilised, and in her piety she conceived a mission to convert the Scots from their native barbarism and Celtic customs: she banned Gaelic from the court, eliminated the out-dated usages of the church in Scotland, and brought Benedictine monks to Scotland. Margaret was a Saxon princess with southern sympathies, sympathies made manifest when she granted Scottish land to her Anglo-Norman friends. The resulting Anglo-Norman settlement, though peaceful and politically intriguing, penetrated the fertile lands to the east of the Highland massif. Once established, the progeny of Margaret's friends formed new clans, among them Bruce, Cunningham, Drummond, Fraser, Grant, Hay, Leslie, Menzies, and Sinclair. Other Norman adventurers, soldiers of fortune and landless knights, were to play critical roles in the acculturation of Gaeldom. Indeed one such adventurer, Walter Fitzalan, eventually became Steward of Scotland; his progeny became the Stewart kings of Scotland.

In the twelfth century, Somerled, Thane of Argyll, himself half Norse, half Scot, established himself as King of Argyll, inaugurating a brief Celtic revival. In 1156 he defeated a Norse fleet, thereby gaining control of Skye, the Inner Hebrides and Argyll. The new Scottish court acted quickly and murderously to dismember Somerled's Celtic dominion. To that end, they sent an army into Argyll, which, however, failed in its objective. The Court signed a peace pact with Somerled in 1159. Four years later, the Scottish court, still nervous of Somerled's independent dominion on its west coast, sent another force against him. Battle was not joined, and to prevent another inconclusive diplomatic solution, Somerled was murdered as he slept, a murder planned, some said, by the Steward of Scotland himself. Somerled's achievement was a short-lived Gaelic revival. Scotland's quarrel with Gaeldom was his legacy.

On Somerled's death in 1164, his lands were divided equally among his three sons. Reginald, also known as Ranald or Ragnal, held the Island of Islay and Kintyre; Dubhgall, the progenitor of Clan Dougall, obtained the other Islands of Argyll and the land of Lorne; Angus inherited the islands of Arran and Bute. Reginald styled himself *Reginaldus Rex Insularum Dominus Argile* and his son, Donald, became progenitor of clan Donald, the future Lords of the Isles.[18]

With Somerled's power broken, the only remaining foreign invaders to be removed were the Norse. Following a series of military engagements, the Treaty of Perth (1266) made the Norwegian lands on the Scottish mainland and on the Isles subject to the legislation of the Scottish crown. From 1354 to 1493, the Lords of the Isles ruled the Western Isles and seaboard and 'In thair time thair was great peace and wealth in the Iles throw the ministration of justice.'[19] With that interlude of internal peace came Gaeldom's long and intimate cultural relationship with Ireland, a relationship that strengthened and prolonged the Celtic lifestyle. This Highland – Irish alliance lasted until the early seventeenth century, when Oliver Cromwell's 'Rigid puritanical rule in arts and morals' sent the Celtic lifestyle in Ireland into a decline from which it never really recovered. With that decline, the torch of ancient Goidelic culture was passed to the Highlands and Islands.

In time, however, greed and acculturation proved the undoing of the Lordship of the Isles. The Lords became greedy for the produce of the fertile lands lying to the east of the Highland massif. They entered an alliance with the English kings, treachery that incurred the wrath of the Scottish crown and formed its determination to exterminate the 'foreign culture' lying to its west. Moreover, many lords, educated in the South, adopted the piety they had learned there. There now arose a clash in values that weakened the internal government of the Lordship. Thus, the Scottish crown forfeited the Lordship in 1493. The legal forfeiture did not, however, mark the end of the Lordship; in fact, Hebridean sea power was to continue until Colla Coitach was hanged from the mast of his own galley in 1647. In her discussion of the 'strange prose poem' in the *Book of Clanranald*, written long after the forfeiture, Dr Isobel Grant marvels at

> . . . the persistence of Gaelic literary traditions among a people whose culture, [was] contemned [sic] by the learned, the powerful, the rich of the alien race who had engrossed the direction of the whole civilization of Scotland . . .[20]

The forfeiture of the Lordship terminated the already weakened executive and administrative control of the western seaboard. Uncontrolled clan warfare followed throughout the Highlands. This inter- and intra-clan feuding bankrupted the region. Raids and smuggling became a way of life. Pirates and smugglers ruled the seaboard.

In fact, clan feuding occurred at all of the important demarcation zones: in the south-west, at the Lowland interface; centrally, at the Perthshire or Central Lowland boundary; at the Northeast interface; and in the West, at the interface between the western seaboard and Inner Isles, and the Outer Isles. At all of those boundaries, culture, lifestyle, religion and commercial interests differed.

Another interface developed in the mainland massif itself, one that separated the people of this area into two groups: those with easy access to salt or fresh water frontage, permitting ease of movement and cultural interchange; and those of the 'backlands.' In the hinterland, inter-clan warfare, family feuds, cattle lifting and robbery were the norm. Those desolate badlands, typified by Rannoch Moor and the highlands of Sutherlandshire, were the haunts of 'broken men' and outlaws who owed no permanent allegiance to any chief. In those regions, Highland feudalism, despotism and cruelty flourished in the midst of the grinding poverty that was the lot of every loyal clansman. In those remote districts, lifestyle went unchanged until the mid-eighteenth century.

Military invasion, legislative control, inter-clan feuding – all had marked the serpentine political history of Gaeldom for centuries. In 1513, another battle, the bloody defeat of the Scots by the English at Flodden, destroyed the flower of Scottish and Highland nobility. At Flodden, the southern bastion of the Scottish nation was breached and active acculturation by England commenced.

One agent of that acculturation, the Protestant Reformation, reached Scotland in 1560. Like previous proselytisation and evangelisation of the Celtic people, the Reformation of the Church paved the way for further cultural changes. John Knox's promise of 'a school in every parish' contributed more to the final acculturation of the Highlands than any military actions or political and economic forces before or after.[21]

In 1603, the Anglicisation of the Scottish court was assured when the Crowns of Scotland and England were united and James VI of Scotland became James I of England. With the Union of both Parliaments in 1707, the cultural independence of the Scottish nation, Highland and Lowland, was endangered.

Another vehicle of cultural erosion is trade, and after the Union of Scotland and England, trade between the Highlands and England flourished. Drove roads, part of the infrastructure for trade, were said to have been in place since the twelfth century. They now became well-used, reaching peak traffic in the eighteenth and nineteenth centuries.[22] In fact, the narrow kyles of the Islands and the hill passes of the drove roads became two-way streets.

The Minch, or Minches, for there are two, provided West Islanders with a drove road of their own. The Islands were surrounded by marine life and crustaceans of many species, from whales to crabs, which constituted a lucrative commercial fishery, particularly in herring for those, invariably from outwith the Highlands and Islands, with the finances and determination to exploit it. The seaway provided access to the mainland markets, particularly Glasgow, and with the advent of the steamship, acculturation of the Outer Isles quickened.[23]

IV

This chapter's brief summary of the creation of *A'Ghaidhealtachd* demonstrates its early impregnability to land attack from the south and east and its relative safety even from seaborne invaders. *A'Ghaidealtachd* was indeed a product of its physical history, one of profound geological upheavals and harsh, unforgiving climatic changes. The resulting security and isolation of the region were responsible for its long-lived cultural purity.

Yet isolation could not prevent internal strife, nor border turmoil. Still, Gaeldom did not fall from force of arms, Flodden and Culloden notwithstanding. Acculturation alone brought it down. That invasion was first accomplished by men of peace; the acculturation they effected brought more rapid and more enduring change than any armed invasion could have.

Notes

1. Samuel Johnson, *Journey to the Western Islands of Scotland* 1773. in *A Tour of the Hebridies Johnson & Boswell*, R.W.Chapman, Ed., London, Oxford, Univ. Press, 1993, 34.

    Johnson, a critical observer of post Culloden Highlands and Islands, continued:

    > The appearance is that of matter incapable of form or usefulness, dismissed by nature from her care and disinherited of her favours, left in its original elemental state, or quickened only with one sullen power of useless vegetation.

2. A.C.O'Dell and K.Walton, *The Highlands and Islands of Scotland*, London, Thomas Nelson and Sons Ltd., 1962, 14.

    Much of the technical information used in this chapter comes from this informative book.

3. Ibid., 19, 22.

4. Ibid,. 55.

5. Ibid., 49–57, 58–60.

6. Since the time of the Druids, seasonal changes, the astronomical compilation of their timings, the importance of the warmth and the life giving rays of the sun had made sun worship, fertility rites and harvest thanksgiving all vital and integral parts of Celtic culture.

7. O'Dell and Walton, Op cit., 37.

8. O.S.A., X (Tiry), 295.

9. O'Dell and Walton, Op cit., 33.

10. Samuel Johnson, Op cit., 30.

11. Charles Withers, 'The Historical Creation of the Scottish Highlands', in *The Manufacture of Scottish History*, Eds., Ian Donnachie and Christopher Whatley, Edinburgh, Polygon, 1992, 144–5.

12. Myles Dillon and Nora Chadwick. *The Celtic Realms*, 2nd edn., London, Weidenfield and Nicolson, 1972. 4.

13. Ian Grimble, *Clans and Chiefs*, London, Blond & Briggs, 1980, 31.

14. W.H. Murray, *The Islands of Western Scotland: The Inner and Outer Hebrides*, London, Eyer Methuen, 1973, 153, 159.

    For further details on specific saints see:

    Edwin Sprott Towill, *The Saints of Scotland*, Edinburgh, The Saint Andrew Press, 1978.

15. Peter Berresford Ellis, *Celtic Inheritance*, London, Muller, 1985, 1.

16. N.S.A.VII (Kilfinichen and Kiliceuen), 306.

17. A.D. Gibb, *A Preface to Scots Law*, Edinburgh, W. Green & Son, 1964, 62.

18. G.W.S. Barrow, *Kingship and Unity* Scotland 1000–1300, The New History of Scotland, London, Edward Arnold, 1981, 108–110.

19. Alexander Grant, *Independence and Nationhood* Scotland 1306–1469, The New History of Scotland, London, Edward Arnold, 1984, 209–215.

20. I.F. Grant, *The Lordship of the Isles*, Edinburgh, James Thin, 1982, 205–6.

21. For a brief summation of the 'Scottish Myth' in which the equality of educational opportunity is assumed to have existed, and of the part played by John Knox and the Reformation see:

    A.Allan McLaren, 'Introduction: An Open Society?' in *Social Class in Scotland: Past and Present*, Ed., A.Allan McLaren, John Donald Pubs., Ltd., 1976, 2–4.

22. A.R.B. Haldane, *The Drove Roads of Scotland*, London, Thomas Nelson and Sons Ltd., 1952, 14.

    For the history of later roads in Scotland see by the same author, *New Ways Through the Glens*, London, Nelson, 1962.

23. O.S.A. XX (Barra), 341.: III (Gairloch), 89–91.

    The minister of Tiree hoped that with the opening of the Crinan canal [opened in 1801] 'there will be an increase in trade in all the Western Isles.' Idem., X (Tiry), 416–7.

3

Am Fasgadh

It is true that of far the greater part of things, we must content ourselves with the knowledge as description may exhibit, or as analogy supply; but it is true likewise, that these ideas are always incomplete, and that at least, till we have compared them with realities, we do not know them to be just.[1]

HOMO SAPIENS SAPIENS (modern thinking man) was never the sole occupant of his niche; he shared the space with other members of the ecological chain. Thus humankind's struggle to satisfy basic needs has always been a struggle to maintain a symbiotic relationship within a chosen ecological niche. The continuance of life for each species has depended on strength, fortitude and ability. Most important, survival has depended on being able to adapt to the changing demands made by the niche. In many places, niches were once freely selected. Migratory members of the niche could move to more suitable sites should one niche prove inadequate. In *A' Ghaidhealtachd*, suitable sites were not numerous, so when the geophysical activity of the present epoch subsided, earlier settlement sites were reinhabited. Thus Highland settlements occupied the same general area as had settlements in the Neolithic Age. In fact, the shore settlements of the earlier Mesolithic Age hunters and gatherers are still being found on the raised beaches of the western seaboard.

The niche supplied man and his animals with water, food, clothing and shelter, although supply varied with changing climate. In Viking times, for example, fig trees grew on Lewis, where now stunted trees struggle to survive.[2] In Gaelic, *fasgadh* means protection, shelter, or refuge. Highland man, like the rest of his naked species, was obliged to shelter himself, his family and his possessions from the elements and from predators. But for Highlanders as for all people, shelter, home, provided much more than protection: it supplied fire for warmth and cooking; a secure resting place in which to regain strength; a locus for a lifestyle that included family, community and culture, as well as privacy and reflection. It was a place to repair physical and mental wear; it resuscitated belief in the future.

Within that sheltering niche, the type of house constructed or adapted reflected the resources available in the niche. Ice, wood, heather, rushes, stones, hides and furs: all were the material of distinctive refuges, all were part of distinctive habitats. Shelter was therefore representative of a region's topography and climate, and shelter and its site reflected and influenced the lifestyle and culture of its people. Such was certainly the case in the Highlands:

> Such are the effects of habitation among mountains, and such were the qualities of the Highlanders, while their rocks secluded them from the rest of mankind, and kept them an unaltered and discriminated race.[3]

At the Highlander's level of subsistence living, house or home meant rudimentary shelter, a response to climate and a product of the building materials available. It was simple, functional, movable and disposable.

In the Highlands and Islands, six factors were fundamental to establishing and maintaining shelter as we have broadly defined it. First was the right to make use of life-supporting land, a privilege later to become synonymous with land ownership. The second, one that followed quickly on the heels of ownership, was the payment of some form of rent for the use of the land. The third factor, the use of kelp as fertilizer and as supplementary food for livestock, though not prerequisite to shelter as such, was nonetheless primary in maintaining the Highlander's ecological niche. (In the late eighteenth and early nineteenth centuries, the kelp industry provided much needed employment as well. In fact, the end of the kelping boom, and in the second decade of the nineteenth century, the sudden demise of the kelp industry, played a cardinal role in the social history of the West Highlanders and Islanders.) Fourth was the necessity of a constant supply of food and fuel. Fifth was the distinctive farming system of the habitat, one that was the result of social and ecological interaction. The sixth factor was adaptive modification of the structure of the house itself, adaptation that mirrored changes in *am fasgadh*. We shall discuss those factors in turn in this chapter.

I

Possession and local democratic control of productive land was the Highlanders' prime requirement for settlement:

> . . . although they lived in a rude, and almost savage state, they seldom suffered under the pressure of famine or destitution. Situated in localities remote from one another, each family had a sufficient extent of land to support a number of sheep and cattle.[4]

The traditional Highland clan structure supplied the requirement for control of adequate land. In clan structure, the new chief had to obtain the sanction of the clan before he could take office, acknowledgement that his power derived from theirs. Because the chief was elected democratically, the clansman followed him by choice, not compulsion; consequently, a clansman felt himself to be of importance in a society whose every commitment was his, and in which he could speak his mind without his loyalty being questioned.[5] The principle of reciprocal responsibility was so well established in Celtic clan culture that Julius Solinus, writing in the third century, could note that 'The King of the Hebudae [the Western Isles] was not allowed to possess anything of his own lest avarice should drive him from truth and justice.'[6] What is more, land belonged to the clan. The full members of the ancient Celtic clans; that is, the natives, not the 'incomers', were virtually classless and enjoyed from their leaders a respect unknown to men of most other countries. In fact, in the traditional system of land tenure, the term 'landlord' is a misnomer. The lord was not a lord of the land, but of the people on it. They had the use of the land (the 'usufruct') and the lord had the 'lordship' — the military and social command of his people.

Later, with the advent of feudalism, democratic control of land was reduced or lost. Feudalism spawned what we know as landlordism, a system of land tenure radically different from traditional clan holdings. Feudalism first appeared in England in the eleventh century, with the Norman invasion of that country. Feudalism is

> that social system which was firmly established in Western Europe in the centuries between the tenth and the seventeenth. Under this system the land was divided into fiefs, large or small, which were held on condition of pledging allegiance and rendering military service to an overlord. The largest fiefs were held by powerful nobles who owed military service directly to the king. In return for the armed services rendered the overlord, he, in turn, was responsible to his vassals for the protection of their lands and persons.[7]

In the fourteenth century, in accordance with then-current Anglo-Norman practice, the Scottish crown granted land charters to favoured individuals for services rendered. This action signalled the emergence of a distinct Celtic feudalism comprising elements of the older Celtic, Norse and Anglo-Norman feudal systems. However, the new feudalism overturned the definition of legal ownership, as well as the principle of a heritor's stewardship of the land. The new absolute power invested in feudal chiefs challenged the Highlander's traditional right to use hill land as common pasture and to hunt wild animals, and it restricted his use of land as a source of fuel.[8] In short, feudalism dismantled the clan system. It did so by a single act of legislation, the Register of Entails, in 1685:

The essential idea of the entail is a diversion of the line of descent usual in heritage. A special line of descent is marked out in the deed of entail and this is safeguarded by prohibitions against burdening the estate with debt, alienating it or altering the order of succession. Disregard of these by the heir of entail in possession involves forfeiture of his rights.[9]

Somers, writing as late as 1848, described the gross injustice of entail:

The law of entail places the heirs in possession in a most humbling and powerless position. While it retains the position of administering the property in hands which have long withered in the grave, it gives its revenues to money-lenders, whose shadowy forms are equally wrapped up from public responsibility. The heir in possession stands before the world as the corporeal representative of these spectred deities, without their power or their wealth, a mark to be shot at for their impunity, and a butt of general contempt. This system might live while it was optional for property to fulfil or evade its obligations; but in that state of stern and compulsory government which is necessary for the Highlands, it is totally impracticable. The heirs in possession must be free agents. They must have power to improve, to borrow, to sell part or the whole of their estates, to bear the burdens of their station, or, if not able, to make room for those who are.[10]

Neither predetermined by previous cultural tenets, nor legitimized by Celtic law, feudalism installed a new class of clan chief, one who wielded absolute power and who quoted English law, by then firmly established in Scotland, even when it violated prevailing Scottish legal precedent, to prove his legal right to do as he saw fit with an estate and those on it. The minister of North Uist commented on the new chiefs' detachment from their people:

The chieftains, for different motives, have withdrawn themselves from their estates, have become unacquainted with their people, whom they visit but seldom, are not so attentive to the ties of consanguinity, and are become less scrupulous in removing the tacksmen from their farms, if a higher offer is made than the possessors can afford to pay.[11]

Absolute power corrupted absolutely. A revealing insight into the extent of feudal corruption in the early seventeenth century can be gleaned from one of the many attempts to abolish it, the Statutes of Iona of July 1609.[12] King James VI (I), in an attempt to establish law and order and to improve the quality of life of the common people by maintaining religion and curtailing the abuses of the chiefs in the rebellious west, forced the most powerful chiefs and chieftains in the West Highlands and Islands to approve the Iona Statutes. The Statutes are lengthy and have been amended several times since 1609, but from even a précis of the reforms they demanded, we can infer the feudal chiefs' abuse of common Gaels:

1. The Church and Clergy were to be maintained.

2. Inns were to be established to relieve the people of burdensome hospitality.

3. The Chiefs' households were to be cut in size, to be supported by themselves, and not by tax on the tenants; and no man was to live on the Isles without a trade or personal income.

4. Sorners were to be punished as thieves. [A sorner is one who obtrudes himself on another for bed and board.]

5. Islesmen in future were not to import wine, but might continue to brew their own ale [an attempt to stop smuggling].

6. Every man owning sixty cattle *must send his eldest son to a lowland school* [italics are mine].

7. The use of firearms was forbidden [to control feuding].

8. Bards who glorified war were to be discouraged.[13]

Inevitably, the change in the fundamental role of the chief and his consequent pre-occupation with power and status led to parasitic exploitation of the clan's major natural resources, human and otherwise:

> But in general, it seems quite contrary to Reason, Justice and Nature, that any one Person, From the meer Accident of his Birth, should have the Prerogative to oppress a whole Community, for the Gratification of his own selfish Views and Inclinations; And I cannot but think, the concerted Poverty of a People, is, of all Oppressions, the strongest Instigation to Sedition, Rebellion, and Plunder.[14]

The chiefs' egotism retarded development of the arts, religion, education, commerce and agriculture. Gaelic culture, centuries in the making and equal to though different from English, Scottish or Irish cultures, was arrested.

This was not of course how the Establishment regarded the demise of the clan system. For the 8th Duke of Argyll, for example, a member of the Scottish Establishment, it was 'the decline . . . of usages of unwritten and unknown law.' For Argyll, feudal control of land meant that backwardness and irresponsibility had been replaced by the progressive rule of law:

> It was the emergence . . . of powers and influences which were embedded in the Legislation of many centuries, and had been from time immemorial the basis of all civilisation. The Chief, as such, lost a power which was checked by no responsibility, and was only by accident connected with any public duty. The Proprietor, as such, became free to exercise powers which were recognised by law, and were, in the nature of things, inseparably bound up with the progress of the country and the advance of agriculture.[15]

Argyll's 'progressive rule of law' had certainly put an end to clan feuding. That in turn meant that landlords no longer had the expense of maintaining fighting men. But dominance was expensive nonetheless. The new Highland gentry needed to generate more money from their estates which, in most cases, were their only source of income. There was advantage to the gentry, furthermore, in keeping money out of the hands of Highland tenants, as Dr Johnson observed after his 'Journey' to the Highlands in 1773:

> When the Laird could only eat the produce of his lands, he was under the necessity of residing upon them; and when the tenant could not convert his stock into more portable riches, he could never be tempted away from his farm, from the only place where he could be wealthy. Money confounds subordination, by overpowering the distinctions of rank and birth, and weakens authority by supplying power of resistance, or expedients for escape. The feudal system is formed for a nation employed in agriculture, and has never long kept its hold where gold and silver have become common.[16]

II

In the traditional clan system, land was used to support clansmen and their animals. Feudalism made land a commodity which earned money for its owners.[17] The notion of land as a commodity to be rented overturned the clan right of use, and so changed profoundly the way Highland society functioned.

The Treaty of Perth (1266) had marked the beginning of Celtic feudalism: it invested legal ownership of all Scotland in the Scottish crown. Clan chiefs held their land as part of a fiefdom, and had a commitment to raise fighting men when required for the army of their feudal superior. They would, in turn, by means of *bonds of manrent*, protect adjacent weaker clans in return for their commitment of loyalty and a roster of fighting men on request. Later, in more peaceful times, the chiefs' duty was to maintain the King's law in their clan lands. Until Culloden, some of the more powerful chiefs were the Heritable Sheriffs of large portions of the country and so had power to hold court, to act as judge and jury, and to execute criminals in the King's name. (The abolition of these local power bases was one of the first punitive acts which followed Culloden.)

In this new feudal role, the chiefs did no menial work and lived the leisurely and, in most cases, the cultured and educated life of proud Highland gentlemen. As the tempo of acculturation increased, chiefs were invariably attracted to the centres of their adopted culture, Edinburgh, London and the cities of Europe. In those milieux, however, wealth was not the number of fighting men one could raise; it was money, and money could be obtained from one source only – from renting land.

To provide for their households and to meet their obligations to their superiors, the chiefs would subdivide clan lands into 'tacks' or large farms, leasing them to family or close relations. The lessees, or tacksmen, were the gentlemen farmers who managed a chief's lands; they were the middle class of the clan, its factors and rent collectors. When necessary, tacksmen would sub-let their own land to others, usually pastoral farmers who raised black cattle, sheep, goats and horses, and who paid their land rent out of the sale of those animals.[18] Together with the tacksmen and chiefs, these tenants represented the *freemen* class of feudal Celtic society.

Below the tenants were the *unfreemen*, the majority of clansmen. To be unfree was not new in the Highlands and Islands: slavery had existed during the Norse occupation, when slaves, called *thralls*, were freely bought and sold. In the early stage of Norse occupation of the Highlands, native Celts were, therefore, 'enthralled' by their conquerors, though they might eventually obtain free status.

The unfree class rarely had legal claim to land. To graze their animals, they leased land from a tenant or tacksman. They paid rent in kind or by service and, when not so employed, were allowed to work their own land. Rising rents made the demand on their time so onerous that in most cases they had only two days in the work week in which to tend to their own land, a shortfall that had to be made up by their women. Though the rights of those unfree sub-tenants, later to be called crofters, were as well guaranteed as any, crofters could not, even by dint of hard work, raise themselves above their station.

At the bottom of this social organization stood the largest class of Highlanders, the cottars, sometimes called scallags: the common agricultural labourers, the lower class tradesmen, and the loyal clansmen of Culloden Moor. Cottars had no connection with the groups above them socially, and they had no rights. They supplied a pool of cheap labour for all. In time, the dividing line between unfree sub-tenant and cottar blurred and a sub-tenant could, at the whim of his superiors or as a result of economic reversal, be made destitute and reduced to the ranks of the cottar.[19]

A cottar fortunate enough to have access to good land could support his family and work off his rent in labour or in kind, raising crops or animals which his superiors then converted into money. Smallholders with poor land, if they had an understanding resident landlord, tacksman or tenant, could exist by working almost entirely for their proprietor by means of *commutation-rent*; that is, by providing services in lieu of money or victual rent. Cottars were generally not told how much time they had to work, though they were told the type of work to be accomplished in various seasons. These smallholders had in fact become agricultural labourers.[20]

The full impact of commutation-rent on the lives of those who laboured under it was staggering. Those who controlled the land used their people's need for it against them, to enslave them or to drive them from it. Those ends were accomplished by legal and political manipulation. To live within feudal society was to live under a law formulated by and for one class, and the legal system protected itself against any radical change to that regime. In 1744, the 3rd Duke of Argyll's instructions to his various chamberlains demonstrates the hold estate owners had on their tenants:

> You are to treat with the tenants of that part of my estate under your management for tacks of the farms where the possessors are under bad character or are not affected to the Government or my interests, and in farms that are now under tacks you are to use your endeavours to introduce tenants that are well-affected to the Government and my family, and as I am informed that my lands are rather too high-rented in these countrys, so that there may be a necessity of some abatement of rent, I do approve that those abatements be chiefly given in those farms where you can bring in people well disposed to my interests.[21]

It was, therefore, impossible during this period for *unfreemen or cottars* individually or collectively to seek redress for a grievance – as their ancestors had once done in an earlier, egalitarian Celtic society.

In estate management, the object for all landlords was profit. Their conduct in pursuit of that end varied, however, from benign paternalism to ruthlessness and rapacity. One landlord whose actions bespeak paternalism was the 8th Duke of Argyll. His management of the huge Argyll estates was agriculturally sound, and his concern for his tenants genuine. His estate was nonetheless the site of tension among tenant crofters. Argyll recognized the fragility of the soil on the island of Tiree. He also saw its great potential, if properly managed, as lush pasture land for dairy cattle. To protect Tiree for its most profitable use, he laid down detailed directives for its management, and he was adamant that his directives be followed:

> In all modern leases there are certain stipulations binding the tenant to observe the rules of 'good husbandry', and often these rules are specified with great minuteness. Their one and only object is to prevent waste and deterioration of the soil. At a time when small tenants were only just rising out of the wretched 'run-rig' system, and when the very elements of good husbandry in the rotation of crops were unknown to them, it was an absolute necessity that the tenants should be bound to cultivate according to the rules laid down for them by those who manage the estate. Neither thirty years ago, nor at the present

moment, can some rules in regard to cropping be dispensed with, — especially in Tyree, where, in addition to all the evils of bad management, there is the special and additional danger arising from 'sand-blowing.'[22]

But such directives, however well-meaning and agriculturally sound, entailed severe strictures for tenants. The Duke's tenants complained. Indeed, the estate orders referred to above were part of the Duke's response to complaints made by the Tiree tenants.

Cregeen's research confirms that the paternalism characteristic of the Duke's grandfather, the 5th Duke, had influenced his grandson, as that grandson's [the 8th Duke's] management philosophy confirms:

> There is another reason why population should increase upon the Duke of Argyll's property. From his estate, small tenants are never removed, *while they behave properly* [italics are mine]. It is no secret in the country that his Grace continued their farms to small tenants at the former rent, though large augmentations were offered by gentlemen who were better able, and would pay their rent more punctually. From the same principle of humanity, it has also happened often, that his Grace, though with loss of rent, ordered farms to be divided into smaller portions, to accommodate numbers that would otherwise be destitute, and obliged, with weak and helpless families, to leave the country.[23]

On other estates, however, rents continued to increase. Johnson describes the plight of one of his hosts: his 'wealth consisted of one hundred sheep, as many goats, twelve milk-cows, and twenty-eight beeves ready for the drover'; yet that man's land rent had in twenty-five years been advanced from five to twenty pounds.[24] Elsewhere, on the MacLeod estates on Skye, rents nearly trebled in 1811.[25]

In the first half of the nineteenth century, the post-war economic depression led many landlords, Highland chiefs as well as newcomers, to raise rents repeatedly to pay for estate improvements and to employ professional factors or estate managers. In the second half of the eighteenth century and in the early decades of the nineteenth century, many landowners had become dependent on the income their estates generated. Moreover, they knew that to be productive, they had to keep up with the improvements in estate management then being introduced by the Agricultural and Industrial Revolutions.

Landlords wanting to make their estates more profitable found a champion in James Loch. From 1812 till his death in 1855, 'James Loch was the major instrument in the direction and execution of the economic policies of the [Stafford] family', and to Loch, the basic problem was that the interior tenants 'had too liberal supplies in former years and the custom of importing meal for them annually, had tended to increase their numbers, their idleness and their attachment to their mountain spots.'[26] In 1816, Loch had drawn up long-term plans for remodelling the Stafford estate. He advised Lady Stafford that successful resettlement of the people from the Sutherland Highlands depended not only on the availability of further suitable coastal lands, but also on gradual relocation:

> I am afraid both from the temper of the people at large as well as the feeling of *government* [italics are mine] we must get them out of the hills gradually though the other course [more rapid resettlement] would be most for their own happiness and comfort.

Richards notes this 'perennial paradox of the Sutherland policies – the need to compel people to do what was designed "for their own happiness and comfort." ' Loch also admitted that the vast numbers involved prevented the idea of comprehensive clearance: 'some' he concluded, 'must never be moved at all.'[27]

Moreover, Loch saw to it that financial relief to the Sutherland estates' tenants was administered selectively. Thus of the £10,000 Lord Stafford spent on tenants' relief in 1817, Loch arranged that coastal settlers, then the most needy, be given first priority, followed by those interior tenants who paid rent directly to the estate. He was adamant that no relief be paid to sub-tenants. They, he argued, were the responsibility of tacksmen:

> It is only common justice that those who are the occasion of such a population being created and multiplied, and who in better years derive all the advantages from their existence, should in the years of scarcity contribute to feed them and feel some of the disadvantages arising from too numerous a population.[28]

Loch's plans for the great clearances of 1819–20 were approved by the Countess (Lady Stafford) and she wrote:

> I should think the experience [of the recent famine] must do something with the people themselves in convincing them of the impossibility in the present state of the world of such a system of society continuing.[29]

But Loch's humanitarian plans were opposed:

> In 1818, Loch's plans for clearing the interior were found unacceptable by the Revd David Mackenzie, Minister of the parish of Farr on the coastal lands of Strathnaver. The minister informed Loch that he could not bring himself in his pulpit, to tell the 220 families to be affected that the removal would 'be for their advantage'. In reply to Mackenzie's letter of concern, Loch assured him that the plan would proceed and the proposed clearance was 'not undertaken in the mere wantonness of power' — it had been most thoroughly considered, with the benefit of the people foremost in the mind of the Stafford family.[30]

And in truth, although the Sutherland clearances are usually cited as the cruellest of the Evictions, Loch himself tried to proceed reasonably:

> He wrote beseeching letters to Suther [the estate factor], to avoid haste, to take two years if necessary, to make the rents 'as moderate as your duty to the landlord and the real interest of the tenant will permit', and to give the people not even the slightest excuse for complaint.

Loch also advised Suther:

> When you find any obstinacy in those who are to be moved and who owe money, you can manage by showing them that if they go quietly they may both get a cheaper lot and be excused their arrears . . . I consider the state of arrears they have got into gives us the right to do so.[31]

Many smaller landowners and their improving managers behaved more selfishly and rapaciously.[32] The minister of Duirinish on Skye noted in the *New Statistical Account* several means which unscrupulous landowners might employ to enrich themselves and beggar their people:

> Thus an avaricious proprietor may at any time increase his rental in this country, by the subdivision of his farms, and for some years he will succeed in exacting every penny of his rack-rent. Again, if he wishes to sell his property, the long rent-roll duly attested will enhance the value of it in the market. If he be desirous of borrowing money, through the same roll he may induce a money lender, ignorant of the actual state of matters, to advance on the security of the property a sum double its actual value. There are here strong temptations for hard-hearted avarice to deepen the evil under which the island already groans, to encourage the increase of the already teeming population, and there is an open door for cruelty on the one hand, and for fraud on the other;[33]

Such landowners met little resistance. In fact, the Duirinish minister, like most of his colleagues, blamed 'the evil' on the ignorance and inertia of the people themselves in submitting to extortion and to want. Indeed, there was everywhere among Highlanders 'the fear of having the fruits of their industry called for by their landlords, many of whom think that they have a right to the earnings of the tenants, except what barely supports life.'[34] Moreover, in some of the estates that engaged in the lucrative venture of kelping, kelpers received no cash for their work if their rent were in arrears. Their wages were merely credited against the rent they owed their landlord.[35] Even in Tiree, the saying ran that ' Mur b'e eagal an da mhail, bheireadh Tiridhe an da bharr' [But for the fear of a double rent, Tiree would yield a double crop].[36]

Rent had become the preoccupation in the Highlands. To the landlord, insufficient revenue from rents meant bankruptcy. To the small sub-tenants and cottars, failure to pay rents could mean eviction, pauperism, starvation and disease. That prospect kept them submissive. It also reinforced in Highlanders a fervent passion to be free from the control of landlords and to acquire permanency of land tenure.

III

The French wars of the late eighteenth century had been a prosperous time for Highland landowners, and for some Highlanders themselves. The wars brought on a boom to kelping estates, at least initially.

In seaboard estates amply supplied with kelp, landowners encouraged their people to move to the shores to engage in this profitable industry; thus they ensured they would be paid rent. 'My grandfather', wrote the 8th Duke of Argyll, 'paid to the people so high a price for their kelp that practically they had no rent to pay.'[37] At first, most who worked at this arduous and at times hazardous occupation could pay their rent with money, so for a short time their future looked good and they deserted the land, 'regardless of the detriment to their corns [oats] and pastures.'[38]

Kelping, introduced first in North Uist in 1735, was seasonal and labour-intensive. Kelp seaweed was gathered from the sea, burned on the beach and the ash recovered. The soda-ash, sodium carbonate, was used in the manufacture of glass, soap and linen. In the south, soda-ash had long been made commercially from barilla, a plant imported from Spain and other Mediterranean countries. When the Seven Years' War began in 1756, the French blockade of Britain reduced the supply of barilla, and those estates with kelping shores made up the shortfall.

It did not take long for landlords of the kelping estates to decide that since the kelp was on their shores, and the soda-ash made from it was produced on the same shores by their own people, then the whole kelping process should be handled by the estate. (We will show in a later chapter that the shore and everything on it between high and low water was, in fact, not legally theirs. That legal nicety they skilfully bypassed.) They bought the soda ash for the price of the labour involved and sold it at market price, in the process making a healthy profit. In addition, their tenant-labourers paid them higher rents. Johnson commented on that point:

> This new source of riches has raised the rents of many maritime farms; but the tenants pay, like all other tenants, the additional rent with great unwillingness; because they consider the profits of the kelp as the mere product of personal labour, to which the landlord contributes nothing.[39]

When the battle of Waterloo in 1815 ended the war with France and with it the blockade of Mediterranean barilla, the Scottish kelping industry soon lost its commercial viability. The final blow to Highland kelping came in the late 1820s, when the traditional method for manufacturing sodium carbonate was replaced by the Leblanc chemical process.[40] The decline of the kelping industry highlighted once again the urgency of the Highland Problem. A redundant and pauperised native population were forced to move once more to find other menial employment. Those who remained haunted the shores in search of edible food. Many of the landlords of the Highland kelping estates faced bankruptcy.[41]

IV

The relocation of the poor to the kelping shores had not been without damage to those regions. For kelpers, the potato was a nutritional staple, since even on wet, windy and salty shoreland, fertilized as it was by seaweed, the potato thrived. But these small coastal potato patches were quickly exhausted, and the poor, always vulnerable to economic depression and crop or fishery failure, were acutely susceptible to any failure of the potato crop.

Highlanders had originally resisted the introduction of the potato. The following observation attests to that resistance. Ironically, it also foretells the impending disaster of over-confidence on the potato as the sole food staple:

> About 15 years ago [*c.* 1775], the present minister was obliged to give over the cultivation of potatoes, except a little for his own private domestic use, because prejudices hindered the people from eating them; but his perseverance in using them in his own family at last convinced the people of their error, and the vast utility of that article . . . *Kail or cabbage of any kind is not used here; since their prejudice against potatoes has been overcome, they chuse to bestow their manure on the latter rather than the former* [italics are mine].[42]

The population had grown quickly during the prosperous kelping period: the buoyancy of the kelp economy had encouraged earlier marriage and larger families; the early abundance of potatoes had provided adequate food supply; and the reacceptance of inoculation (variolation) and the discovery of vaccination kept more people alive. The 8th Duke of Argyll observed that

> The potato had been introduced earlier, and had served well to support the growing multitudes. The population of Tiree had increased more rapidly than the population of Glasgow, so that from 1769 to 1802 it had increased from 1,670 to 2,776, and in 1846 it had mounted up to 5,000.[43]

The extent of what had become a dangerously rapid increase in population can be gleaned from census returns like those that follow. These figures are for Scotland as a whole, and for three representative Highland counties:

	Scotland	Argyll	Inverness	Ross & Cromarty
1755	1,265,380	66,286	59,563	8,084
1795	1,526,492	76,101	73,979	55,430
1801	1,608,420	81,277	72,672	56,318
1811	1,805,864	86,541	77,671	60,853
1821	2,091,521	97,316	89,961	68,762
1831	2,364,386	100,973	94,797	74,820
1851	2,888.742	97,371	96,500	82.707[44]

This dramatic rise in the population of the Highlands occurred despite substantial pre-war emigration. The increase was attributed to Highlanders' large families, and additionally to such diverse influences as whisky distilling, the fisheries and the rise of crofting (sub-tenancy).[45] (Not until the late nineteenth century would the population of the Highlands and Islands start to decline.[46]) When population growth made it necessary to subdivide squatters' land, their small lots, never adequate as a prime supporter of life, became dangerously crowded, the potato patches barely large enough to sustain life.[47]

In fact, most estates in the coastal regions had never been able to supply sufficient grain to meet local demands. The shortfall was usually made up by the proprietors' purchase of grain, usually in bulk from mills in the Lowlands and the North-East. The meal was sold to the people at cost for cash, or its price was included in land rent.[48] In Tiree, 'We bought cargoes of Indian meal [maize], and gave it out to the people in wages for systematic drainage of the land.'[49] A chief sometimes provided such relief by raiding the nearest source of food. A resident heritor might do so by buying or transferring food from better supplied areas within his estate(s). The fact is that most parishes could not produce enough grain to last more than a few months in any year. Thus Highland sub-tenants and cottars, farming poor land, usually at the wrong time in the season, were extremely vulnerable to any failure in the supply of other food staples, particularly since the potato itself was available for only nine months of the year. That circumstance created in the Highlands a dependency made more urgent by increasing population.

By the nineteenth century, local assistance was no longer customary. Crop failures and population increase inspired a plea for relief from all quarters of the Highlands.[50] The demand was for immediate release of estate land to the common people so that they could support themselves, and for the establishment of viable local industries so that the spiritual, moral and physical harm of unemployment could be forestalled – and rents once more paid.[51]

V

That the Establishment treated the Highlands like colonies to be exploited was a conclusion many drew from its disregard for how its improvements endangered the food supply. Establishment landowners showed a similar disregard for Highlanders' need for fuel. Trees were scarce and stands of timber privately owned. On some estates, peat was in short supply. In regions where peat was unavailable, dried animal manure had to be used.[52] Worse, some landlords deliberately made fuel-collecting difficult to force people to move from potential sheep walks.

Peat was essential for warmth and cooking. Without it, a township died. Proprietors knew this. To force people to relocate, they would deny peat-cutting rights on traditional sites. This increased the labour intensity of working the peat by increasing the distance to the new peat bank. In the south, coal, a much better fuel, was available, but it was subject to a coastal tax if transported by sea. This coal tax, while it prevented the depletion of Scottish coal, caused further hardship in areas where peat reserves were inadequate:

> The fuel used in this parish is peat, which, from the frequent rains in this watery climate, becomes very precarious. Last summer not above half of the fuel was got home, and even that in very bad condition. But it is hoped that the legislation will adopt proper measures to take the duty off an article so universally and absolutely necessary as coal.[53]

The Government was aware that the coal tax, like other legislation enacted to protect the industrial south, would have devastating consequences for the Highlands:

> I have been assured, that, in these islands, the expence [*sic*] of the customhouse-officer to discharge a cargo of coals, amounts, in many cases, to more than four times the duty on the coals; and if the cargo be small, it will sometimes be more than double the prime cost of the coals.[54]

Yet the coal tax was not repealed until 1793.

Circumstances in the West Highlands and Islands had become desperate. Many considered them to be beyond recovery. The population had outgrown its supply of food, and in many districts, its supply of fuel as well.

VI

We turn now to the fifth fundamental of early Highland settlement, the traditional farming system of *am fasgadh*, and to its reorganization under feudalism. The choice of a site for a Highland township had originally depended on the holding capacity of the land. A township was a small, irregularly sited but compact grouping of family houses. It was the nucleus of *am fasgadh*. In the pre-Culloden period, arable land was subdivided by the common people into unfenced and unenclosed narrow strips, each approximately 20 to 40 feet wide, on low land or ridges. Pasture land was held in common. This system, called *runrig*, gave households equal portions of land, though the quality of the portions varied. To avoid dissension within the township, lots were drawn for each portion, often annually, which meant that the quality of a family lot would vary according to the draw each year. These arable plots were further subdivided into the 'inbye' or infield near the house, and the 'outbye' or outfield, invariably on higher ground some distance from the township.

The grazing capacity of communal pasture land, the *souming*, was an estimate of the number of each class of animal, cattle, sheep, goats or horses, that the pasture could support. The number of animals each individual would be allowed to keep came from that estimate, but it was predicated also on the capacity of the individual's inbye or runrig to provide sufficient fodder for wintering his animals. The latter calculation was vital, since if fodder was not provided, the health of the family, no less than that of the livestock, would be in jeopardy.

Most townships also had access to the 'rough grazing' provided by the steep, higher hillsides for pasturing horses and sheep. But it was the autumn grasses and hay from the lower pasture lands that had to be conserved at all cost for the final pre-winter conditioning of the animals. Similarly, good spring and summer pasture was imperative, particularly for cattle, which, unlike sheep and goats, were limited to lower and gentler slopes. If the winter had been early and severe, the weakened cattle would have to be carried out of the house to the nearest spring grazing. When they were strong enough to travel, they would be moved to the lush summer grass of the upper hillsides, the *àiridh* or shieling, to which the township had a traditional right of summer grazing. This annual spring and summer migration of animals for fattening was no romantic Highland excursion to a sylvan setting. Moving herds between two different environmental regions was a 'transhumance', an essential part of the pastoral lifestyle of many peoples.[55] Loss of seasonal grazing for the few cows that cottars and sub-tenants owned endangered their supply of milk, one of the staples of their diet.

Runrig was, true to Celtic culture, logical, fair and democratic: each niche different; all subject to the vagaries of climate and nature in general; the fragile economy of each dictating the carrying capacity of its livestock and its human population. But the runrig system was not perfect. One of its major drawbacks stemmed from its lack of enclosure. Farm stock and wild animals strayed on to arable plots. To keep them out demanded continual supervision, usually by the elderly and the children.[56] Repeated violation of the runrigs by the animals of any member of the township led to discord. A second disadvantage inherent in the runrig system had a greater impact on farming. Each runrig tenant realized that any toil on the rig other than that required for the yearly sustenance of family and livestock would benefit only the incoming user, he who had drawn that lot for the next year. Thus the Highlander adopted a philosophy of 'sufficient unto the day', one that fuelled criticism of him as being lazy and unambitious.

In fact, Highland farming philosophy generally was scorned. So, too, were many more practical and productive features of Highland farming. For example, the inferiority of Highland horses, in breed, size and strength, was constantly criticised. It was noted also, quite correctly, that in some regions the pasture was of such poor quality that it could not properly feed the black cattle and the excess populations of horses that grazed on it.[57] Even the Highlanders' method of ploughing was deemed outmoded and needlessly labour-intensive:

> The farmers of this country are utter strangers to the mode of abridging labour. It is no uncommon thing to see 12 men and 20 horses at work in a farm, which three men and four horses would, on an improved plan, labour to much better purpose.[58]

What critics failed to acknowledge or appreciate was that most Highland farming methods, crude as they might have appeared, had evolved over centuries to accommodate a specific ecological niche. Highlanders' methods were invariably compatible with the site, though technology may have rendered their tools outdated for more general use.[59] For example, in the Outer Isles, the modern Lowland plough, pulled by two heavy draught horses and fitted with a deeply cutting coulter, was ineffective, as was the heavy Scots plough pulled by four small horses or oxen. The small plots of rocky soil could be efficiently turned only by the manual foot plough, the *cas-chrom*, with which twelve men working in line could dig an acre a day.[60] Furthermore, 'In the old caschrom days every inch of the ground was cultivated even among the boulders where the best soil is often to be found and which no plough can go near.'[61]

In fact, many Lowland improvements were simply not transplantable to the Highlands and Islands, where farming in the Lowland sense was impossible. For instance, unlike Lowland farmers, many Highlanders could not devote themselves full-time to farming. They had to fish, in the inshore white fishery for ling and cod, and when possible in the herring fishery. Critics and improvers alike operated often out of gross ignorance of those Highland realities. Another of the realities they knew nothing of was the fact of the Highland year. The Highland year started, weather permitting, with sowing, April 1 to the end of May; kelping followed from May to August; the harvest was made from September 1 to the end of October; manuring took place all winter. All of this work was primarily estate work; that is, service performed in lieu of rent money. Timing and success were determined by the weather. If operations were delayed for any reason, the time remaining for personal croft work was drastically limited.[62] Moreover, peats were cut and dried between April and the 1st of September and could only be stacked in good weather. It took 30 men to supply the peat requirement of a tacksman, and only when that job was completed could the men and their families collect their own fuel. Peating was labour-intensive and time-consuming even when whole families worked at it, so it left little time for families to prepare their own land.[63] When peating delayed ploughing and sowing of their own crops, Highlanders' late crop might be destroyed overnight by the first autumn gale.[64]

For the Highland cottar and subtenant, the system of *runrigs* and commutation rents presented one set of hardships. For the Highland landowner, it presented a very different set. Runrigs often got in his way, and land rents did not return enough money. So landlords, being the only group with the power to effect change, began to re-evaluate their estates and to convert them into more productive operations. The land was obviously unsuited for the large-scale commercial farming grown so popular and profitable in the south. Highland landowners elected, therefore, to engage in large-scale grazing of Lowland sheep, a venture which had proved lucrative at the Lowland/Perthshire boundary since its introduction there in the last decades of the eighteenth century. This undertaking required clearing the people, their townships and their animals from the hillsides and glens, and particularly from the lower grasslands, which would be vital to grazing sheep in winter.[65] No Lowland sheep farmer would consider paying the high rental which such rich grazing lands commanded unless the land was cleared.

The traditional *runrig* system of land use stood in the way of estate profits. To make way for lucrative sheep farming, landlords moved their people to the inferior lands of the estates. With these clearances, crofting began.[66] The primary effect of this change was the break-up of the traditional township and its communally-held land. Its replacement distributed land as permanently-divided croft holdings to be worked by one man. Croft lands were inferior, usually running inland, often steeply, from the seashore or loch side. They were narrow strips of land unsuitable for letting to sheep farmers or for conversion to sporting estates. In crofting, pasture land was still held as community pasture, but the best of it remained with the tenant. In the Sutherland estates, where people were moved from the rich pasture land of the interior tableland to the coast, with its steep cliffs and narrow coastal plain, crofts were little more than small potato patches.

Crofts stretched for miles along loch sides or on each side of a glen, disrupting the close sense of community that the traditional *runrig* township had afforded. Furthermore, crofters at the extremes of the townships might find themselves permanently disadvantaged because their crofts were distant from essential facilities, such as the peat bank, potable running water, the church, the school and, in a fishing community, the site of the beach, safe harbour and pier.[67] In 1841, the minister of Duirinish commented on the social aspects of the shift to crofting:

> The people have become less social, but much more peaceable in their conduct towards one another, and more temperate than they formerly were. It was, as is well known, customary for neighbours to visit each other's houses nightly, and to while away part of the long winter evenings, in reciting tales and traditions, singing songs and playing some musical instrument. Now, all this is completely given up . . . Each family confines itself to its own dwelling, or if a visit is paid, the time is spent in retailing the silly gossip of the day. People certainly may be far more beneficially employed than the old Highlanders used to be; yet we conceive the change in their habits to be a subject of regret on various grounds. The traditions of a country – the only source of information concerning bygone days in the absence of written records – are always interesting and instructive; and it is to be lamented that the traditions of the Highlands have been to a great degree irrecoverably lost.[68]

Additionally, and no matter the system for apportioning land, much of the Highlands and Islands was remote and inaccessible. For all practical purposes, the wheel might not have been invented. There were no roads, and therefore, no carts. Everything had to be carried on the back of man or beast. Furthermore, in some coastal areas, such as the east coast of Harris, a community with access to a rich and diverse fishery, croft lands ran along the rocky, indented coastline and extended steeply upwards into an equally rocky backland almost completely devoid of soil. In this desolate landscape, agricultural improvements were limited; the plough was of no value; a horse could not even make the ascent into the croft land. The minister of Harris commented on such coastal crofts:

Not only the poorness of the pasture, but the ruggedness of the ground disables him [the crofter] from keeping a horse, to lead the manure to his ground; for he often has it to carry through paths entirely impassable by the country *gearrans*, [the small hardy Highland horse] though they are perhaps the best climbers of their kind in the world.[69]

In these crofts, no machine relieved Highland men of the back-breaking labour that the most rudimentary cultivation entailed. Nor were Highland women spared. Rather, they worked without interruption from sun up to sundown:

Much of the hard work around the townships fell to the women. They not only spun, dyed, wove, and waulked, they made the family's clothing. They dug the soil along with the men, harrowed, reaped, gathered and stacked peats at the bank, bore the peats home in creels, cut grasses and heather for thatch or rope making, carried the heavy bales long distances, collected seaweed, spread manure, milled grain, mended nets, and cooked and washed for large families. On top of all such work they bred and reared numerous children, of whom a large proportion died in the first two weeks after birth. Despite all the trials, they sang their way through life.[70]

To cultivate such areas, the crofter and his wife created lazybeds or *feannagan* by carrying loads of peat and seaweed from the shore, filling the space between the rock ribs with peat and covering this with seaweed. These small, sheltered, but incredibly labour-intensive plots could yield a surprisingly large crop of potatoes. In Harris and similar landscapes, the crofting portion of the crofter/fisherman's lifestyle had to be sacrificed or drastically limited for him to survive. And the Achilles heel in crofting as in the runrig system was its dependence on the potato and on imported meal. Failure of either could spell disaster.

The fact that their would-be improvers were now mainly absentee landlords who relied on their local representatives for action and advice did nothing to reassure Highlanders. They knew that each landlord regarded their lowland sheep farmers as the support of an estate, and crofters and scallags as its ruin. It was reported, for example, that in 1840, in the parish of Sleat,

there are 225 families, comprising upwards of 1100 individuals, located in different parts of the parish, who pay no rents, deriving their subsistence from small portions of land given them by the rent-payers for raising potatoes. These are a burden to the proprietor, insomuch as they destroy the land in cutting fuel and turf; and are a grievous burden to the inhabitants generally, from the extent of pauperism prevailing among them.[71]

In fact, the death of a lifestyle that authorities saw as outmoded and non-profitable was inevitable. Its replacement by thousands of sheep managed by a few Lowland shepherds could not be forestalled.

VII

Just as the original location of *am fasgadh* was a function of its physical geography, so too was the Highlander's house, no matter how wretched it may have appeared to others. Traditional Highland black houses, *taigh dubh*, were the property of the owners themselves and were free from rent. The house was built primarily of local stone, since the ancient forest cover of the region had long before been destroyed. Much of the forest in Lewis, the Uists, Skye, Kintyre and the Argyll islands had been destroyed in 1098 by King Magnus Bareleg of Norway in a punitive raid on his Hebridean compatriots.[72] Those forests that survived the Vikings, indiscriminate grazing and lack of reforestation, the first industrialists levelled in their search for fuel. Where suitable stone was not readily available, the Highlander used turf divots.

While most houses were freestanding, advantage was often taken of a rock or hillface to act as a side or end for the structure, thus giving it the appearance of a lean-to. Having no large trees to supply wood for roof supports (*cabair*), particularly for the ridge-pole or roof-tree (*cabar-droma*), Highlanders salvaged from the shore any long pieces of wood they found. Understandably, such wood was extremely valuable. (That fact was not lost on the factors and land officers during the time of the evictions. They made a point of destroying salvage wood so that shelters could not be rebuilt. Likewise, a landowner could threaten rebellious tenants by reminding them that all flotsam and jetsam found on the foreshore was the property of the estate and could not be removed without permission.[73])

The roof of the Highland house also reflected the material at hand: straw, heather, rushes, turf divots or a mixture of those materials might be used in its construction, and all roof material was secured with hand woven ropes of heather or straw held snug by heavy stones tied to their extremities.

The walls of the black houses represented distinctive accommodations to changeable weather. Their ends were rounded, not gabled; the walls were low and doubled, the space between them filled with an insulation of rubble and earth, upon which vegetation grew and livestock inevitably grazed. These walls were five to nine feet thick. Another innovation prevented the roof from being blown off by strong winds: the roof rested on the inner wall rather than overhanging the outer wall, as it did in southern construction. While this design kept the wall damp, it also kept the roof on.

Given its roof and wall design, the door of the black house was very low. Some reported that the house could be entered only by stooping or crawling. The second opening in the house was the smoke vent, a hole in the roof made above but to the side of the centrally-placed peat fire. This asymmetry prevented heavy rain from extinguishing the fire. The home fire burned day and night, for warmth but also in observance of the ancient Celtic/Druid ceremony of Beltine.[74] (The custom of keeping the peat fire alive all night, known as *smooring*, was a ritual performed for centuries in the Highlands.) These, then, were the basic external features of the Highland black house. Regional modifications were minor: for example, a second door and even rudimentary windows were in some places added.

Inside, some black houses measured approximately fifty by twelve feet, that space being divided to provide shelter for the animals separate from the family. The floor consisted of hard-packed soil. Care was taken to ensure proper drainage of the animals' quarters. To that end, the house was built on a naturally sloping site, with the family's quarters at the high end. In more ambitious constructions, the family's quarters were raised six inches or so above that of the animals. In all homes, drainage out of both compartments was provided, though during prolonged wet weather, the movement of man and beast would turn the drainage path and the external approach to the door into a quagmire.

At one end of the house, usually but not necessarily that occupied by the cattle, was the midden or dunghill, where all waste products were stored till the annual clean-out in the spring. Everything that could be used to fertilize the ground was stored here, including the heavily-sooted inner surface of the thatched roof, which was removed during reroofing and added to the midden. In some areas, especially in the towns, middens were kept outside the house, usually against the house wall. Descriptions of these middens are common in nineteenth-century reports of the lifestyle of the Highland poor. The report from the town of Inverness is typical:

> Hence among the dwellings of the poorer classes stagnant pools very frequently occur, and the drainage in these places, naturally bad enough, is often purposely obstructed by the people for the purpose of adding to their dung-hill heaps or middens, which, as manure for their potatoe-grounds, form the chief treasures of the poorer cottagers and labourers . . . Most of them are provided with small back courts or gardens, in which a few common vegetables are grown; but their principal value is as stances for pig-houses and dunghills, which, in many instances, are improperly allowed to rest upon or touch the dwelling houses; while it is not to be disguised that cases exist where the pig, the horse, and

cow, all live under the same roof with their owners, and the manure allowed to accumulate there also . . . Amidst such a combination of unwholesome circumstances it is rather wonderful that malignant fever does not very greatly prevail in this town.[75]

The household midden, though repulsive to non-native proprietors and 'tourists', was vital to Highlanders.[76] Further, the black house was simply a product of the architectural school that had developed throughout the millennia and that was responsible for other functional structures like wheel houses, brochs, duns and hillforts or settlements.[77] When it suited their purposes, the Establishment condemned the Highlander's house as being unfit for human habitation. The truth is that the Highlanders' shelter, like all other elements of *am fasgadh*, was ideally suited to topography and environment, and to the lifestyle it supported.

Notes

1. Samuel Johnson (1709–84), *A Journey to the Western Islands of Scotland*, in *A Tour to the Hebrides*, Johnson & Boswell, Ed., R.W. Chapman, London, Oxford, Univ. Press, 1930, 35.

2. W.H. Murray, *The Islands of Western Scotland*, London, Eyre Methuen, 1973, 167.

3. Johnson, Op cit., 42.

4. N.S.A., XIV (Portree), 225.

5. Murray, Op cit., 151.

6. Ibid., 150–1.

7. *Dictionary of Sociology*, Ed., Henry Pratt Fairchild, Totowa, New Jersey, Rowman & Allanhead, 1970.

8. In a modern review of land ownership and use in the Highlands one writer suggests that 'Perhaps, the term "ownership" is now redundant, and ought to be replaced by "stewardship".' This term, he implies, 'conceives different layers of "stewardship" that involve matching obligations as well as privileges.'
   Land Ownership and Use, Ed. John Hulbert, Longforgan, Dundee, The Andrew Fletcher Society, 1986, Foreword, v–vi.
   Ownership of land in Scotland has always conferred political, social and economic advantages. Advantages which provided power to the 'Establishment'. For example, we have seen that the laws of entail were used to prevent an estate from being broken up and that landowners claimed complete monopoly over the resources of their land. But under feudalism this relationship did not exist. By 1621, an act ensured that hunting became an exclusive right of property. The Scottish system of landownership,

therefore, is different from that of the rest of Britain because it is defined by Scots law. Furthermore,

> The Scottish system is also unique in the modern world because the method by which land is owned is still legally classified as feudal (England, for comparison, abolished its feudal tenure in 1290) . . . However, despite the power of landownership, the control that landowners have over their land is relative. Land owners in Scotland can use their land as they please, subject to the constraints of their feudal title to the land, statutes and common law. The title or authority by which landowners own their land is derived from the highest authority in Scotland. In legal theory this is God, but in practice it is the Crown, who is the ultimate owner of all Scotland and is known as the Paramount Superior. Any landowner is thus a vassal of the Crown. The essential character of Scotland's feudal tenure is that this need not be a direct relationship. Anyone, when he disposes of land he owns, can maintain an interest in that land. He, as a vassal of the Crown, is then the superior of the new owner, who becomes his vassal. There is no limit in Scots law to the number of times this process, known as subinfeudation, can be repeated over the same piece of ground. At each stage, the superiors can limit the extent of possession conveyed by reserving rights to themselves and by imposing additional conditions and burdens on the vassals . . . For too long, the land of Scotland has been subject to one ruling idea, developed as legal theory and expressed as law. Scotland's feudal system has been the Law of the land for nine centuries . . . The future lies with a modern Scottish system that rewrites the Law of the Land.

Robin Callander, 'The Law of the Land', Ibid., 1, 6, 11.

9. A.D. Gibb, *A Preface to Scots Law*, Edinburgh, W. Green & Son Ltd., 1964, 68–9.

10. Robert Somers, *Letters from the Highlands*, On the Famine of 1846, (1848), Reprint, Perth, Melvin Press, 1985, 165, 178.

11. O.S.A., XIII (North Uist), 310.

12. In the Outer Isles, James VI had already attempted genocide, to be followed by colonisation of the territory by Lowlanders. But unlike the plantation of Ulster, this attempt failed miserably and the Chiefs' law, not the King's, prevailed in the west.

13. Murray, Op cit., 202.

   A ninth statute consisted of Enactments to ensure implementation of the preceding acts. It would take at least a century before the effect of the Statutes was evident but by virtue of their oath and signature, James VI had, in fact, included the chiefs in his Scottish parliament and the prospect for a unified Scottish nation was never so promising. The next hundred years, however, as a result of acculturation, saw the decline of Gaeldom and the Scottish nation: the monarch soon became an absentee king engrossed with English affairs, and in 1707, the absentee monarchy was followed by the presence of a token Scottish 'parliament' in London. Scotland was 'governed' by a 'manager' appointed by England.

14. Edward Burt, *Letters From a Gentleman in the North of Scotland to His Friend in London*; (*c.* 1720–30), 2 vols., 2nd edn., London, 1759, I, 59.

15. Duke of Argyll, *Scotland As It Was and As It Is*, 2 Vols., Edinburgh, David Douglas, 1887, 231–2.

    See also: Rosalind Mitchison, *Lordship to Patronage Scotland 1603–1745*, London, Edward Arnold, 1983, 116–7, 122.

    The Duke of Argyll's comments about the backward and irresponsible clan system reveal that he regarded the process as one of acculturation, but he also epitomised what is now termed by some, the 'Whig Interpretation of History':

    > What is discussed is the tendency in many historians to write on the side of Protestants and Whigs, to praise revolutions provided they have been successful, to emphasise certain principles of progress in the past and to produce a story which is the ratification if not the glorification of the present.

    H. Butterfield, *The Whig Interpretation of History*, New York, W. W. Norton & Company Inc., 1965, Preface v.

16. Johnson, Op cit., 103.

17. It was not until the nineteenth century that land measurement in acres came into use. Before this period, the conception of the size of a portion of land was based on the number of cattle that each portion of land could support. Murray notes that this concept arose following the Norse colonisation of Scotland at which time each homestead paid one penny as *Skatt*. Measures of land were named and valued on a standard based on the weight of silver. Hence, eighteen- or twenty-penny lands made an ounce land, and eight ounces made one merk or pound land.

    The size of a penny-land could vary even within the same island and was related always to the agricultural potential of the land, the poorer land being larger in area, but usually somewhere between 600 and 1000 acres. A tacksman might lease as many as twenty penny-lands, the smaller tenants with penny-lands and the sub-tenants half-penny lands, while the cottars subsisted on farthing-lands and often half farthing lands. A township commonly held a penny-land.

    For further information on Highland land evaluation consult:

    Donald Macdonald, *Lewis: A History of the Island*, Edinburgh, Gordon Wright, 1978, 68–9.

    W.H. Murray, *The Islands of Western Scotland*, London, Eyre Methuen, 1973, 184.

    G. Whittington and I.D. Whyte, Eds., *An Historical Geography of Scotland*, London, Academic Press, 1983, 49–51.

    O.S.A., X (Harris), 367–8.: XIII (North Uist), 310.,(Barray) 330–1.

18. For a detailed breakdown of the Highland social system, particularly in the Outer Isles, see: O.S.A., X (Harris), 361–371.

19. O.S.A., XIII (North Uist), 311.

20. O.S.A., VI (Loth), 315–7n.

21. E.R. Gregeen, 'The Changing Role of the House of Argyll in the Scottish Highlands', in *History and Social Anthropology*, Ed., I. M. Lewis, London, Tavistock Pubs., 1968, 175.

    Another Argyll estate directive provides an indication of the political mood of the first half of the eighteenth century:

    I would have it made a condition of the tacks that every tenant should take an oath of allegiance and a promissory oath never to raise or encourage any rising in rebellion against the present Government.

22. The Duke of Argyll, *Crofts and Farms in the Hebrides*, Edinburgh, David Douglas, 1883, 62.

23. O.S.A., XIV (Kilfinichan and Kilviceuen), 189.

    For a brief review of the 5th Duke's estate management policies see: Cregeen, Op cit., 175, 180–7.

24. Johnson, Op cit., 33.

25. Revd R.C. MacLeod of Dunvegan, *The Book of Dunvegan*, 2 Vols., Aberdeen, 3rd Spalding Club, II, 113.

26. Eric Richards, *The Leviathan of Wealth*, London, Routledge & Kegan Paul, 1973, 202.

27. Ibid., 198.

28. Ibid., 201–2.

29. Ibid., 203.

30. Ibid., 204–5.

31. Richards notes that accumulated rent arrears on the estate had been £16,319 at the end of 1816 and they were rising rapidly.

    Ibid., 204.

    For further information on the Highland Clearances with detailed notes see: Kenneth J. Logue, *Popular Disturbances in Scotland* 1780–1815, Edinburgh, John Donald, 1979, 'The Clearances' 54–74.

32. For an authoritative review of the changes in the economics of the Highlands see: Malcolm Gray, *The Highland Economy* 1750–1850, Edinburgh, Oliver and Boyd, 1957, 75–86.

33. N.S.A., XIV (Duirinish), 344.

34. O.S.A., XIII (North Uist), 317.

35. Malcolm Gray, 'The Kelp Industry in the Highlands and Islands', *Economic History Review*, 2nd Series, IV, 1951, 207–8.

36. Quoted by Cregeen, Op cit., 182.

37. George Douglas Campbell, 8th Duke of Argyll, in *Scottish Diaries and Memoirs* 1746–1843, 2 vols., Ed. J.G.Fyfe, Stirling, Eneas Mackay, 1942, II, 576.

38. O.S,A., X (Harris), 359–361.

39. Johnson, Op cit., 73.

40. Bruce Lenman, *An Economic History of Modern Scotland* 1660–1976, London, B.T. Batsford Ltd., 1977, 126–7.
      Murray, Op cit., 215–218.

41. For a survey of kelping, its origins, expansion, profits, conditions of the work force, landholding system and the resulting population growth see: Gray, Op cit., 1951 and 1957.
      Hunter (1976), Op cit., 16–31, 39–49.

42. O.S.A., XIX (Uig), 285, 286.

43. George Douglas Campbell, Op cit., 576.

44. 1755, Alex. Webster, in *Scottish Population Statistics*, ed., James Gray Kyd, Edinburgh, Scottish Academic Press, 1975, 82–3.
      1795, Sinclair, *Analysis*, 1825.
      1801–51, *Census of Scotland*.

45. Murray, Op cit., 215.

46. If we divide Scotland into three areas representing roughly the Highlands, the Lowlands and the narrow Central Belt which lies between, we get the following distribution in 1755, in 1861 and at the date of the last census in 1951 . . . In 1755 the population of the Highland Area was 652,000, with a population density of 31 persons per square mile. In 1861, the same area had a population of 1,020,000, and a density of 48 persons per square mile. In 1951 the population was 1,000,000 with a density of 47 . . . It will be seen that in the middle of the eighteenth century more than half of the population [of Scotland] lived north of the Central Belt, but by 1951 only one-fifth of the population were in this district, which constitutes more than 70 per cent of the area of Scotland. More dramatic still, however, is the fact that by 1951 three-quarters of the population were concentrated with a density of 900 persons to the square mile into the Central Belt, which comprises but one-seventh of the area of Scotland. These figures indicate the profound changes which have taken place since the middle of the eighteenth century in the regional distribution of our population.
      James Gray Kyd, Op cit., xviii–xix.

47. Allan Fullerton and Charles R.Baird, *Remarks on the Evils at Present Affecting the Highlands & Islands of Scotland* etc., Glasgow, William Collins, 1838, 16–7.

48. O.S.A., XIX (Stornoway), 259: XIII (North Uist), 304–5; (Barray), 330: III (Gairloch), 89–90: X (Harris), 360–1.

49. George Douglas Campbell, Op cit., 577.

50. N.S.A., XIV (Strath), 314.

51. O.S.A., XX (Thurso), 516–7.

52. Alexander Fenton, *The Shape of the Past – Essays in Scottish Ethnology*, 2 Vols., Edinburgh, John Donald, 1985 & 1986, I, 96–101.

53. O.S.A., XII (Jura and Colonsay), 333.

54. James Anderson, *An Account of the Present State of the Hebrides and the Western Coasts of Scotland* etc., A Report to the Lords of Treasury, Edinburgh, 1785, Intro., xxxii.

55. N.D. MacSween, 'Transhumance in North Skye', *Scottish Geographical Magazine*, LXXV, No 2, 75–88.
    Ian D. Duff, 'The Human Geography of South-Western Ross-Shire (1800–1929)' Ibid., XLV, No 5, 1929. 282–4.
    John Frodin, 'Transhumance in Sweden', Ibid XL, No.5, 1924, 303.

56. O.S.A., X (Harris), 357.

57. O.S.A., XIX (Barvas), 266–7: (North Uist), 325: XX (Kilmadock), 79: II (Blair-Atholl), 469.

58. O.S.A., XII (Jura and Colonsay), 321.

59. Murray reports that in the mid-twentieth century, in some areas, particularly in the Outer Isles, *runrig* integrated with crofting still remained the system of choice, but with longer terms of allotment.
    Murray, Op cit., 222.

60. Murray, Op cit., 185.

61. Osgood Mackenzie. *A Hundred Years in the Highlands* (1921), new edit., 1988, Edinburgh, The National Trust for Scotland, 151.

62. O.S.A., XIII (North Uist), 316

63. Fullarton and Baird, Op cit., 17.

64. For an insight into peat cutting and 'The people's daily round and common tasks' see: I.F. Grant, *Highland Folk Ways*, London, Routledge & Kegan Paul, 1961, Chapter IX.

65. O.S.A., VIII (Kilmalie), 427n.

66. Some Highlander families were evicted more than once. The family of Mr John MacKenzie, a vice-president of the Assynt Crofters trust, was evicted three times. The final MacKenzie croft is on the inhospitable coast of Eddrachillis Bay at Culkein Drumbeg (the 'grazing of the township of Drumbeg'). Here Mr MacKenzie carries on the crofting tradition. His

modern house, ironically, is built on fertile land. When a boy, he had witnessed his grandfather laboriously create this land by carrying soil and seaweed from the shore to level ground. It was the grandson, however, who would regain the land lost by the crofters of North Assynt. John MacKenzie (an elder of the Free Church) and his associates won their victory against the Establishment, not by the rattling of claymores, by wild charges, or by wilder political rhetoric, but by negotiating as shrewd businessmen and as equals with the representatives of the North Lochinver Estate.

Personal interview Robert Mathieson/John MacKenzie, Culkein Drumbeg, May 1995.

67. A.T.A. Learmouth, 'The Population of Skye.' *Scottish Geographical Magazine*, 66, No. 2, 1950, 97–9.

68. N.S.A., XIV (Duirinish), 358.

69. O.S.A., X (Harris), 352.

70. Murray, Op cit., 195–6.

71. N.S.A., XIV (Sleat), 319.

72. Murray, Op cit., 167.

73. In Scotland, the foreshore had traditionally belonged to the proprietors, whereas in England, it was the property of the Crown. The British Government did not claim its right to Scottish foreshore until the mid-nineteenth century by which time, fortunately for the Highland proprietors, the kelp boom was over. The Scottish landowners, however, did form an association to protest their claim and as the result of a test case they won their right to the foreshore.

Confirmation of the power of a heritor over all facets of his estate is attested by the lesson learned by a parish minister who, much to his chagrin, took on his patron and lost:

Upon the shore of the glebe, which extends about ¾ of a mile, grows a profusion of sea-weed, of the right sort fittest for kelp: to this the present incumbent thought he had a right; and that he might convert this sea-weed to his own benefit, as a small addition to his small stipend; but in this he unexpectedly found himself opposed by the family of Reay [the heritors], who thought fit to dispose of this very sea-weed, as well as the rest on the estate by lease to a Peterhead company; and upon his giving interruption to them, he was obliged to defend himself in a process for damages before the Court of Session, who, after considerable expense and trouble to the incumbent, thought fit to decide the affair against him. He is thus deprived of the benefit of the whole sea-weed growing on his glebe, which was useful to him for other purposes, as manure to his land, and pasture to his cattle in the cold season of the year.

O.S.A., VI (Edderachylis), 281n.

74. Each year on May 1st, the fires of every household were extinguished and then relit symbolically from the rays of the sun, the 'sacred fire of Bel', to ensure a fresh start in the new year.

75. *Reports on the Sanitary Conditions of the Labouring Population Of Scotland,* B.P.P.(Lords) XXVIII, 1842, No.17. 'Sanitary Report on the town of Inverness, North Britain', by George Anderson Esq., Solicitor in Inverness.

76. John MacCulloch, *The Highlands and Western Isles of Scotland,* Four vols., London, Longman, 1824, II, 465–6.

    It is beyond the scope of this book to examine further the structure of the black house, its regional variants, or its close but more modern cousin, the *taigh geal* or white house. Incidentally, the early white house was internally as black as any black house. Much research is available on the structure and the manner of life in these houses. See also:

    Alexander Fenton, Op cit., Vols 1&2: idem, *The Island Black House,* Edinburgh, HMSO, 1978.

    For further information and for numerous photographs of Highland houses still occupied in the first half of the twentieth century see:

    Colin Sinclair, *Thatched Houses:* A contribution to the Social History of the Old Highlands, Edinburgh, Oliver and Boyd, 1953.

77. Richard Feacham, *Guide To Prehistoric Scotland,* London, B.T. Batsford Ltd., 1977, 27–8, 94–5, 100–4, 162–3, 175–7.

4

Health

Is righ gach slàn.[1]

(A healthy man is a king.)

THE LOGICAL BEGINNING in any study of health would be a clear and universally accepted definition of what comprises a state of health. But health is a relative concept, varying among cultures, and within the same culture at different periods and among different groups. Such differences in perceptions of 'health and the good life' complicated the application of health 'improvements' in the Highlands and Islands.

A very early concept of health was simply the absence of obvious disease. That definition is not only superficial, as a glance at Fig. 1 will show, but is wildly outdated. Observations made in this century have expanded and deepened our understanding of health. For instance, in 1948, the World Health Organization (WHO) published its definition of health, one that has been criticized but has not to date been superseded. Health, the WHO said, 'is a state of complete physical, mental, and social wellbeing, and not merely the absence of disease or infirmity.'[2] Ten years later, after a decade of National Health Service in Britain, the Medical Officer of Health for Ilford, Essex, made the following observations on the distinction between health and disease:

> Man, like other organisms, is evolving continuously, for better or worse, within his environment; and when a person's contact with his environment, internal or external, is deleterious, he is bound to suffer some damage, though this may not be permanent or even appreciable . . . To maintain his equilibrium with his environment, man and his species are in perpetual struggle . . . In the living there is no such thing as complete health, any more than there is complete disease (which is death): each organism is somewhere between the two . . .[3]

The complexities of 'that damned word health' have also been widely debated in the USA. In his paper, 'The Social Nature of the Definition Problem in Health', American Dr Sander Kelman attempts to isolate the social basis of health. His analysis sheds light on the cause of ill-health generally and is germane to our discussion of the ill-health which followed the Highland Clearances:

Although the recognition of the social basis of many diseases and ill health goes far back in medical history, the greatest boost probably came with the publication of the Chadwick Report in England and the Shattock Report in the United States in the mid-19th century. Since that time there has been a great deal of writing on social epidemiology and the environmentalist approach to health, . . . for it is clearly in conflict with the biological and individual orientation of the classical school, still very much the predominant methodology. Yet the purpose of this paper is to show that even if their differences could be resolved, the substance of 'health' is still not defined . . . To generalize, the bio-individual school encounters major difficulty whenever it seeks to impose a generalized germ theory on a pathology the etiology of which is a complex dialectic between the organism and socially induced stresses.[4]

Establishment voices in the nineteenth century Highlands and elsewhere would have cried foul to such inclusive interpretations of health – as they would to the implications of judgements like the following:

Health care providers and their clients need to be aware of the power of culture when they make health care decisions. They also need to reflect on the differing beliefs, values, attitudes, and world views that affect both their behaviour and the behaviour of the client.[5]

Such observations clearly demonstrate the emergence in this century of a broader definition of health and an appreciation of the intimate interrelationship among social conditions, disease and medicine. Broader interpretations of health were not unknown by some members of the Scottish medical profession, even in the eighteenth and nineteenth centuries, although they would not have been generally accepted. To an Establishment invariably classically educated at select English private schools and universities, notions of health, disease and medicine were inherited from an 'approved' history. To the poor and illiterate clansman, health and disease alike were supernatural forces, beyond his control.

That the nineteenth-century Scottish Establishment, even to some extent the medical Establishment of that time, were ignorant of the broader causes and effects of health and disease helps explain much of their medical thought and practice. That they nonetheless understood fully the basic principles of public health and yet were inert, laggardly or hostile in the face of serious public health problems was inexcusable.[6]

I

Let us look more closely at the Highlander's understanding of health and disease. For him, the world was animated by the will of the gods and sundry other mythological beings, or later, by the will of a Christian God. And for him, 'all things, animate and inanimate, [were] endowed with personal indwelling souls.'[7] That animism affected his lifestyle and culture and shaped his understanding of the causes of health and ill-health.

In Celtic mythology, the cult of the Mothers was fundamental: Mother Earth was regarded as a source of fertility.[8] Celts also believed that certain wells, rivers, trees and animals had patron gods or goddesses. The Celtic cults were maintained by Druid priests, who taught that the soul did not die, but passed into another body, and so there was little to fear from death. One student of Celtic mythology, Nora Chadwick, argues that although Celts held a strong belief in an after-life, there is little evidence to suggest that they believed in sin and punishment.[9] The orally-transmitted Irish sagas, written down later in Christian Ireland, show clearly that there was a naturalness with which men, women and gods met and with which they passed in and out of the natural and supernatural spheres. Many of the prominent figures in Irish mythology were gods, or had gods for parents, to whom the actions, good or bad, of those mythological figures were usually attributed.

Such cults were not, of course, unique to Celtic peoples. In the western 'Cradle of Civilization', traditionally believed to be Mesopotamia, the gods were similarly believed to be all-powerful beings who sent illness and disease as punishment for sins. The supernatural was rationalised: disease and calamity followed bad behaviour; fortune followed virtue. The ancient Hebrews also believed that disease was a punishment for sin but that disease was meted out, not by a multitude of gods but by God himself, their own Jehovah.[10] In ancient India, all the gods affected health and disease.[11] The ancient teachings of Hinduism gave rise to a traditional Indian healing, based on Ayurvedic (knowledge of life) medicine. The traditional practitioners of Ayurvedia defined life as

> the union of body, senses, mind and soul, and in this context consider positive health as the blending of physical, mental, social, moral and spiritual welfare. The moral and spiritual aspects are here stressed and thus give new dimensions to man and the system of medicine by which he maintains his health.[12]

Hindu ideas of health and medicine were to find their way into the Middle East, eventually influencing Greek medicine, and by way of the Arabists, they reached Europe. Their effect on European medicine in general was minimal, but it is tempting to speculate that the Celtic peoples, who had inherited so much of their legal system from India, might also have been familiar with Ayurvedic medicine.[13]

The continuance of Druidism as the bedrock of Highland culture fostered the spread of naturalistic medicine:

> The inhabitants of these islands do for the most part labour under the want of Knowledg' of Letters, and other useful Arts and Sciences; notwithstanding which Defect, they seem to be better vers'ed in the Book of Nature, than many that have greater Opportunities of Improvement. This will appear plain and obvious to the judicious Reader, upon a View of the successful Practice of the Islanders in the Preservation of their Health, above what the Generality of Mankind enjoys; and this is perform'd merely by Temperance, and the prudent use of Simples; which, as we are assur'd by repeated Experiments, fail not to remove the most stubborn Distempers, where the best prepar'd Medicines have frequently no Success. This I relate not only from the Authority of many of the Inhabitants, who are Persons of great Integrity, but likewise from my own particular Observation. And thus with *Celsus*, they first make Experiments, and afterwards proceed to reason upon the Effects.[14]

II

The medical Establishment practised a very different medicine. Theirs was theory and practice rooted in Egyptian and Greek antiquity and in the European science of the Middle Ages. In Europe, Greek civilization had, after hundreds of years of cultural diffusion, absorbed the medical knowledge of other ancient cultures.[15] Greeks adapted and improved the medical lore of other cultures before the fifth century BC, the age of Hippocrates. While it is true that prior to Hippocrates, Greeks had endowed many gods and animals with healing powers, Greek medicine was even then secular as well as religious; it recognized natural as well as supernatural causes for disease. The Pre-Hippocratic age of the philosopher–scientist, the fifth century BC, applied the new secular approach to human problems. Socrates defined 'healthy' as 'the name which is given to the regular order of the body, whence comes health and every other bodily excellence.'[16] His analysis of the relationship between health and disease is thus that 'they both have pleasures and pains, but in health the pleasure exceeds the pain, and in sickness the pain exceeds the pleasure.'[17]

The fifth century BC is traditionally regarded as the age of Hippocrates.[18] Insomuch as the Hippocratic School did not believe that illness was punishment but rather the result of natural causes, the physician's duty was to assist nature and so restore a state of harmony. Hippocrates explains this harmonious state thus: 'A man is at his best possible condition when there is complete coction [of the humours] and rest, with no particular peculiar power or property displayed.'[19] This fixation with the 'humours' remained an integral part of medical thought, and influenced treatment until the eighteenth century. The Hippocratic goal of harmony was to be achieved by treating the patient in his own environment.

In the post Hippocratic period, medical sects began to appear. By the 3rd century BC, they had spread throughout the Eastern Mediterranean. In the same period, Greek medicine reached its peak in Alexandria. Physicians were influenced by the teachings of Plato and his students. Those Dogmatists, as they were called, relied in their medical practice on reasoning rather than observation. Their deductions were at times brilliant. Witness Aristotle's scintillating observation about the part which the body's own resistance to disease, that is, natural immunity, plays in health:

> Men are called healthy in virtue of the inborn capacity of easy resistance to those unhealthy influences that may ordinarily arise; unhealthy, in virtue of the lack of this capacity.[20]

Yet the Dogmatists failed to correlate their deductions with the disease process and with the theory of the cause of disease current at the time. That failure spawned faulty theories and therapies which were to survive, though ameliorated by Arabist practice, into the Middle Ages.[21]

The Roman Empire eclipsed Greece, first, as the centre of knowledge, and then by the mid-second century BC, as the cultural centre of the Western World. The Roman world attracted Greek physicians and men of letters who pursued their studies there and infiltrated all aspects of learning.[22] Traditional Roman medicine had been inherited from the Etruscans, and contained both secular and religious elements. The latter consisted of practices like divination from the entrails of animals, the use of prognostic charts and the atonement of the gods. Those religious practices survived to play a decisive role in the course of Western medicine.

The Roman Empire was the site, moreover, of one of the most potent influences on the development of medicine. In all of its aspects, the coming of Christ, the story of his ministry, crucifixion, death and eventual resurrection, Christianity played a seminal role in the development of Western medical thought and direction. The miracles of healing performed by Christ and the subsequent transfer of this gift to his disciples re-established the power of the supernatural in curing disease and, by implication, in its cause.[23] The Judaic belief that disease was a punishment for sin or a sign of divine disfavour remained the basic explanation of illness. In that respect, the coming of Christianity retarded medical innovation for centuries. Christianity did, however, inaugurate a ministry to the sick in the form of various nursing orders. Triage, an integral part of Greek medicine, was replaced with an active concern for the terminally ill.

Hippocrates had not conceived medicine to be concerned with terminal illness:

> In general terms, it is to do away with the suffering of the sick, to lessen the violence of their diseases, and to refuse to treat those who are overmastered by their diseases, realizing that in such cases medicine is powerless.[24]

Christianity's return to the supernatural notwithstanding, the influence of Greek medicine grew. Perhaps the most famous Greek physician in Rome during this period was Galen (*c.* AD 130–200). Galen opposed the medical sects then flourishing in Rome. He was an ardent proponent of the teachings of Hippocrates, especially the unity of the living organism and the power of nature in the maintenance of health. In several places his works reveal his lack of respect for Judaism and Christianity. His position stood somewhere between Stoicism and Christianity: he accepted the natural law of Stoic philosophy, but rejected its astrological corollary; he rejected all ideas of Christian miracles, but was a firm believer in God as the supreme creator of the universe in all its parts.[25]

By the fourth century, Rome became the epicentre of a series of religious changes that were to have repercussions for medical practice in Europe and eventually in Gaeldom. In 321, St Anthony initiated monasticism, and in 325, the Council of Nicaea established basic Christian dogma. In 391, the Roman Empire, once having simply favoured Christianity, began to require it. The Early Christian Church was no longer recognized, and in the next few centuries Roman Catholicism established itself throughout the Empire.

Those changes at the centre were, however, not soon felt at the periphery. In Ireland, for example, the Celtic Church would remain true to the teachings and example set by the Early Christian Church until the fifth century. This early Celtic Church had readily adapted to the Age of the Saints, a period which in Dark Age Europe was to be called the Age of Faith, the period in which people lost confidence in their ability to survive by their own efforts and acknowledged their dependence on saints.[26] In this period, approximately 500–1000 saints replaced the old gods and demi-gods. These saints, like the gods before them, figured large in people's quest for miraculous cures for disease. Saints were believed to possess intercessory powers with God, the foremost intercessory in this group being the Virgin Mary. This cult followed the custom of the Greeks and earlier peoples in linking diseases with specific saints. So erysipelas, a common, acute infectious skin disease, was called St Anthony's fire. In the Highlands, 'charms' were used to cure diseases among humans and animals. The charm below is a cure for erysipelas (Rose):

Eolas na Ruaidh [Charm for Rose]:

When this charm is applied, the point of a knife or a needle, or the tongue of a brooch or of some other sharp instrument, is pointed threateningly at the part affected. The part is then spat upon and crossed three times in the names of the three Persons of the Trinity, whether it be the breast of a woman or the udder of a cow.[27]

When the Western Roman Empire fell under the tide of new 'barbarians' from the north in AD 476, Europe entered the Dark Ages. It is significant to recall that non-Romanized early Celtic Ireland was a cultural replica of pre-Christian Celtic Europe, and therefore 'barbarian'. Its religious conversion had been to an early Christianity, which was then superimposed on a traditional European Celtic social framework.

The cleavage of Christian Europe into a Western portion with Rome as its centre, and an Eastern (Byzantine) portion, more populous and wealthier, based in Constantinople, contributed to the making of the European Dark Ages. One of the great losses in the Age was the loss of written texts:

. . . the zealous anti-Hellenism of the Christian Church led to the physical loss of much of the Greek and Roman writings that were the basis of Western civilization.[28]

In any case, since most of the medical texts of this period were written in Greek, the medical knowledge was available only to a few scholars, mainly Celts, or to those who had Latin translations. Fortunately, the spread of Islam into south-eastern Europe in the seventh century, and the Arabs' desire to seek out the knowledge of the classical Greek and Roman worlds, ensured the translation into Arabic of those works still extant. Those translations were studied by all so-called Arabists, whose numbers included Christians, Persians and Jews as well as Muslims. The translations were retranslated into Latin, errors and all, during the Middle Ages.

Islam spread westward across the countries of the Mediterranean Basin and then into Spain. Like so many other religions, Islam taught that Allah caused illness as punishment for sins. Cures were to be obtained through prayer, or by seeking divine help through the agency of a physician. Ibn Khalduun (1332–1406), the Arab historian, made clear the position of medicine in Muslim countries. He conceded Galen's position as the leading authority on medicine, and went on to explain that medicine is not Mohammed's priority:

Civilized Bedouins have a kind of medicine which is mainly based on individual experience. They inherit its use from the SHAYKHS and old women of the tribe. Some of it may occasionally be correct. However, it is not based on any natural norm or upon any conformity (of the treatment) to the temper of the humours. Much of this sort of medicine exists among the Arabs . . . Muhammad was sent to teach us the religious law. He was not sent to teach us medicine or any other ordinary matter.[29]

Islam's priority may not have been medicine, but the Arabic World nonetheless produced some outstanding physicians. Avicenna's (980–1037) medical teaching was, for example, still part of the medical curriculum of British universities until the seventeenth century.[30] The Arab physician Rhases (850–923) is credited with contributing to the Hebrew aphorisms of Isaac Judaeus, a Jewish physician in Egypt. One can assume that those aphorisms were known to the legendary Highland medical family, the Beatons. The Beatons (MacBeaths) had been physicians to the Lord of the Isles and the Kings of Scotland. The Beatons' practice extended, in fact, from the fourteenth to the eighteenth centuries, during which time they used a Gaelic medical text that represented four successive layers of medical knowledge: Greek, Muslim, Continental and Gaelic. Thus, the Arab-Muslim influence had found a direct route, early, to the Highlands.[31] A sampling of those Hebrew/Arab aphorisms, as selected by Lyons and Petrucelli, follows:

Most illnesses are cured without the physician's help through the aid of nature.

If you can cure the patient by dietary means, do not turn to drugs.

Do not rely on cure-alls, for they mostly rest on ignorance and superstition.

Always make the patient feel that he will be cured when you are not convinced of it, for it aids the healing effect of nature.[32]

Another Arabic influence on health care is worthy of note. Islam did not originate hospital care, but it was an exemplar of a healthy hospital environment. The richly-endowed hospital, the Al-Mansur, founded in Cairo in 1283, was the most modern of its time.[33] The Christian West had much to learn from Islam about hospital care. Early Christian hospitals were mere offshoots of monastic medicine, the 'leprosories' and 'lazerettes', places where recoveries were regarded as miracles. Christians were, after all, more concerned with saving the soul than with restoring the body.[34] Haeger notes that 'hospitals' had existed much earlier, in Sri Lanka around 500 BC, and in India about 260 BC.[35] And in the Middle Ages, the Christian church ran hospitals for the poor and a 'domus leprosorum' in Scotland, east of the Highland line.[36]

By the eleventh century, the Dark Ages became the Middle Ages, a five-hundred-year era of nationalism, feudalism and the struggle for religious control over the citizens of evolving nation states. That control entailed arresting the spread of Islam. Hence the Crusades. All of those impulses made the Middle Ages a time of wars, famines, destitution and disease. It was the age of the Black Death, of leprosy and the 'sweating sickness', or Sudor Anglicus, a disease of unknown etiology, possibly influenza, which killed strong men in days and which first appeared in England in 1485.[37]

Such was people's misery that the help of anybody, saint, 'doctor', quack or mystic, who had the reputation for easing suffering was petitioned. Their misery also made ignorant people look for a scapegoat to punish as the cause of their travail. In the Western World, Jews, a suitably foreign minority, became a conspicuous target and were put to death by burning.[38] The Age had another outcome too, however: a new respect for the contagious nature of disease and a recognition of the need for basic laws to govern public health. Those attitudes influenced the management of communicable diseases from that time onward.[39]

Despite the suffering which characterized it, this period was known too for the establishment of famous universities. Several new medical schools autonomous from the Church advanced medicine significantly. The reputation of the Salerno school, situated south of Naples, was at its zenith from the 11th to the 13th centuries, its graduates universally respected. This 'Domus Sanitatis', as it was called, advanced the art of surgery, hitherto despised by Arabs and Christian priests alike. In Italy, the schools of Padua and Bologna soon followed Salerno's lead and became progressive medical schools, as did Montpellier and Paris later in France. While Paris prevailed as the world's centre of education, it was free-thinking Montpellier, situated like Salerno at the border of the Islamic and Latin worlds, that first admitted Arabs and Jews, thus exhibiting its freedom from episcopal control. The teachers in these medical schools of the Middle Ages provided the basic stimulus for later advances in surgery, medicine and therapeutics.[40]

Without question, medical practice was improving. The Middle Ages brought science to bear on medicine, and the new medical schools set high standards. Still, the absence of a uniform method of certification for medical practitioners permitted a wide range of qualifications: from the learned, university trained, academic Doctor of Medicine who lacked practical training; to the skilful, experienced surgeon; to the cleric; to the unlettered quack. The discrepancy in practitioners' knowledge and skill haunted the medical profession for centuries. Nor did it go unnoticed by their patients.

By the end of the Middle Ages, surgery had developed into a well-defined science with its own rich technical literature. It would, by embracing the Aristotelian emphasis on experimentation, continue to advance 'until the controversy generated by the Reformation and Counter

Reformation all but stamped out intellectual discourse.'[41] Discourse and dissemination of the new medical knowledge was, of course, greatly facilitated by another development of the Middle Ages, the movable printing press.[42]

The Reformation and the Counter-Reformation generated religious passions, none of them salutary for medicine. In fact, religious intolerance during this period led to the same scape-goating and persecution that had marked the Dark Ages. This time, however, it was no longer necessary to blame misfortune on Jews. This time, in the Catholic South, a Protestant heretic would do nicely, as would a papist in the Protestant North.[43] North and South, witches were among the most convenient targets. In Scotland, an Act Anent Witchcraft, legislated in 1563, imposed the death penalty for anyone found guilty of witchcraft. This act, the first of its type in Europe, remained on the Statute Books until 1736. Smout notes, however, that even during the height of the witch-burnings, no witchcraft trials took place in the whole of the Hebrides, nor in most of the mainland Highlands, two of the most superstitious areas in the country. He explains that anomaly thus:

> They held . . . to the older medieval view, that some witches did good, some did harm, and all should be tolerated for fear of stirring up a hornet's nest of the supernatural.[44]

The next Age was transitional: the Renaissance moved people away from intolerance and bigotry. Discussion and inquiry were possible once more. In medicine, significant progress was made. Anatomy and physiology, the building blocks of modern medicine and surgery, were established. The concept of disease and its treatment, or 'practica', became the focus of serious intellectual discussion at the new medical schools.

The Renaissance transition completed, the seventeenth century ushered in the Age of the Scientific Revolution. Medicine became a science. Before that could happen, however, three major influences from earlier centuries had to be reckoned with. Aristotelianism, Galenism and Paracelsianism all delayed the advance of medical theory and practice and contributed to a growing mistrust of the medical profession.[45] Aristotle's original teachings had been altered over the centuries to accommodate cultural change. By the seventeenth century, Aristotelianism was a mix of astrology and medicine and Aristotle's vital contribution, observation followed by experimentation, had been neglected. Chance observation had become the norm. For example, the followers of Galen (130–200), a Greek physician practising in Rome, distinguished themselves by their use of plant medicines. They had, though, strayed from Aristotle's example of experimentation. In fact, they rarely accepted his findings as he had described them. One exception among them was the English physician, William Harvey (1578–1657). Harvey is known principally for his brilliant practical investigations on the circulation of the blood, published in 1628.[46]

The legacy of another early physician was a mixture of rational and religious elements. Philippus Aureolus Theophrastus Bombastus von Hohenheim (1493–1541) or Paracelsus, which name means 'the equal of the Roman physician Celsus', was a leader of medical thought, even though he may not have been a qualified physician. Paracelsus believed in astrology and in the physician's ability to harness the astral forces and direct them to heal. As the constellations changed, he maintained, so must diseases and their treatment. He was trained in chemistry and popularized the use of minerals, as opposed to the plant medicine of the Galenic physicians. His insatiable thirst for knowledge and his willingness to use that knowledge to challenge and criticise his colleagues' methods made them detest him:

> The apothecaries are my enemies since I refuse to empty their jars. My prescriptions are simple and have no need of forty or fifty ingredients. I aim not to make apothecaries rich, but to cure patients.[47]

Haeger has abstracted a few aphorisms from Paracelsus' writings which give an insight into the mixture of reason and religion in his work:

> Just as God created all illnesses, he has created a specific remedy for each of them. They exist everywhere in nature, for the whole world is a pharmacy and God is the highest pharmacist.
>
> He who is happy always gets well.
>
> Knowledge of nature is the precondition for medical science.
>
> A doctor's personality can act more powerfully on a patient than do all the remedies he prescribes.
>
> The doctor is only nature's servant, not its overlord.[48]

His advice that medicaments are poisons, and that only right dosage prevents their toxic effects was, unfortunately, not taken to heart by the medical profession. Its failure to heed that advice, and its tendency rather to prescribe injudiciously, produced a lay opinion that the treatment was worse than the disease, an opinion that prevailed over the next few centuries. In fact, while some still attributed ill-health to the perversion of nature's rules, many blamed physicians for making people sick. A Highland proverb, '*Cul an leighis ris an léigh*', reminds us that 'A doctor avoids medicine for himself.' The writings of major literary figures of the eighteenth and nineteenth centuries are a terrible indictment of the medical profession and its treatment of the sick,[49] as are many similar observations by Scottish writers. The parish minister of the Island of Colonsay, reporting in the *Statistical Account* of the late eighteenth century, observed dryly:

> The inhabitants are robust and healthy; they live in the same simple manner as their brethren in Jura, and have neither lawyer or surgeon in the island.[50]

Adam Smith (1723–1790) too had something to say regarding the medical profession's 'speculative physicians', who ignored or undervalued the body's natural defence mechanisms:

> Some speculative physicians seem to have imagined that the health of the human body could be preserved only by a certain precise regimen of diet and exercise, of which, every, the smallest, violation occasioned some degree of disease or disorder proportioned to the degree of the violation. Experience, however, would seem to show that the human body frequently preserves, to all appearances at least, the most perfect state of health under a vast variety of different regimens; even under some which are generally believed to be very far from being perfectly wholesome. But the healthy state of the human body, it would seem, contains in itself some unknown principle of preservation, capable either of preventing or correcting, in many respects, the bad effects of even a faulty regimen.[51]

Among common people in Scotland, lack of faith in the profession was near universal. One of Burns's poems, 'Death and Dr Hornbook', makes that evident. In the poem, Death admits that Dr Hornbook was responsible for more deaths than he:

> Whare I kill'd ane, a fair strae death
> By loss o' blood or want of breath,
> This night I'm free to take my aith,
> That Hornbook's skill
> Has clad a score i' their last claith,
> By drap and pill.[52]

People of all classes, rich as well as poor, recognized the danger of establishment medicine. Mitchison saw the irony in the fact that those who could afford it were those most endangered by it:

> . . . the late seventeenth century was a time of generally high mortality and also of pernicious ideas on infant feeding and medical treatment of the sick to which the rich, because they could afford to pay doctors, were particularly subject.[53]

The intellectual tempo of the seventeenth century was not duplicated in the next hundred years. Advancement was slowed by the tyranny of medieval dogma, still influential in medicine as in other spheres:

Undoubtedly the vista unfolded in the previous century by the genius of Newton, Descartes, Boyle, and Bacon led men away from a blind belief in authority to a new faith in progress and the inexorable triumph of the human spirit. Nevertheless the physician, always noted for his conservatism, has seldom been able to keep pace with contemporary scientific advances, especially in other fields, or to put such advances to immediate practical use. The men of medicine could hardly disregard the rapid succession of startling advances in physics and chemistry, but the resultant revival of interest in the systems of the iatrophysicists and iatrochemists did nothing to advance the practice of medicine, and it may have contributed to a period of stasis and decline.[54]

The more serious problem in eighteenth century medical practice was not excessive conservatism, however, but excessive speculation, unsupported by scientific fact or experimentation. To be sure, in Europe and Britain, widely separated medical researchers were using new inventions such as the microscope to unlock the secrets of human histology and pathology. Not until the second half of the nineteenth century, however, would the new science of bacteriology shatter the *status quo* by proving the direct association between germs and disease and thereby lay the foundation of modern medicine.

IV

We can see the influence of many classical and Celtic concepts of health, disease and treatment in the Highlands and Islands during the eighteenth and nineteenth centuries. The conversion of the Celts to Christianity had been, as we have said in an earlier chapter, relatively easy and had resulted in a Celtic Christian superstructure built upon a pagan base.[55] A century later, a Presbyterian minister on Cape Breton Island remarked on that same mixture of beliefs among Highland immigrants:

> Perhaps the only bad traits that they brought with them to Cape Breton were their superstitions regarding witches, fairies, ghosts, etc and their fondness for whiskey.[56]

The pagan base of Celtic Christianity aside, the Judaic belief that disease was a sign of divine disfavour was endorsed and remained a strong tenet among the Calvinists of the Highlands and Islands. During the time of the cholera epidemic of 1832, at a meeting held at Callernish in the Parish of Uig, Lewis, on 11 February, 1832, it was stated that 'it would be the Will of Providence to visit the Island of Lewis with the awful scourge.'

Those words suggest that the writer believed the poor of Lewis would be spared simply because they were God-fearing. In fact, the contents of the letter from which those words were taken reveals a fairly informed understanding of the relationship among health, disease and prevention, though it makes equally clear the prevailing conviction that health and disease are ultimately matters of divine intervention. A further letter dated 23 February notes that

> The Clergymen and principal Inhabitants are doing all in their power to introduce cleanliness, which is the very first thing to be attended to. Should it be the Will of Providence to visit the Island with the malady, there can be little doubt the poor people will come off much better, than dissipated starved persons in towns, for there in many instance, they have no coals, food or any other comfort, whereas in the Lewis, they have warm houses, plenty of the best of fuel, good water and altho their diet is not sumptuous yet they have it regular, such as their Breakfast dinner & supper, of sometime animal food, good fish, Bread, potatoes milk and butter. – together with that when their regular habit of living is taken into view, I humbly think they have a better chance.[57]

Pagan though he might be inclined or judged, even the most confirmed backslider was apt to seek the help of his Christian God while the threat of cholera morbus hung over Lewis.

In point of fact, however, the practice of medicine by the West Highlanders of the eighteenth century, as by most 'primitive' peoples, consisted in the basic concept of assisting nature to cure ill health. That principle was integral to their way of life. Dr Alexander Macleod (1788–1854), a surgeon practising in North Uist in the early nineteenth century, used in his practice the ordinary pharmaceutical drugs but he also used herbs and commonsense injunctions about diet and exercise:

> . . . he was greatly in the habit of preparing medicines from the local herbs. The use of local herbs had on the Highlanders a double effect – the therapeutic effects of their active principles, and the effect caused by the somewhat superstitious respect that they are regarded with. Dietary and exercise were two of his standard remedies, and in enforcing these he had to exercise his great knowledge of the people to ensure that his directions were being carried out.[58]

Moreover, in the absence of hospitals or religious hospices, the patient was treated at home. Interestingly, modern medical practice has since recognized the value of domiciliary care and treatment. In fact, the merits of that early holistic Highland medicine have since been recognized. Dr Hugh Cameron Gillies, in an article on the Beatons written at the beginning of the twentieth century, expressed his scepticism of 'modern therapeutics' and resisted the tendency to regard Highland doctors as ignorant or charlatan:

I am by no means sure that we have made such immense progress as is generally
supposed from the medical and surgical position stated in this book [*Regimen
Sanitatus*, circa 1500] . . . The source of this text is admittedly not original. We
meet with references to Hippocrates, to Galen, to Avicenna, Rhases, and others
most regularly on almost every page. This is as it certainly should be in a medical
or scientific work.[59]

As Dr Gillies's comment suggests, Highland medical theory was more
classically based and Highland medical practice more holistic than most
Establishment medicine. Indeed, Establishment medicine took a tack
antithetical to Highland practice. Establishment medicine was part of
Establishment industry, where profits were to be made in therapeutic
medicine, with its emphasis on drugs and apparatus. The Highland maxim
that an ounce of prevention is worth a pound of cure offered no promise
of profit.

The Establishment encouraged therapeutic medicine at the expense of
preventive medicine. As less research attention was paid to prevention, it
became increasingly more costly and therefore far less remunerative than
the quick fix of therapy.[60] It was less expensive as well to ignore the basic
social and environmental causes of many diseases. To ensure Highlanders a
healthy and disease-resistant environment was simply too costly for the
Establishment even to contemplate it.

Establishment physicians of the eighteenth and nineteenth centuries,
carried on the wave of medical advances, naturally disapproved of medical
practice and practitioners who did not hold with their views. Highland
doctors like the legendary Beatons were dismissed as parochial purveyors
of 'rural' medicine. But the reputation of qualified Establishment physicians
was so bad, that by the eighteenth century, 'quack' doctors were in some
areas of Scotland still regarded as being better than their qualified
counterparts:

> Quack doctors were in request for surgical operations as well as for drugs, and
> in the estimation of the Kirk-Session might be regarded as more skilful than a
> qualified surgeon. In the Kirk-Session records of Shotts there is noted '1730, to
> Mr. Green, the mountebag, for couching John Roger's wife's eyes, £9:6 Scots.'[61]

For effective medical attention, Highlanders had to rely throughout the
nineteenth century on Highland physicians – of whom there were scarcely
enough.

So the situation was to remain while the Establishment continued to
link improvement with enhancement of their own investments, to the
detriment of Highland culture and health. The criticisms of Establishment
medicine presented here are criticisms of its medical practice and its

reliance on therapeutic armamentaria. We must, of course, nonetheless acknowledge that the Highland Establishment did, as did the Establishment of every country, help finance the research of eighteenth and nineteenth century anatomists, physiologists and pathologists, research which took medicine a quantum leap forward in understanding bacteriology.

Notes

1. *Is righ gach slàn* is a very old Gaelic proverb, one that the Caledonian Medical Society chose as its motto.

2. The World Health Organization, in *Everyman's United Nations*, 8th edn., New York, United Nations Pubs., 1968, 509.

3. I. Gordon, MD, 'That Damned Word Health', *The Lancet*, 20 September, 1958. 638–9.

4. Sander Kelman, 'The Social Nature of the Definition Problem in Health', *International Journal of Health Services*, Vol., 5, No., 4, 1975, 625–642.

5. Gary L. Kreps and Barbara C. Thornton, *Health Communication Theory and Practice*, 2nd, edn., Prospect Heights, Illinois, Waveland Press Inc., 1992, 167.

6. Ferris J. Richey in his paper, 'Medical Rationalization, Cultural Lag, and the Malpractice Crisis' *Human Organization*, Vol. 40, No. 2, 1981, 97, suggests that the rationalization of the physician's role is retarded by traditional and charismatic features inherent in professionalism and the healer's role. In other words, the formal rationalization of the physician's role is shown to lag behind the formal rationalization of the other cultural realms.

7. 'Animism', *Dictionary of Sociology*, Henry Pratt Fairchild, Ed., Helix Books, Rowman & Allanheld, Totowa, New Jersey, 1970,

8. Myles Dillon and Nora Chadwick, *Celtic Realms*, 2nd edn., London, Weidenfeld and Nicolson, 1972, 13–14.

9. Nora Chadwick, *The Celts*, London, Penguin Books Ltd., 1970, 150.

10. Albert S. Lyons and R. Joseph Petrucelli, II, *Medicine, An Illustrated History*, New York, Abradale Press, 1987.
    The book covers the history of medicine from prehistoric times to the twentieth century and is profusely illustrated.

11. J.P. Mallory, *In Search of The Indo-Europeans*, London, Thames and Hudson Ltd., 1989, 106–7 and passim 222–265.

12. From 'Principles and Practice of Traditional Systems of Medicine in India', (working paper presented by M.A. Razzack to a WHO meeting on the Promotion and Development of Traditional Medicine, Geneva, 1977. World Health Organization, Technical Report Series No. 622.

13. Dillon and Chadwick, Op cit., 11–12, 199–200.

14. Martin Martin, *A Description of the Western Islands of Scotland*, (circa 1695) 2nd edn., Edinburgh, Reprint, James Thin, 1970, X–XI.

15. Lyons and Petrucelli, Op cit., 153–229.

16. *The Dialogues of Plato.* 2 vols., translated by B. Jowett, New York, Random House, 1937, I, 'Gorgias', 504.

17. Ibid., II, 'Laws' V, 734.

18. Today we do not know much of this legendary healer. We cannot say for sure even that he ever existed. Nor do we know whether he was an individual or a composite figure representative of a particular school of thought. The Hippocratic Oath, held so sacred by Western medicine, barely survives as a genuine document. We do know that the present document, deemed to be the true Oath, which links the newly qualified medical practitioner with the famous Greek School, has been amended several times. The original Oath, for example, forbade surgery. This censure can be taken as an indication of the ineptitude of surgery at that time, or of a schism between the societies of physicians and surgeons during the period. Furthermore, prohibitions against abortion and contraception were not part of the original oath. Their insertion can be interpreted as accommodations to the religious beliefs of the Christian era.
    For further discussion of the influence of Hippocrates see:
    George Merikas, MD, 'Hippocrates: Still a Contemporary', *Humane Medicine*, Canadian Medical Association Pub., Ottawa, Vol. 8. No. 3, July 1992.
    Lyons and Petrucelli, Op cit., 207–217.
    Hippocrates 6 vols., English translation of Vol., I by W.H.S. Jones, London, William Heinemann, 1923, I, 291–301.
    The introduction and Jones's notes are a mine of information on Hippocrates: his writings, the interpretation of previous translators and their errors and misinterpretations of the subject matter.

19. Jones, Ibid., *On Ancient Medicine*, 1., XIX, 53.

20. Richard Mckeon, Ed., *The Basic Works Of Aristotle*, New York, Random House, 1941, 24.

21. One aspect of Plato's thoughts on government addresses Public Health. His ideal State was one in which government provided for the health of its citizens by preventing poverty and over-population.
    The Dialogues of Plato, Op cit., 'The Republic', Book V.

22. Lyons and Petrucelli, Op cit., 231–251.

23. 'Then he called his twelve disciples together, and gave them power and authority over all devils, and to cure all diseases.'
    The Bible, Authorized (King James) version, Luke 9:1.

24. *Hippocrates*, Op cit., *The Art*, II, 193.

25. J.S. Pendergast, 'Galen' in *Encyclopaedia Britannica*, Chicago, Vol., 9, 1958, 972–3.

26. Chadwick, Op cit., 195–6.

27. Alexander Carmichael, Carmina Gadelica, Hymns and Incantations, 2 vols., Edinburgh, T and A. Constable, 1900, II, 2–3.
    For further insight into the prevalence of this cult in the Highlands and Islands see: William MacKenzie, *Gaelic Incantations Charms and Blessings of the Hebrides,* Inverness, Northern Counties Pub. Co. Ltd., 1895.

28. Lyons and Petrucelli, Op cit., 295.

29. Ibn Khaldun, *The Muqaddimah:An Introduction to History*, Translated from the Arabic by Franz Rosenthal, Edited and abridged by N.J. Dawood, Princeton, N.J., Bollingen Series, Princeton Univ. Press, 1969, 386–7.

30. Lyons and Petrucelli, Op cit., 310.

31. Derick S. Thomson Ed., *Companion to Gaelic Scotland*, Oxford, Blackwell Pub., Ltd., 1983. 195–6.
    Cameron Gillies, commenting on the *Vade Mecum of the Macbeaths* (Beatons), noted that a Scot, Bernard de Gordon, born in France, was a teacher at Montpellier in the early fourteenth century and that he wrote the *Lilium Medicinae* which the MacBeaths possessed and rendered into Gaelic.
    Dr H. Cameron Gillies, *Regimen Sanitatis* – The Rule of Health – A Gaelic Medical Manuscript of the Early Sixteenth Century or perhaps older, Glasgow, Univ. Press, 1911, 12.
    Martin Martin reported on the great reputation of a Neil Beaton in Skye, an 'unqualified' physician:
    He considers his patient's constitution before any medicine is administered to them . . . He treats Riverius's *Lilium Medicinae* (early 17th century) and some other practical pieces that he has heard of, with contempt; since in several instances it appears that their method of curing has failed, where his had good success.
    Martin Martin, Op cit., 197–8.
    For more information on the Beatons see:
    John Bannerman, *The Beatons: a medical kindred in the classical Gaelic tradition*, Edinburgh, John Donald, 1986.
    Dr J.J. Galbraith, 'Medicine among the Gaelic Celts', *Transactions of the Gaelic Society of Inverness*, XXXIX/XL, 1942–1950, 63–78.

32. Lyons and Petrucelli, Op cit., 315.

33. Knut Haeger, *The Illustrated History Of Surgery*, New York, Bell Publishing Co., 1988, 70–1.

34. Lyons and Petrucelli. Op cit., 317.

35. Haeger, Op cit., 70.

36. Ian B. Cowan, 'The Medieval Church in the Highlands', in *The Middle Ages in the Highlands*, Ed., Loraine MacLean of Dochgarroch, Inverness, The Inverness Field Club, 1981, 96–7.

37. Lyons and Petrucelli, Op cit., 349–351.

38. Ibid., 351.

39. Ibid., 355.

40. Ibid., 337–362.
    Haeger, Op cit., 69–93.

41. Lyons and Petrucelli, Op cit., 369.

42. For a more detailed review of the impact of this Age on medicine see: Ibid., 368–423.
    Haeger, Op cit., Chapter 4, Surgery in the Renaissance.
    Nancy G. Siraisi, *Medieval & Early Renaissance Medicine*, Chicago, Univ., Press, 1990.

43. Lyons and Petrucelli, Op cit., 388–9.

44. T.C. Smout, *A History of the Scottish People* 1560–1830. London, Fontana Paperbacks, 1982, 188–9.

45. See: Lyons and Petrucelli, Op cit., 'The Seventeenth Century', 426–423.

46. William Harvey, *An Anatomical Disquisition on the Motion of the Heart and Blood in Animals*, Ed., E.A. Parkyn, London, Everyman's Library, No., 262, J. M. Dent & sons Ltd., 1907.

47. Haeger, Op cit., 103.

48. Ibid., 103.

49. Sir Francis Bacon, *Advancement of Learning*, translation of Ellis and Spedding, Ed., John M. Robertson, (1905), Freeport, N.Y., Books for Libraries Press reprint, 1970, 103–4, 136.
    John Milton, *Paradise Lost*, in *The Poetic Works of John Milton*, 2 vols., Ed., Helen Darbishire, Oxford, Claredon Press, 1952, Vol I, 255.
    Johnathan Swift, *Gulliver's Travels*, Toronto, The Macmillan Co., of Canada, 1946, 295–299, 326.
    Jean Jacques Rousseau, *Discourse on the Origin and Foundations of Inequality Among Men, on the Social Contract*, translated and edited by Donald A. Cress, Indianapolis, Hackett Pub., Co., 1983, Part one, 123.
    Immanuel Kant, 'The Metaphysical Elements of Ethics', in *Kant's Critique of Pure Reason and Other Works on the Theory of Ethics*, translated by Thomas Kingswell Abbott, 6th edn., London, Longman Green and Co., Ltd., 1909, Reprinted, 1967, 295.
    Leo Tolstoy, *War and Peace,* translated from the Russian by Constance Garnett, New York, The Modern Library, Random House Inc., n.d. 735.

50. O.S.A., XII (Jura and Colonsay), 328.
    Martin Martin also noted in his *Description*, Op cit., 233, that on Jura 'Blood-letting and Purging are not us'd here.'

51. Adam Smith, *An Inquiry into the Nature and Causes of the Wealth of Nations*, New York, The Modern Library, Random House Inc., 1937, 638.

52. William Wallace, *Poetical Works of Robert Burns*, 'Death and Dr Hornbook, A True Story', London, W.& R. Chambers Ltd., 1908, 44.

53. Rosalind Mitchison, *Lordship to Patronage Scotland 1603–1745*, The New History of Scotland, London, Edward Arnold, 1983, 112.

54. Lyons and Petrucelli, Op cit., 467.

55. Peter Berresford Ellis, *Celtic Inheritance*, London, Muller, 1985, 82–3.
    O.S.A.,V (Logierait), 'Superstitious opinions and Practices', 82–85.
    In the mid-eighteenth century, a parish minister on the Isle of Mull also lamented the ease of this conversion when reporting on the character of his flock:
    A dash of superstition is mixed up with their feelings, and may be traced to some opinions handed down by their ancestors, perhaps from the time of the Druids.
    N.S.A.,VII (Kilfinichen and Kilviceuen), 307.
    The parish minister of Duirinish on Skye also worried about his flock's spirit of true religion: 'there is much superstition, the sure concomitant of ignorance, still lingering among them.'
    N.S.A., XIV (Duirinish), 346.

56. Revd John Murray, *The History of the Presbyterian Church in Cape Breton*, Truro, N.S., News Publishing Co. Ltd., 1921, 265.

57. Seaforth Papers, Scottish Records Office (SRO), Edinburgh, GD46\13\215(6).
    This, the first portion (The remainder of the letter was not preserved) of a letter dated 23rd February 1832 to the Hon. Mrs Mackenzie of Seaforth, the proprietrix, was in the handwriting of Alexander Stewart, factor of Lewis. It contained a copy of the minutes of the meeting held at Callernish on the 11th February 1832 respecting the actions to be taken to ameliorate the effects of the impending cholera epidemic. The contents of the letter certainly do not support the contention that all was to be left in the hands of Providence.

58. M.D. Macleod, MB, 'An Doctair Ban' [The fair haired doctor], *Caledonian Medical Journal*, IV, (1899–1901), 12–3.
    See also Dr J.J. Galbraith, Op cit., 63–78.

59. H. Cameron Gillies, MD, 'A Gaelic Medical Manuscript of 1563', *Caledonian Medical Journal*, V, (1902–04), 42–3.

60. Gordon, Op cit., 639.

61. Quoted by Henry Grey Graham, *Social Life of Scotland in the Eighteenth Century*, 2 vols., London, Adam & Charles Black, 1899, II, 210, n. 3.
    'Couching' is the treatment of cataract by the pulling down of the lens so as to allow the visual image to reach the retina unimpeded.

5

Nutrition

Bless the table and fill the stomach. Thou who didst send us this meal, may thou send us another, from meal to meal, until the final meal.[1]

THE HIGHLAND ESTABLISHMENT believed that the common people, given their traditional subsistence diet in assured supply, were better fed than the 'dissipated' population of the crowded towns, those 'dark smoky wynds, vennels and closes' of the fast-growing industrial centres of the Lowlands. They were right. The basic Highland diet had much to commend it, as contemporary nutritional studies showed. In 1869, Hutchison, 'Reporting on the Dietaries of Scotch Agricultural Labourers', observed:

> Whether inland or sea-coast, highland or lowland, the great staples for sustaining life amongst the peasantry of Scotland are oatmeal and milk. In this particular, the difference between the English and the Scotch labourers is very decided; for while the use of oatmeal in the sister country is almost unknown, it forms the leading article of daily sustenance amongst 90 per cent of the families of the labouring classes in Scotland . . . The high dietetic value of oatmeal is a very important feature, where its use is so universal in any district or country as it is in Scotland; and when taken in connection with milk as the other staple article of food and nourishment, its competency to afford a great amount of physical nutriment is considerably enhanced, and we find that as a nutritive agent, milk is almost unequalled.[2]

Similarly, a comment published in the Quarterly Journal of Agriculture in 1836 praised the diet of agricultural labourers in Scotland over that of urban labourers in England:

> An English labourer thinks himself starved, if he does not daily eat butcher-meat and white bread, and drink malt liquor; whereas in Scotland milk and meal [oat-meal] make a plentiful house, and our ablest ploughmen take nothing more. Potatoes, which the children of our gentry prefer to bread, are regarded with considerable scorn by labourers in the south of England.[3]

Moreover, the efficacy and healthfulness of the simple Highland diet has been repeatedly confirmed by researchers during the last few centuries, most recently by two Medical Research Council's studies, one dental, the

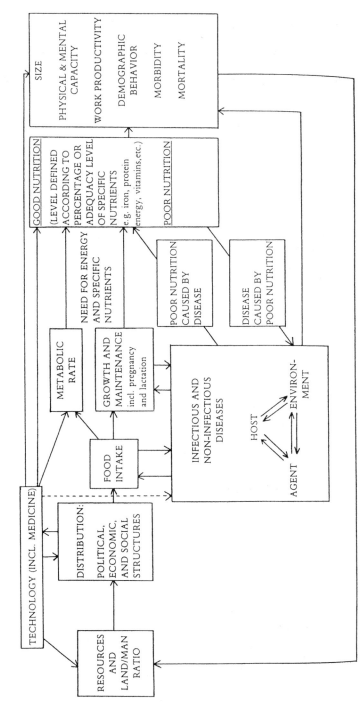

Figure 3. A Holistic Approach to Human Food Nutrition

other nutritional. The Council's dental study compared the dental health of rural Highland children with that of urban children and concluded that

> the dietary of the *rural* children of Lewis included a relatively high proportion of fat soluble vitamins and mineral salts, thus providing a more abundant supply of nutritional factors necessary for the proper development and calcification of the teeth than is available in most parts of Britain. There was also a high carbohydrate and first class protein content and a *moderate supply of vitamin C* [italics are mine]. On the other hand, the Lewis *urban* dietary, apart from vitamin C, included a much lower proportion of protective and a correspondingly higher proportion of non-protective food materials.[4]

The same Council's nutritional study examined the diets of 58 families in the Highlands of Scotland and compared the findings from that analysis with the results of earlier dietary studies made in St Andrews on the east coast of Scotland, in Cardiff (Wales) and Reading (England). The Council found that Highlanders consumed more protein, fat and carbohydrate than did the families in the St Andrews study. Although the proportion of 'first class protein' was low (two per cent), it was still higher than that found in Cardiff and Reading.[5]

By many measures, then, the basic Highland diet was deemed nutritious. What eighteenth- and nineteenth-century Establishmentarians failed to acknowledge, however, was that the quantity and quality of people's food supply was uncertain at best, and that the destruction of their lifestyle had stripped them of other elements necessary to health. Good nutrition is, of course, a matter of the quality and quantity of food, but it is also a matter of factors like fuel and clothing. In fact, it is related to lifestyle generally. Thus too little exposure to the sun, a circumstance of the urban poor, was implicated in the disease of rickets, which raged among them. The contamination of raw and prepared food and of drink also produced nutritional problems and disease. In all, faulty nutrition, defined broadly as here, left Highlanders susceptible to a range of diseases.

Although the Highland Establishment did not recognize the relationship among destitution, nutrition and disease, the laity did. As did the parochial doctors in Scotland:

> Most unquestionably destitution (by whatever means produced) is the great source of disease among us; and there is no doubt that if efficient means can be had for checking and repressing it, disease, in a great measure, will also be checked, the persons most affected being those who, from poverty or dissipation, do not receive even the necessaries of life.[6]

Highlanders who found themselves by choice or compulsion relocated to the new and heavily-populated industrial towns were part of the body of poor drawn from all parts of Britain in search of work. Their common goal was to survive in this new cultural milieu, one that most of them regarded as better than the rural poverty they had known. In 1785, the Lords of the Treasury were apprised of the poverty that moved Highlanders to look for work elsewhere:

> Such being the unavoidable consequences of allowing a people to remain wholly in detached hamlets, we ought not to be surprised at the poverty in those regions, nor at the indolence imputed to them. They are indeed industrious; but that industry is unavailing, — They make great exertions; but these exertions tend not to remove their poverty. Is it a wonder, if, in these circumstances, they should sometimes think of moving to happier abodes?[7]

Circumstances had become so desperate that the wonder was only that more did not go. Two prominent historians, researching the data from the Poor Law Commission Report of 1844, suggested why many stayed:

> Perhaps the most surprising feature of the present day, as indeed of 1843, is that so many people continued to live with poor prospects in remote and beautiful places. It only goes to prove what every economic historian knows, that man does not live by economic considerations alone.[8]

For many others, however, the reward for going was irresistible. Manual labour, though gruelling, or factory work, though it reduced them to extensions of a machine, at least provided a wage. But the cities they found work in were hardly happier abodes. However destitute conditions were in the Highlands, they were not the squalor then prevalent in the industrial centres of Lowland Scotland and England. To one observer of that scene,

> Everything that meets the eye or ear tells of slavish labour united to brutal intemperance . . .
> I was assured that some houses, with a family and only two rooms, took as many as 14 single men as lodgers . . . An infatuated love of money, for no purpose but to minister to a degrading passion for ardent spirits, seems the all-pervading of action in this quarter.[9]

Furthermore, in the cities and towns, their nutritional problems worsened because there they consumed highly refined, adulterated and badly preserved food.[10] Here is Hutchison again, 'Reporting on the Dietaries of Scottish Agricultural Labourers' in 1869:

> In the neighbourhood of large towns we found the labourers complain much of the difficulty of obtaining milk, even in scanty supplies, and this scarceness of so important an article of diet leads to the *substitution of treacle [molasses] and water, or sugar and water, and in a few instances of beer* [italics are mine]. None of these can in any way be compared [as regards nutritive properties] with milk.[11]

Thus the degradation of the industrial towns where they found work, no less than their destitution at home, deprived Highlanders of their traditionally simple but nutritious fare: milk, oats, potatoes, fish and a limited intake of meat. That deprivation proved a serious danger to health, in particular to the body's defence mechanism. Malnourished wherever they lived, Highlanders were prey to disease.

I

According to McLaren and Meguid, malnutrition means nutrition disordered as a result of any deviation from the normal; undernutrition includes starvation, semi-starvation, hunger and underfeeding, as well as hidden hunger and misfeeding. Hidden hunger, McLaren and Meguid explain, may be present even though a person does not complain of hunger, if his diet lacks nutrients essential for proper metabolism.[12]

Poverty can spell under-nutrition, even for suckling infants, if they are breast-fed longer than normal – a not uncommon circumstance among poor Highlanders. The parish minister of Assynt noted the length of weaning in families of his parish:

> The Highland girls of this parish for the most part marry at the age of betwixt 16 and 21 years; the lads at that of betwixt 20 and 25. There are some instances of women bearing children to the age of 50 years at least. It is no uncommon sight to see a grandmother give her breast to her own grandchild to suckle. Some fond mothers nurse their children for two years. Other mothers nurse their infants for three; and truly the narrator has seen a boy at his mother's breast at the age of four years, and then break hasle-nuts under his teeth.[13]

The result of this delayed weaning is a large, pale infant who, although he may look well enough fed, is in fact not only dangerously undernourished, but is also anaemic because the milk he has been fed is so low in iron. Furthermore, prolonged lactation can be destructive to the health of an under-nourished, overworked mother. In the Highlands, delayed weaning was one of the causes of high infant and maternal mortality. Furthermore, by 1868, food distribution within the family had become seriously imbalanced: a review of rural dietaries in Scotland showed that by that time, male wage-earners had begun to receive the bulk of meat and other protein, thus concentrating the effect of poor diet on women and children. This in turn led to a gender-oriented disease pattern.[14] To deprive housewives was particularly dangerous because, as we saw in Chapter 3, the seasonal crofting and fishing economy of the Western Highlands made the housewife an indispensable worker in the family.

Among the Highland poor, malnutrition was the result too of what had become a staple food, *uisge-beatha* or the 'water of life.' This quick source of energy was readily available to the poor, and the local (or smuggled) product was cheaper and naturally thought to be much superior to the government-controlled 'parliamentary' whisky. From Lewis, Martin Martin reported:

> Their plenty of Corn was such, as dispose'd the natives to brew several sorts of Liquors, as common Usquebaugh, another call'd Trestarig, idest, Aqua-vitae, three times distill'd, which is strong and hot; a third sort is four times distill'd, and this by the Natives is call'd Usquebaugh-baul, idest, Usquebaugh, which at first taste affects all Members of the Body: two spoonfuls of this last Liquor is a sufficient Dose; and if any Man exceeds this, it would presently stop his Breath, and endanger his Life. The Trestarig and the Usquebaugh-baul, are both made of Oats.[15]

Used with discretion, alcohol was a valuable nutritional supplement to the Highland subsistence diet. Quickly metabolised, whisky produced instant if short-lived warmth and energy. But like mother's milk, it was not a complete diet. As the economy of the Highlands and Islands worsened, cheap whisky increasingly afforded temporary relief from the stark realities of life, but only at great cost to the body. Many ministers detected the onset of chronic alcoholism in their parishes, and while many themselves were not averse to a 'dram', they could not ignore the causes for and the effects of over-indulgence among their parishioners as among their colleagues.

II

As we have said, Highlanders' diet was uncertain in quantity and quality. Moreover, their diet was often deficient in one or more of the essential food groups. Of those six groups, protein takes pride of place, being required not only for the maintenance of the human body, but also for its growth, repair, reproduction and lactation. Protein deficiency can be destructive to life, especially during the formative periods of intra-uterine life, infancy and childhood.[16] Adults can survive long periods of insufficient and inferior protein intake but children, particularly very young children, cannot.[17] That fact alone helps explain the high infant mortality rates during the frequent periods of starvation in the Highlands, as well as during the nutritional trauma of a prolonged nineteenth-century voyage in an emigrant ship, and the subsequent struggle for survival in a new country.

As late as the mid-nineteenth century, Highlanders were driven to eat seaweed and shellfish during periods of famine.[18] But shellfish, oysters, clams and other mollusca have little nutritional value except for their iron and iodine content. Highlanders' only seaborne source of protein other than fish was crustaceans; that is, lobsters, prawns and crabs. Crustaceans are about 18% protein and so make a valuable contribution to the diet.[19]

The specific dynamic action of protein allows it to replace fat and carbohydrate as a source of energy, making it a valuable source of food for those exposed to cold. Protein deficiency was customary in the Scottish Highlands and in Cape Breton, to which Highlanders emigrated, because crop failures and fish scarcity were common.[20] That deficiency meant an immediate decline in health and in resistance to disease, especially because Highlanders were so often exposed to inclement weather in the unsuitable habitats to which they had been evicted, and during the severe winters in Cape Breton.

Protein may be obtained from animal or vegetable sources. Vegetable sources are, however, regarded as second-class for growth function. But in the Highlands, where arable land was at a premium, the poor rarely butchered livestock. Meat was confined to the chief's table, as Reay Tannahill noted:

> Where the clan chief's table held oatcakes and brose, mutton and venison, salmon and herring (and a good deal more besides), the peasant would sit down to the first and the last, and think himself fortunate.[21]

And Hutchison observed that

> In Skye, the dietary of the lower classes is more deficient, both in quantity and nutritive value, than in any other district of Scotland . . . One family in this island we found had not seen butcher meat for five years, and there are many who never tasted beer or cheese![22]

(Hutchison's Report provides an informative glimpse of Highland diet and daily life in the mid-nineteenth century. A selection of his observations are reproduced as Appendix A of this book.) Johnson too commented on the absence of meat in the diet of the small sub-tenant Highland farmer:

> Their food is not better than their lodging. They seldom taste the flesh of land animals; for here are no markets. What each man eats is from his own stock. The great effect of money is to break property into small parts. In towns he that has a shilling may have a piece of meat; but where there is no commerce, no man can eat mutton but by killing a sheep.[23]

In short, the rural population of eighteenth-century Scotland lived on oats, barley, kail and some dairy produce. Only occasionally did they eat fish.[24] Furthermore, from the 1770s onwards, the Highland diet was comprised increasingly of the potato which, though it contained more than

20% of starch, provided only 2% of protein. Potatoes are also low in minerals such as iron and calcium and provide only small amounts of the B vitamins and vitamin C. Thus the potato, when it became the major component of a Highlander's diet, had to be consumed regularly in large amounts to supply sufficient nutrients.[25] In the West Highlands and Islands, the normally higher intake there of fish was therefore of fundamental importance as a source of non-plant protein. Moreover, while cereal proteins provide relatively little of the 'essential amino acids', lysine and methionine, fish protein provides relatively higher concentrations of those same acids, an important fact since amino acids are necessary for protein synthesis. Absence of any of the ten essential amino acids stops protein synthesis.[26]

The second major food group, fat, is necessary for energy production. It supplies from 10 to 40% of the total energy requirement. McLaren and Meguid suggest that the higher figure is assigned where the energy source is unsaturated fat of animal origin.[27] Fat can also be stored in the body as a reserve of energy and as a soft insulation against trauma and cold. Deaths resulting from cold; that is, from hypothermia, were wrongly diagnosed until the late twentieth century, when the full significance of the insulating property of fat became apparent. Moreover, McLaren and Meguid observe that certain unsaturated fatty acids, in which the liver and tissue oils of fish like mackerel, herring and cod are rich, have antithrombotic effects on platelets and therefore may be important in preventing clotting of the blood in the coronary arteries.[28] Finally, fat, like dietary protein, contains essential fatty acids. Accordingly, some fat intake is mandatory.

In the eighteenth century, the source of dietary fat varied with economic status. By that time, Highland clansmen had become a mainly agricultural work force, while the economy of the West Highlands and Islands was essentially pastoral, augmented by seasonal fishing and indifferent agriculture. Yet in that pastoral and agricultural lifestyle, one obvious source of dietary fat, the pig, was not part of Highlanders' diet, and for good reason:

> Not being a ruminant it competed directly for human food. It could not be milked, and milk was by far the most important food product of the domesticated animal.[29]

Burt gives another reason for the absence of swine on Highlanders' farms:

> Those People have no Offal wherewith to feed them; and, were they to give them other Food, one single Sow would devour all the Provisions of a Family.[30]

But in the south-west Highlands, where the traditional lifestyle had not been disturbed and runrig remained, as in the parish of Killin, pigs were more plentiful:

Since potatoes have become more plentiful, swine have become more numerous. There are about 150 of them at present in this parish.[31]

That exception aside, the major sources of fat throughout the Highlands were fish and dairy products, both perennially at risk from the vagaries of nature, from any ecological disturbance in the habitat, and from inept legislation.

The development of a Scottish fishery as a solution to the Highland problems was promoted by the government. But the legislation proposed to establish that fishery was unrealistic and revealed Establishment ignorance of conditions in the Highlands. A coastal fishery is always precarious. Even a bountiful catch, if it cannot be safely preserved by drying or salting, can give rise to a temporary gluttony, or to the ingestion of rancid fish. Without dependable and efficient preservation, commercial fishing could not be undertaken. Salting was the key to the Highland fishery, yet although the government offered a bounty to encourage herring fishing, any local attempts to improve the fishery were handicapped by the taxation of salt, an irony that James Anderson reported to Their Lordships:

> This change, so devoutly to be wished, has been, along with other things, most effectually prevented from taking place, in consequence of a system of Salt-laws, which the Legislature, ill informed with regard to those distant and hitherto neglected parts of the empire, have thought proper to enact [Imposed 1712, in violation of the Treaty of Union]. These laws, as they present stand in the Statute-book, tie up in the most effectual manner, the hands of the poor natives of these coasts, and absolutely debar them from entertaining the most distant hope of ever engaging in those fisheries *on their own account*, while they continue in force. This gives an additional power over them to those superiors already mentioned [their masters], whose power was formerly but too great, which serves to rivet the chains of those poor people still faster than they were before.[32]

Before the importance of hygienic and preservative measures against the deterioration of food were fully understood, rancid fat was always a problem to health. Tannahill makes the interesting observation that oats and rye, two 'weeds' which flourished in most of Scotland, helped to ameliorate the effects of rancid fat. In particular oats, which had become the main crop, had a salutary anti-oxidant effect:

> Nutritionally, they [oats] were to prove valuable, for although they have a lower protein value than wheat or rye, they are higher in calcium and iron, and have certain anti-oxidant properties that delay deterioration in other foods and even protect against the effects of eating rancid fats.[33]

Many episodes of disease states reported to have followed heavy intakes of fish and milk were almost certainly the effect of rancid fat in those foods, exacerbated by a reduced intake of oatmeal, in that diners sated with fish and milk would have consumed less anti-oxidizing oatmeal.[34]

The third food group, carbohydrate, forms the largest component of the diet of most people of the world and produces most of their energy requirement. Potatoes and cereals are excellent sources of energy and, providing the cereals have not been over-refined or adulterated, they will provide a wide range of minerals and vitamins, particularly B complex from cereals and vitamin C from potatoes.

Cereals may also contain some of the essential amino acids so necessary for the building of body tissue, but they are never in themselves a satisfactory supply of all essential acids. For example, most cereal protein is deficient in methionine. A diet that contains a mixture of cereal and legumes tends to reduce the deficiency inherent in each and have an improved 'biological value'.[35] However, the introduction of the potato, with its bountiful yield and ease of cultivation, meant that fewer legumes were grown in the Highlands and Islands. Thus Highlanders' reliance on potatoes created a dangerous void in the food chain. That reliance, in Scotland and later in Cape Breton, is understandable however, because, as Currie and Mearns point out, carbohydrate crops are cheaper to grow:

> The demand for energy is primary, and the yield of food energy from an acre of land is higher for cereal crops than from legumes in the ratio of about 3:1 and higher than for meat produced from crops in the ratio of about 9:1, hence, where pressure of population is heavy, the consumption first of animal products and then of leguminous plants tend to fall, and the consumption of cereals and, in consequence, carbohydrate rises markedly . . . The percentage of energy derived from fat is much more variable and is in inverse proportion to that derived from carbohydrate . . . Economic pressure lowers fat and raises carbohydrate consumption, because carbohydrate is cheaper than fat.[36]

Though cheaper to produce, the potato, and certain cereals which formed the carbohydrate supply, were never certain crops and when they failed, the resulting absence of carbohydrates, particularly during pregnancy and infancy, was a regular threat to Highlanders' health.

As to the other food groups, the mineral requirements for proper nutrition, always minimal, were adequately provided by the sustained normal diet of the Highlanders. Normally, vitamin requirements were met as well, largely because the potato, when taken in large quantities, provided adequate intake of vitamin C. The vitamin C content of the potato declines naturally with storage however, so that using old and rotting potatoes or eating seed potatoes to ward off starvation provides less vitamin C than is required, a deficiency that is most serious when people are near starvation. Scurvy was always a threat, therefore, to the Highlanders' health, especially if the pre-potato seasonal sources of vitamin C – berries, green vegetables, and milk – were poor.

Water, the last food group, was normally never in short supply, thanks to the climate of Old and New Scotland, but it was often not potable. In particular, the impurity of most urban water supplies guaranteed a continuous and often fatal presence of enteric diseases. The oft-quoted text from Isaiah has no better application than to the relationship among water, sanitation and health: 'Woe unto them that join house to house.'[37]

Woe also to those who suffered together in the crowded coastal strips following the nineteenth-century evictions, and to Highland emigrants in crowded and vermin-infested emigrant ships and city tenements. Everywhere, what joined house to house was neighbours' alimentary tracts and their vermin.[38]

III

Most Establishment landowners were not ignorant of the effects on their people of crop failure and poor fish catches. In the main, their estate improvements had caused the starvation their tenants suffered:

> 'There has been grown', says the Duke, [the 8th Duke of Argyll] 'more corn, more potatoes, more turnips; there has been produced more milk, more butter, more cheese, more beef, more mutton, more pork, more fowls and eggs.' But what becomes of them? The Duke must know that the ordinary food of the common people is meal and potatoes; that of these many do not get enough, that many would starve outright if they were not kept alive by charity. Even the wild meat which their fathers took freely, the common people cannot now touch. A Highland poor-law doctor, whose district is on the estate of a prominent member of the Liberal party was telling me recently . . . how insufficient and monotonous food was beginning to produce among them diseases like the *pellagra* in Italy [caused by a deficient intake of the B vitamin Niacin (nicotinic acid)], when I asked him if they could not, despite the gamekeepers, take for themselves enough fish and game to vary their diet. 'They never think of it', he replied; 'they are too cowed. Why, the moment any one of them was even suspected of cultivating a taste for trout or grouse, he would be driven off the estate like a mad dog.'[39]

This hunger in the face of plenty was typical in the nineteenth century. It was the case as well during the Irish famines, when

> The face of the country is covered with ripe corn while the people dread starvation . . . The grain will go out of the country to pay rent . . . Glorious

weather, superb crops and cheap food could not help the penniless unemployed masses.[40]

The landowners had in their estate improvements disturbed the customary if uncertain seasonal food supply of the Highlanders and their animals. Evicted from their traditional niches and relocated to smaller, barren plots, Highlanders could at least for a time grow potatoes in abundance. But that dependency on the potato meant, as we have said, a great reduction in the amount of grain and legumes produced locally; that in turn meant a dependency on imported grain. Figures from the village of Plockton in Wester Ross illustrate how the dependence developed and how dangerous, nutritionally, it was. Highlanders turned to their poor land 'to yield no more than a tithe of their subsistence.'[41] This land provided a better crop of potatoes than one of corn or barley:

> On one of the best managed lots, I find that a piece of land which used to yield twelve bolls of potatoes, has returned four bolls of barleymeal . . . however, . . . for three bolls of barleymeal, or two bolls of oatmeal, for twelve bolls of potatoes, is a much more common return. The difference, in point of utility to a family, between the two crops may be easily estimated. A boll of meal is 140 pounds, in weight; a boll of potatoes is four cwt., or 448 lbs. Five lbs. of potatoes are considered equal in point of nourishment to one pound of oatmeal; . . . it follows . . . that the life-sustaining power of two bolls of oatmeal bears the same proportion to that of twelve bolls of potatoes as does [approximately] one to four. It is difficult to determine the precise quantity of nourishment necessary to maintain a human being in health and vigour, but I believe a family of five – two adults and three children – will live as the Highlanders live, that is, they will not die suddenly of starvation, upon five pounds of oatmeal per day, or twenty-five pounds of potatoes. And . . . while twelve bolls of potatoes would sustain a family of five during thirty weeks and five days, the two bolls of oatmeal which the Highland crofters have reaped this year as a substitute, are only sufficient to sustain such a family during eight weeks.[42]

If Establishment landlords were indifferent to the effects of their avarice on the Highland population, Establishment merchants were even more callous. They routinely adulterated food and failed to preserve it properly. In fact, during the potato famines of the 1840s, one merchant, Alexander Bannantyne, was charged with adulterating the meal of the Highland Relief Fund.[43]

IV

> The potato is the true root of Scarcity, which promises to let Famine at defiance. The poorer sort of people dine and sup chiefly on potatoes, in the season of them.[44]

Any discussion of the importance of the potato in Highland life must note the great watershed in the history of the common people of the Highlands and Islands, the potato famines of the mid-nineteenth century. The famines, not Culloden, were the epicentre of the social upheaval in the West Highlands and Islands. For a majority of the population, the potato famines broke the last tenuous bonds of the ancient Celtic clan system and exposed the enormity of the gap between the haves and the have-nots. In so doing, the famines set the scene for the popular uprisings to come.

The vagaries of climate in the late 1840s hastened the spread of potato blight and its devastation of the potato crop.[45] But neither climate nor blight was the prime cause of the famines. Rather, the primary cause was the dependency of a population in so vulnerable a region on one food crop. That dependence was the fault of the Highland landowners, most of them non-residents and non-agriculturalists.[46] As we have noted, most landowners were well aware of the failure of the crop and of the famine it produced. In a series of letters published in the *North British Daily Mail* in 1847, one writer chastised the new owner of the estate of Glenelg Proper for allowing his people to starve:

> It can surely not be any advantage to a proprietor to have fertile land lying waste at one end of a glen and people starving at the other . . . It would be a good thing if the Highland proprietors could be brought to feel that it is a personal disgrace to fail in providing for their people, when the resources of their estates are amply sufficient to secure that end. Mr Baillie [from Bristol, England] is a merchant, who enjoys a capital reputation on the Exchange, and would shrink from the idea of insolvency as from the cholera or the plague. Yet to be owner of an uncultivated and undeveloped estate, like Glenelg Proper, and at the same time have hundreds of people upon it destitute of food, and dragging out existence by a miserable dependence on the charitable offerings of the British public, is a species of bankruptcy not less dishonourable than a downright stoppage of payments.[47]

While the potato famines of the nineteenth century were not confined to the West Highlands and Islands, their effects were most devastating there, particularly in the small, crowded and isolated new townships and villages in that area. The misery in those villages was far greater even than in Ireland, although the Irish famines [1845–9] were more publicised and politicised.

The Irish population were at least dispersed throughout four provinces and a greater land mass and therefore had access (in theory), as did similarly afflicted commoners in most of Britain, to other sources of food. In Scotland, the death toll from the famines in the potato-dependent regions was staggering: thousands of deaths from 'uncomplicated starvation'; thousands more from hypothermia; and more thousands from communicable diseases whose onset and spread were also precipitated by hunger.[48]

Often starving, usually without clothes or fuel, living in new settlements that could not sustain them, defenceless against diseases for which they had developed no immunity, Highlanders were condemned by their evictors to disease and death. Nor was the situation much improved for many of the Highlanders who in the 1830s emigrated to Cape Breton, as the Revd John Stewart reported from there in 1833:

> I have baptised the child of a parent lying on a pallet of straw with five children in a state of nudity. I have baptised where neither father, mother, nor children could venture out in their tattered rags. I have seen dwellings where six or eight of a family lived for five weeks on the milk of a cow, without any other food. I have endeavoured to afford the consolation of religion at a dying bed, in a habitation where no food existed but what was supplied by neighbours who could ill spare it.[49]

The famines threw the already threatened Highland lifestyle into imminent danger of cataclysmic break-up. The plight of the people could no longer be ignored. The British government had already had some experience in famine relief in Ireland. In the first two years of the Irish famine, the British government had 'behaved with considerable generosity', though without effect:

> In 1847, eight millions [pounds] were advanced to enable the Irish to supply the loss of the potato crop and to cast about them for some less precarious food . . . The result is that they have placed more dependence on the potato than ever and have again been deceived.[50]

In 1847, the government decided that the support of the destitute in Ireland should come from the poor rates. The Irish Poor Law system was badly organized, however, and in most destitute areas, it was quickly bankrupt because local rates could not be collected to finance it. The poor law system was not, however, the government's most serious mistake in dealing with the Irish famines:

> Neither during the famine nor for decades afterwards were any measures of reconstruction or agricultural improvements attempted, and this neglect

condemned Ireland to decline . . . Seed rose in price, far beyond the reach of
the famine-stricken Irish, but the Government would not assist with seed, in
spite of the successful distribution by the Society of Friends. The Irish small
tenant was inevitably driven back on the potato; he was penniless, starving,
ignorant; the only crop he knew how to cultivate the potato . . . He had no
choice.[51]

The British government approached the Highland famine no less ineptly.
For generations, they had seen in the West Highlands and Islands only
superb scenery and excellent sporting estates. That the population was small,
unorganized and therefore politically anonymous guaranteed that the
government would ignore their plight. Ignore it they had for decades. As
early as 1822, one correspondent had warned about famine in the
Highlands:

> The distress of the Irish attracts great attention from the public; and the
> generous spirit shown on this subject does much honour to the British nation.
> There are, however, people still nearer on our own doors who are at this
> moment suffering very severely in silence; I mean the inhabitants of the West
> Highlands in general but more especially those of the Hebrides . . . I am not
> so well informed in regard to the North, or the North-east Highlands, though
> I have reason to believe they are in a very bad condition; but in the West
> Highlands and Islands, the same scenes that now occur in Ireland will most
> assuredly be found soon if they are not relieved.[52]

When the government did take action, the difference between the Irish
and Highland famines soon became apparent to Sir Edward Pine Coffin
and his staff, sent to the Highlands from Ireland to organize the relief.[53]
Coffin had been knighted for his relief work in Ireland. By October 1846,
he and his assistant, Captain Pole, understood the severity of the Highland
famine:

> The importance of establishing these depots [food depots] is so great, at least
> on this western side of Scotland, where commercial enterprise is hardly to be
> trusted for a regular and sufficient supply of imported food, that I hope the
> arrangements for the purpose will be hastened as much as possible. The chief
> benefit will be felt by the smaller proprietors, who may exert themselves for
> the assistance of their people, and I think that the mere presence of the depot
> may operate as a stimulus to their exertion, and, under proper regulation, tend
> to encourage that of the people themselves, by proving to them that they are
> not abandoned, and that food is insured to those who can and will labour for
> it. Inactive resignation to calamity seems to be a leading feature of their
> character, which must, if possible, be converted into industrious energy: and it
> is the more to be deplored, because the absence of clamour and agitation may,
> in contrast with the state of Ireland, be supposed to indicate a comparative

superiority of condition, which I am, however, persuaded does not exist. I believe on the contrary, that the Highlander, or at least the native of these naturally poor and remote islands, has fewer resources, and less inducement to exert himself, than the Irish peasant, and that his condition deserves proportionably more watchful attention.[54]

That the Highlander had far 'fewer resources . . . than the Irish peasant . . .' had been attested by another observer. Alexander Mackenzie, editor of *The Celtic Magazine*, found during a fact-finding mission to County Mayo that Irish peasants were better off than their Highland cousins:

> I have always been led to believe that the small tenants of Ireland were in a far worse position than the corresponding class in the north of Scotland – the Highland Crofters. If it had been possible for me to have had any conceit on this question, knowing as I did so well, the miserable – the almost unspeakably miserable – condition of my own crofting countrymen, it would have been completely knocked out of me by my present visit to what is universally admitted to be one of the very poorest districts in Ireland. I do not feel quite prepared to express a decided opinion as to the comparative means of subsistence of the two peoples – the quantity and quality of the food they consume – but as to the superior outward appearance and substantial nature of the dwellings of the Irish peasants over those of my Highland countrymen there is no question at all. Indeed, there can be no comparison.
>
> *I always had the idea that an Irish cabin was nothing but a mud or turf hut, and since I landed in the country I was always expecting to meet with such, but I have not seen one, though I have touched the Atlantic on the West Coast of Mayo, and gone through the poorest part of the county, taking it all over, in the whole of Ireland. On the contrary, the people have substantially-built stone houses with stone gables, and chimneys at both ends or in the middle of the houses, in most cases with white-washed walls and straw thatched roofs, done in the best, and, in some cases, in an artistic manner. The Irish cabin of my imagination does not really exist, and the actual dwelling of the Irish peasant in the very poorest localities is not to be compared for a moment with that of the Highland crofter in the West Highlands and Islands – in South Uist, Barra, and portions of Skye, and the greater portion of Lewis. The mere comparison brings the blush to my cheek* [italics are mine].[55]

In the Highlands, the famines caused a severe shortage of the meal being used to replace potatoes, which then forced up the price of grain. In Tobermory on the Isle of Mull, the normal price of a boll (140 pounds) of meal was approximately 16–20 shillings. By November 1846, the price had risen to 26–28 shillings.[56] Feeling 'great alarm at the continued advance of prices' of the lifesaving meal and at the inability of the poor to live with these inflated prices on the 'ordinary wages of labour', Coffin wrote to his superior, Charles Trevelyan, Assistant Secretary of the Treasury, advising him of the gravity of the situation. True to Establishment *laissez-faire* policy, Trevelyan replied: 'We cannot force up the wages of labour, or force down the price of provisions without disorganising society.'[57]

V

The British Establishment's handling of the Highland potato famines was indicative of their general economic philosophy. Trevelyan's response to the Highland grain shortage was not individual callousness, for Trevelyan was not one of those 'evill disposed persons . . . without pity towards poore men, [who] by their engrossing of grayne and other abuses will make want amidst plentifulness.'[58] Trevelyan was simply a member of an Establishment whose guiding light was the primacy of the market. That economic philosophy was enunciated by an Establishment economist, David Ricardo (1772–1823), whose interest and forte were currency and banking. Ricardo was no social philosopher; for him, a labourer was merely an instrument of capitalism.

The Establishment used the words of another theorist to justify their actions in the Highlands. Adam Smith was the leading social philosopher of the time. And certainly it was true that Smith had allowed that

> By pursuing his own interest [a man] frequently promotes that of the society more effectually than when he really intends to promote it.[59]

But the Establishment cited Smith selectively, equating his *laissez-faire* philosophy with their own unbridled individualism. They distorted his theory in that they neglected Smith's qualifying observations, observations like the following:

> The Statesman who should attempt to direct private people in what manner they ought to apply their capitals, would not only load himself with a most unnecessary attention, but assume an authority which could safely be trusted, not only to no single person, but to no council or senate whatever, and which nowhere be so dangerous as in the hands of a man who had folly or presumption enough to fancy himself fit to exercise it.[60]

Far from giving *carte blanche* to the improvers, Smith condemned their greed:

> As soon as the land of any country has all become private property, the landlords like all other men, love to reap where they never sowed, and demand a rent even from its natural produce. The wood of the forest, the grass of the field, and all the natural fruits of the earth, which, when land was in common, cost

the labourer only the trouble of gathering them, come even to him, to have an additional price fixed upon them.[61]

And he laid out plainly the responsibilities of those who benefited from the people's labour:

Is this improvement in the circumstances of the lower ranks of the people to be regarded as an advantage or as an inconveniency to the society? The answer seems at first sight abundantly plain. Servants, labourers and workmen of different kinds, make up the far greater part of every great political society. But what improves the circumstances of the greater part can never be regarded as an inconveniency to the whole. No society can surely be flourishing and happy, of which the far greater part of the members are poor and miserable. It is but equity, besides, that they who feed, clothe, and lodge the whole body of the people, should have such a share of the produce of their own labour as to be themselves tolerably well fed, clothed, and lodged.[62]

In fact, Smith was not a typical nineteenth-century capitalist. His theory of the division of labour and his belief that labour is the chief creator of value is more radical socialist than capitalist.[63]

The improvers had no champion in Adam Smith, but they did find support among their own numbers. They founded the Highland Society of Scotland in Edinburgh in 1784.[64] Initially, the objectives of the Society were the improvement of the Highlands and Islands and the preservation of the language, poetry and music of the Gael. Two years after its foundation, however, it became the Royal Highland and Agricultural Society of Scotland, the body solely responsible for the promotion of agriculture in Scotland. Most Highland landlords, by our definition the Highland Establishment, joined the Society.[65]

Throughout the nineteenth century, Establishmentarians commercialised agriculture to extract more revenue. To raise grain prices, they repealed the grain market controls and nationalised grain markets. Higher prices made for great discontent among the poor everywhere. Because discontent among the workers in populous urban centres seemed the greater threat, the government ensured food supply for those areas, at the expense of rural communities. Aristocratic paternalism was replaced by State social control. Nonetheless, it had become clear that concerted public agitation would indeed effect official action. In the Highlands, however, paternalistic control was still strong enough to slow public agitation, even in the face of starvation. Public protest would not gather momentum there until the second half of the nineteenth century.

Members of the Establishment with property in the Highlands and Lowlands were fully aware of the social unrest and the 'Radical Wars' then developing in Britain. They were even more sensitive to the spirit of insurrection smouldering in Lowland Scotland. Any sign of similar disorder on their own estates in the Highland glens and islands was to be quelled. On Skye, in 1884, a minor fracas over the non-payment of rent led them to petition the authorities for military aid. As requested, a detachment of Royal Marines and gunboats was sent to the Western Isles.[66]

VI

Destitution, faulty nutrition and disease are inextricably linked. In the traditional ecological niches of the Highlands, subsistence was always precarious. Yet Highlanders' traditional diet had reflected their niches and had kept them reasonably healthy. Later estate improvements compromised or confiscated those settlements. One improvement, introduction of the potato, destroyed the dietary balance and ultimately condemned Highlanders to destitution and disease.

The extent of that destitution had been well known by the British and Scottish Establishments for centuries.[67] Yet landowners and government policy-makers alike encouraged Highlanders' dependence on potatoes and misquoted economic theorists like Adam Smith out of self-interest, while merchants contaminated food for their own gain. In fact, Establishmentarians proceeded virtually uninterrupted on a course which they knew endangered the lives of the indigenous people of Scotland.

Notes

1. This is a translation of part of a grace said before a meal in the Isle of Skye. Its austerity reveals not only the true blessing of food but also the uncertainty of continued nourishment.

   In the eighteenth century, Robert Burns in the Lowlands penned another simple grace which also captured the blessing of good health as well as revealing the continual nutritional uncertainty of the poor:

   Some hae meat and canna eat,
   And some wad eat that want it:
   But we hae meat and we can eat,
   Sae let the Lord be thankit.

   William Wallace, *Poetical Works of Robert Burns*, Edinburgh, W. & R. Chambers, Ltd., 1908, 489.

2. Robert Hutchison, 'Report on the Dietaries of Scotch Agricultural Labourers', *Transactions of the Highland and Agricultural Society of Scotland*, 4th Series, 2, 1868, 4, 5.

3. "Comparison of the Poor-Laws of England and Scotland', *The Quarterly Journal of Agriculture*, Vol., VI, June 1835 – March 1836, 19.

4. J. D. King, 'Dental Disease in the Island of Lewis', *Medical Research Council*, Special Report Series, No. 241, London, H.M.S.O., 1940, 59–60.

5. E.P.Cathcart, A.M.T. Murray and J. B. Beverage, 'Studies in Nutrition : An Inquiry into the Diet of Families in the Highlands and Islands of Scotland', Medical Research Council, Special Report Series, No. 242, London, H.M.S.O., 34–6.

6. Report, by William Stevenson, Esq., Surgeon, 'On the Sanitary Conditions and General Economy of the Town of Musselburgh and Parish of Inveresk, in the County of Midlothian' in *Report on the Sanitary Condition of the Labouring Population of Scotland,* 1842, B.P.P. XXVIII, 133.

7. James Anderson, *Account of the Present State of the Hebrides and the Western Coasts Of Scotland . . . A Report to the Lords of Treasury*, Edinburgh, 1785, Intro., xxxiv.

8. Ian Levitt and Christopher Smout, *The State of the Scottish Working Class in 1843*, Edinburgh, Scottish Academic Press, 1979, 263.

9. Thomas Tancred in *Report of Commissioners to Children's Employment Commission on Employment of Children in Mines and Collieries*, vol., ii, B.P.P. 1842, XVII, 313.
   Reports of industrial pollution, squalor and human degradation in the industrial centres are well documented. Migration to the industrial centres was typified by the following observations regarding Glasgow:

> During periods of active immigration and rapid growth, as in the early decades of the last century [the nineteenth], the number of immigrants may largely outnumber the surplus births, and come to form a considerable proportion of the total population. So recently, indeed, as 1871 only 47 per cent of the population of Glasgow had been born within its borders; in 1911 this had increased to 62 per cent.

A.K. Chalmers, *The Health of Glasgow:An Outline 1818–1925*. Glasgow, Bell and Bain, 1930, Intro. v.

A report from the Medical Officer of Health for the first quarter of 1869, after downplaying the effects of climatic causes as a major cause of ill-health in the case of Glasgow and Greenock, noted:

> But in the permanently acting causes of high death rates and especially in the low standard of domestic comfort, the overcrowding, general squalor and physical degradation which are the unhappy characteristics of a large part of the population; and that these again are the direct results of permitting generation after generation to be brought up in houses of worse construction, in which morality, decency and cleanliness are alike impossible.

Idem, 77.

10. For a modern approach to the problems of current nutrition see: John Burnett, *Plenty and Want: A Social History of Diet In England From 1815 to the Present Day*, London, Scolar Press, 1979.

 Time, April 6, 1992, The cover story reads: 'The New Scoop on Vitamins – They may be much more important than doctors thought in warding off cancer, heart disease and the ravages of aging – and, no, you may not be getting enough of these crucial nutrients in your diet.'

 A. Stewart Truswell, *ABC of Nutrition*, 2nd edn, London, *British Medical Journal.* 1992, 89–99.

 Dr W.W. Yellowlees, *Food Health in the Scottish Highlands:* Four Lectures from a Rural Practice, Clunie Press, Perthshire, Scotland, 1985.

 René Dubos, *Man Adapting*, New Haven, Yale Univ. Press, 1980, Chapter VI, 'Nutrition and Infection.'

 Mabel Louise Dubbin, *Forty Years A Nurse Thirty-Two A V.O.N.* [a district nurse] *An Autobiography,* Sydney, Martin Equipment Ltd., Pubs., 1975, 94. Dubbin cites evidence of rickets in the industrial section of Sydney, Cape Breton, a result of faulty nutrition.

11. Hutchison, Op cit., 5.

12. Donald S. McLaren and Michael M. Meguid, *Nutrition and its Disorders,* 4th edn., Edinburgh, Churchill Livingstone, 1988, 1, 96–7.

 Hidden hunger is prevalent in the twentieth century world as a result of poverty, or changing social custom. As a contemporary social custom, excessive faulty dieting, while reducing calorific intake, exposes the body to many deficiency diseases. Among the poor, under-nutrition is the result of the intake of cheap energy-producing carbohydrates. The current popularity of cheap, fast-food outlets, also known as 'fat food outlets' is proof of this need for instant energy. Such excessive calorific intake, from high carbohydrate diets, especially when associated with an increasingly sedentary lifestyle, gives rise to obesity and eventually to the medical complications of malnutrition. See:

 A. Stewart Truswell, Op cit., 41–6.

13. O.S.A., XVI (Assint), 207.

14. Rosalind Mitchison, 'Malnutrition in Scotland since 1700, and its Social Consequences', *The Society for the Social History of Medicine*, Bulletin No., 38, 1986, 17–8.

 This unbalance 'may have contributed to the socially divisive theories of the Social Darwinists.'

15. Martin Martin, *A Description of the Western Islands of Scotland* (circa 1695), 2nd. edn., Reprint, Edinburgh, James Thin, 1970, 3.

16. B.C. Guha, 'The Role of Fish in Human Nutrition' in *Fish in Nutrition*, Eds., Eirik Heen and Rudolf Kreuzer, London, Fishing News (Books) Ltd., 1962, 40.

Derrick B. Jelliffe and Patrice Jelliffe, 'Breast Feeding and Infant Nutrition in Developing Countries' in *Nutrition, Food, and Man: An Interdisciplinary Perspective*, Eds., Paul B. Pearson and Richard Greenwell, Tucson, Arizona, Univ. of Arizona Press, 1980, 11–20.

17. Vernon Young and Nevin S. Scrimshaw, 'The Physiology of Starvation' in 'Food', Readings from *Scientific American*, San Francisco, W.H. Freeman and Co., 1973, 49–50.

18. O.S.A., XVII (Small Isles), 285.
 N.S.A., XIV (Kilmuir), 271.

19. McLaren and Meguid, Op cit., 16.
 The cockle, found in abundance on many shores, provided, when cooked in milk, a common source of food during periods of famine. The tissues of the cockle, however, contain less protein and fat than those of the oyster and mussel. Furthermore, shellfish are commonly infected with typhoid bacilli and other pathogenic organisms. When ingested they are also associated with allergic reactions. Local tradition and customs may also play an important role in food selection and indeed, 'one man's food may be another man's poison.' For example, the lobster did not hold the honoured place among poor Highlanders as it does in today's society. Similarly, until recently, mackerel in the West Highlands was regarded as a scavenger fish and not suitable as food.

20. Sir John Sinclair, *Analysis of the Statistical Account of Scotland* (hereafter Analysis), Two Parts, Edinburgh, Constable & Co., 1825, Part Second, 38.
 James Hunter, *The Making of the Crofting Community*, Edinburgh, John Donald, 1976, 50–53.
 Robert J. Morgan, 'Poverty Wretchedness and Misery' The Great Famine In Cape Breton 1845–1851', *Nova Scotia Historical Review* VI, 1986, 69–104.

21. Reay Tannahill, in *A Companion to Scottish Culture*, Ed., David Daiches, London, Edward Arnold, 1981, 127.

22. Hutchison, Op cit., 7.

23. Dr Samuel Johnson, *A Journey to the Western Islands of Scotland* [1773], in *A Tour to the Hebrides*, Johnson and Boswell, Ed., R.W.Chapman, Oxford Univ. Press, London, 1930, 92.

24. Mitchison (1986), Op cit., 17.

25. Mclaren and Meguid, Op cit., 12.

26. Guha, Op cit., 39–40.

27. McLaren and Meguid, Op cit., 34.

28. Ibid., 33. See also A. Stewart Truswell, Op cit., 1–5.

29. Tannahill, Op cit., 127.

30. Edward Burt, *Letters from a Gentleman in the North of Scotland* etc., 2 Vols., 2nd edn., London, 1759, I, 142.

31. O.S.A., XVII(Killin), 383.
    This parish, one of the highest in Scotland, was on the land of the Earl of Breadalbane, a relative of the House of Argyll. In many respects the people were more fortunate than those on northern estates. It was reported that Breadalbane's people were now sober, regular and industrious. They are, in general, rather in easy than in affluent circumstances. They pay their rents punctually, and live comfortably. Most of the farms in the lower part of the parish are divided among several tenants. The arable and pasture ground being separated, each has his own division of the arable, and the cattle feed in common in the pasture ground. In this manner they live harmoniously together; and *possessions descend, particularly on the Breadalbane estate, from father to son* [italics are mine]. Ibid., 384.

32. Anderson, Op cit., 34, and 181–192.

33. Tannahill, Op cit., 127, 128.

34. O.S.A.,VI (North Knapdale), 259.; XII (Jura and Colonsay), 320.
    Johnson makes an interesting comment which may be germane to this topic:
    Fish in fair weather they need not want; but, I believe, man never lives long on fish, but by constraint; he will rather feed upon roots and berries. Johnson, Op cit., 92.

35. Johan E. Hoff and Jules Janick, in 'Food' Readings from *Scientific American*, Op cit., Intro., 4.
    Leslie Sue Lieberman, 'Biocultural consequences of Animals Versus Plants as Sources of Fats, Proteins, and Other Nutrients', in *Food and Evolution*, Eds. Marvin Harris and Eric B. Ross, Philadelphia, Temple Univ. Press, 1987, 225–253.

36. J.R. Currie and A.G. Mearns, *Hygiene*, 2nd edn., Edinburgh, E.& S. Livingstone Ltd., 1945, 135–151.

37. *The Bible*, Authorized (King James) Version, Isaiah 5:8.

38. J.P. Day, *Public Administration in the Highlands and Islands Of Scotland*, London, Univ., of London Press Ltd., 1918, 300.
    See also: Enid Gauldie, *Cruel Habitations A History of Working Class Housing 1780–1918*, London, George Allen and Unwin Ltd., 1974, 87, 138.

39. Henry George, 'The Reduction to Iniquity'. *The Nineteenth Century*, XVI, No., 89, 153.

40. Cecil Woodham Smith, *The Great Hunger Ireland 1845–9*, London, New English Library, pb, 1977, 298.

41. Robert Somers, *Letters From the Highlands on the Famine of 1846*, (1848), Reprint, Perth, Melven Press, 1985, 71.

42. Ibid., 71–2.

43. Thomas Johnston, *The History of the Working Classes in Scotland*, Glasgow, Forward Pub. Co. Ltd., 1920, 276.
    See also Karl Marx, *Capital*, Ed., Friedrich Engels, New York, The Modern Library, 1906, 193–4 n4, 273–6.

44. O.S.A. XIX (Bendothy), 351.

45. Potato blight is caused by a fungus, *phytophthora infestans*. It was, and still is, a common disease of potato crops throughout the British Isles, Europe and America. The unfortunate climatic conditions during the 1840s allowed the infestation to spread rapidly and to recur in successive years, thus not permitting the expected relief which normally follows a bad harvest. Not only were the potatoes unfit to eat but there were no seed potatoes left for the next year's planting. The human suffering that followed was inordinate.
    The control of the infestation, in normal climatic conditions, was as yet not fully appreciated. The preventive measure, was, when found, simple and expedient, and consisted of spraying the crop with a solution of copper sulphate.
    For further information on the potato in general and its importance to the Highlands of Scotland see:
    Redcliffe N. Salaman, *The History and Social Influence of the Potato* (1949), Cambridge, Univ. Press, reprinted 1970. 346–385.

46. In fact, 'One of the greatest evils with which the Highlands have to contend, is the almost universal absenteeism of the landlords.'
    Allan Fullarton and Charles R. Baird, *Remarks on the Evils at Present Affecting the Highlands & Islands of Scotland* etc., Glasgow, William Collins, 1838, 51.
    'In some estates both proprietor and his factor were absentees.'
    James Hunter, *The Making of the Crofting Community*, John Donald, Edinburgh, 1976, 61.
    Estate problems related to non-resident heritors were constantly identified in the *Statistical Accounts*.

47. Somers, Op cit., 92.

48. In the remote Scottish Highlands and Islands, migration made famine, morbidity and mortality data even more difficult to assess. In Ireland, the effect of the famine in certain areas can neither be denigrated by the above statements nor can the mortality rate be accurately estimated due to an unwillingness of the people to be registered in the census of 1841. 'In the four provinces of Ireland the smallest loss of population was in Leinster, 15.5 per cent, then Ulster, 16 per cent, Connaught's loss was greatest, 28.6 per cent, and Munster lost 23–5 per cent.'

Woodham-Smith further noted that in the census of 1841, the population of Ireland was given as 8,175,124; in 1851, it had dropped to 6,552,385. 'The Census commissioners calculated that at the normal rate of increase the total should have been 9,018,799, so that a loss of 2_ million persons had taken place.' These figures do not reveal the cause of death since the process for collecting vital statistics was not available.
Woodham-Smith, Op cit., 409.

49. Revd John Stewart, quoted in 'Sketch of Missionary Proceedings at Cape Breton, From August 1833, to December 1836', PAM. No. 3303, Beaton Institute, University College of Cape Breton (Hereafter B.I., U.C.C.B.), n.d., 16.

50. Woodham Smith quoting Lord John Russell the Whig Prime Minister. Op cit., 406.

51. Ibid., 406.

52. 'Scarcity in the West Highlands', *Inverness Courier*, Thurs, 13 June 1822, 3, col. E. Reprint of a 'Letter to the Editor from A Highlander', published in the *Scotsman*, Edinburgh, 28 May, 1822.
See also: J.C. Beckett, *The Making of Modern Ireland 1603–1923*, London, Faber and Faber, 1981, 292–3.

53. *Correspondence Relating to the Measures Adopted for the Relief of the Distress in Scotland,* (Hereafter Correspondence) British Sessional Papers 1847,
Sir G. Grey to Sir J. M'Neill, 2 September, 1846, 6.
loc cit., Treasury minute, 8 September, 1846, 14.
Sir George Grey was Home Secretary in Lord John Russell's administration and MacNeill was in charge of administering the Poor Law in Scotland.

54. Sir E. Coffin to Mr. Trevelyan, 17 October, 1846, Ibid., 109.
Charles Trevelyan, to be knighted in April 1848, was the Assistant Secretary to the Treasury.

55. Alexander Mackenzie, 'Ireland and the Irish Land Act, from a Highland Point of View.' *The Celtic Magazine*, Inverness, A. & W. Mackenzie, Vol. X. 1884–85, 63–4.

56. Ibid., letter Mr. Stewart to Mr. Trevelyan, dated Morven, 1 December, 1846, 195.

57. Ibid., letter Mr. Trevelyan to Sir E. Coffin, January 13, 1847. 275–6.
In a letter, Sir John M'Neill to Mr Trevelyan, dated 10 October, 1846, Idem., 80, MacNeill states:
On the west coast, however, and in some of the Islands, they appear to expect Government to form stores on the spot for the sale of provisions at a cheap rate. I confess I have some apprehensions of evil consequences from their having set their minds upon this measure, for fear they will

abstain from purchasing in the market, in the hope that the Government will give them cheaper supplies, and that thus, independent of the evil of delay, the whole deficiency would have to be supplied from the Government stores instead of the half only, as I ventured to suggest in my letter to Sir George Grey.

58. Louise A. Tilly, 'Food Entitlement, Famine and Conflict', in Rotberg and Rabb, Op cit., 135, n.2.

59. Adam Smith, *An Inquiry into the Nature and Cause of the Wealth of Nations*, New York, The Modern Library, Random House Inc., 1937, 423.

60. Ibid., 423.

61. Ibid., 49.

62. Ibid., 78–9.

63. Gladys Bryson, *Man and Society; The Scottish Inquiry of the Eighteenth Century*, (1945), New York, Reprints of Economic Classics, Augustus M. Kelley Pubs., 1968, 215.
    . . . there is considerable agreement that his doctrine of the natural order, which bespoke freedom of economic enterprise motivated by self-interest, has been consistently used as a rationalization of capitalism, even though Smith may not so have intended it.
    Ibid., 212.

64. The founders included Sir John Sinclair, President of the Board of Agriculture (1798 and 1806–13.) and owner of extensive estates in the North and in the Lowlands of Scotland. He was the organizer of the first *Statistical Account*. The Highland Society's first president was the 5th Duke of Argyll.

65. Smith had shrewdly noted that
    People of the same trade seldom meet together, even for merriment and diversion, but the conversation ends in a conspiracy against the public, or in some contrivance to raise prices.
    Smith, Op cit., 128.

66. Hunter (1976), Op cit., 149–153.

67. For example, as late as the mid-nineteenth century, a connection between poor nutrition and insanity among paupers and the beneficial results which followed an increased intake of food had been reported.
    Scottish Lunacy Commission, Report of Lunatic Asylums in Scotland, Edinburgh, 1857, 142

6

Ill-Health

The man who owns the boil and the man who squeezes it see the matter from different points of view.[1]

TRACING EXACTLY THE EFFECT of the Clearances on Highlanders' health is not easy. One reason for the difficulty is the scarcity of first-hand reports. The region saw relatively few travellers, only a minority of whom were able to converse directly with the natives in Gaelic. We must depend almost exclusively, therefore, on the anecdotal reports of Gaelic-speaking Highland parish ministers as recorded in the two *Statistical Accounts of Scotland* (1791–8 and 1845). Furthermore, the medical terminology and the description of diseases in those *Accounts* do not match English accounts at that time, let alone those of this century. Finally, the *Accounts* report signs and symptoms only, never an ideal basis for identifying causal pathology. Yet they tell us much about the extent and severity of disease during and after the Clearances. Furthermore, more recent discoveries and cultural studies of the effects of dislocation and acculturation help us extrapolate causal pathology from the *Accounts'* signs and symptoms.

I

In their native glens and islands, Highlanders had acquired a natural immunity to the common infectious diseases, albeit such natural immunity was bought at the price of a high mortality rate among the weakest members of a family and township. For example, puerperal or childbed fever was a frequent and serious complication of domiciliary midwifery. Giving birth in a Highland black house would certainly have exposed women to bacterial contamination and the risk of infection. That so little is reported in the *Accounts* about mortality from childbirth probably attests to the efficacy of women's immune systems, and their ability to survive the treatment, invariably blood-letting or evacuant therapy, of the midwife or knee-woman (*Bean-ghluine*), or the surgeon.[2]

The great social changes that Culloden ushered in reduced greatly

Highlanders' natural immunity, by exposing them to alien diseases and by leaving them destitute and malnourished. To understand the impact of those changes on Highlanders' health and resistance to disease, we must know something of several immunological concepts: immunity and host resistance to disease; the virulence of the invading organism; and the methods by which a host becomes infected.

Benenson defines immunity to disease as 'that resistance usually associated with the presence of antibodies or cells having a specific action on the micro-organism concerned with a particular infectious disease or on its toxin.'[3] Immunity is relative: an ordinarily effective protection may be overwhelmed by a strain of organism of unusual virulence, by an excessive dose of the infectious agent, or by exposure to the agent through an unusual portal of entry. Though we still do not fully understand immunity, for our purpose we can classify immunity as either natural; that is, specific to species, race and individual, or acquired. Acquired immunity may be further classified as naturally or artificially acquired. Furthermore, naturally-acquired immunity may be passive, antibodies being transmitted via the placenta to the foetus or to the suckling infant with the first breast milk. Such immunity lasts for about six months, and the specific immunity pattern donated reflects the mother's previously successful encounters with infectious diseases. It also reflects 'the disease pattern of the ecological niche of the mother.'[4]

Naturally-acquired immunity may also be active, the result of an attack by a disease organism or its toxin. Such immunity is more permanent, and may even confer lifetime immunity, as is the case following smallpox. Furthermore, and of cardinal importance to understanding disease patterns among Highlanders, this immunity is conferred even by sub-clinical infections, in which the infected person shows no recognizable clinical evidence of the disease. Finally, immunity may also be artificially-acquired, by injection of an antiserum. Artificially-acquired immunity is also long-lasting, usually assuring protection for years.

In the period under study here, immunity to infectious disease was acquired naturally, the result of a previous attack of the disease, or, as in the case of smallpox, it was acquired artificially, by prophylactic smallpox inoculation (variolation).[5] Inoculation by another procedure, vaccination (with cowpox), was introduced at the end of the eighteenth century. By 1800, vaccination had become widely practised and accepted in Lowland Scotland, and use of the procedure quickly spread throughout the Highlands and Islands.

The West Highlanders, so long as they remained in their native niches, eventually became resistant to those infectious diseases that were endemic there. Their isolation accounted for their legendary good health and longevity, qualities that were hailed in observations like the following:

> There is no country in Europe, whose inhabitants are more distinguished by their healthiness, – their longevity, – or the inconsiderable number of the diseases to which they are liable, than those of Scotland.[6]

Sinclair quoted the French naturalist Buffon (1707–1788), who had remarked upon that Highland hardiness:

> . . . the mountainous district of Scotland [is] the most distinguished for longevity; and indeed, there is no country, where in proportion to its population a greater number reach from 60–80, and even 90 years of age and upwards, in full possession of all their faculties, both corporeal and mental, than in that part of Great Britain. This is more to be wondered at, since, though the climate of Scotland be healthy, the great body of the people have not, by any means, the conveniences of life which are necessary 'to nurse old age.'[7]

(Highland hardiness and longevity are attested to also, and eloquently, in the literature of the Gael in Cape Breton.)

Highlanders' immunity was, however, fatally compromised by the Clearances. The destitution and malnutrition that dislocation occasioned undermined their immunity to some diseases, like tuberculosis, making it a common killer among all age groups. Furthermore, the Clearances introduced new diseases, for which Highlanders had developed no immunity and to which they were extremely vulnerable. On the isolated island of St Kilda, which lies approximately 41 miles northwest of North Uist, a severe epidemic of what was called the 'common cold' followed the visit of any boat from the mainland.[8] Measles, now regarded as commonplace in the immunized urban centres of the western world, was (and still is) particularly virulent among unprotected populations. An epidemic of measles was reported among the unprotected population on one of the Faroe Islands in 1846.[9] And in Argyll, an epidemic of measles brought into a parish school by a runaway herd boy from another parish infected 51 of the scholars: 'It spread over the country in a short time; but contagious as it was, it was not mortal.'[10] In 1914, however, with the mobilisation of the Territorial Highland Division, Highland soldiers were recruited from relatively isolated communities and transferred to England. There the Division experienced in three months 518 cases of measles, 67 of them fatal.[11]

II

Let us look more closely at the process of infection from communicable disease and how that process was influenced by conditions after the Clearances. A host is said to be infected and a disease infectious when microbes or certain other living agents enter the body of a human being or animal, where they multiply and produce a reaction. The body's reaction may or may not be accompanied by outward signs of disease. Furthermore, the mere presence of organisms within the body does not constitute disease: the alimentary and respiratory tracts, for example, both contain normal flora of domesticated indigenous organisms living in a state of symbiosis or commensalism. The danger occurs when these organisms (commensals) translocate to another body system. Translocation occurs because the host's resistance to disease is lowered during an episode of poor or faulty nutrition, or because of long exposure to inclement environmental conditions. In other cases, some of the domesticated organisms take advantage of the body's depressed defence mechanism and invade at their usual location; that is, they become pathogenic and produce disease.

Infectious, disease-producing microbes are classified as those that cause disease in healthy persons by virtue of their virulence, and that come directly or indirectly from animals, persons ill of the disease, or carriers of the disease; and those that normally enter the host only at times of injury, of lowered resistance such as poverty can create, or when the organisms themselves are more virulent, as happens in major epidemics, when they overwhelm and penetrate the body's normal defence.

As Schwabe points out, animal infection is usually associated with human infection, a point highly significant in the Highland lifestyle:

> Depending upon how one splits or lumps infections caused by closely related organisms, the agents of approximately four-fifths of all described infections of man are shared in nature by other vertebrate animals. These shared infections are called Zoonoses.[12]

Infectious disease is also caused by opportunistic invaders. Those invaders arrive during natural catastrophes which break down the body's defence mechanism. In tuberculosis, for example, the body does not kill the invading organism; it defends itself by locking up the invader in its tissues. When a host's resistance collapses, the body's retaining wall breaks down. The initial tubercular lesions are reactivated and the bacilli spread rapidly throughout the defenceless host. Tuberculosis need not be traced, therefore, to a public locus; rather, it may occur sporadically in otherwise healthy poor families, introduced there by any family member who suffers from severe malnutrition, invariably the result of alcoholism or sexually-transmitted disease. Such dissipation was common in all social classes in the Highlands and Islands.

Exogenous infections enter the body by well-defined routes called portals of entry. Every pathogen has a preferred portal but may make use of many. The organisms which cause pulmonary tuberculosis (*Mycobacterium tuberculosis*), pneumonia, smallpox and measles normally enter the body via the respiratory tract, but *M. tuberculosis* can also enter via the alimentary tract, sometimes in the milk from an infected cow, to produce tuberculosis of the lymph nodes of the neck (Scrofula or King's evil), the bones and the viscera.

Sinclair's *Analysis* of 1825 noted that consumption (phthisis or tuberculosis) had become more frequent among the young, but was most often fatal during the middle period of life. Sinclair also reported that a generation earlier the disease was extremely rare and seldom mortal.[13] He classified The Scrofula as a separate disease but linked it with the formation of tubercles in the lung [the tubercle is the primary lesion of tuberculosis], which ultimately produces consumption: 'The evil seems to be rather on the increase', he speculated, 'from their own carelessness, and intermarriages of the unsound with the healthy.'[14] In that observation, Sinclair had recognised the danger of infection from close contact with a known focus of infection, and he had made the connection among tuberculosis, nutrition and lifestyle.

The digestive tract was the customary portal of entry for those disease organisms that cause typhoid fever, cholera and dysentery. For those diseases, the vehicle was usually contaminated food or drink. After the Clearances, contaminated water was a constant threat to the people of the crowded coastal strips of the Mainland and the Islands. It was to remain a threat in Old and New Scotland until the twentieth century.

The presence of disease-specific organisms within the body does not in itself give rise to a state of disease, a fact which confused the early microbiologists. This confusion was particularly noticeable in diphtheria cases (known to Sinclair as the croup or *cynache tracheali*). Furthermore, the absence of the characteristic membrane at the back of the throat, diagnostic of the classical form of diphtheria, does not mean that the disease is not present, for the lesion may present itself on some other mucous surface. The lay healer or physician was thus understandably misled into making a wrong diagnosis. Further, it was later shown that only the toxin-producing strains of the organism caused severe and untreatable diphtheria. Those strains ravaged the Highlands. Sinclair's *Analysis* reported them as 'the most fatal disorder to which children are liable.'[15]

III

Normally, infection occurs only if four conditions obtain. The first is that the pathogen must have a portal of entry. Typhoid bacilli, if simply applied to the skin, will not produce typhoid fever. A second consideration is the virulence of the organism. An organism transferred from a case of a fulminating disease to a new victim, especially if that person has been weakened by malnutrition, exposure, or by a concurrent disease, will usually produce a fatal or malignant form of the fulminating disease. The third prerequisite for infection is the number of invasive organisms present. Most healthy people can withstand a light exposure to pathogenic organisms. In fact, this is the basis of inoculation for some infectious diseases. But a heavy inoculum delivered to a newborn infant, for example, and derived from an admiring but coughing tubercular grandparent in a Highland black house guaranteed the death of the infant from tuberculous meningitis within weeks. Such cross-infection was a constant source of disease in the over-crowded sites to which Highlanders were removed during the Clearances, in the urban ghettos to which many migrated, and in the emigrant ships and pioneering settlements to which many others fled. A former Medical Officer of Health for Glasgow, describing the health of the city from 1818–1925, was of the opinion that although early in the eighteenth century 'the population of Glasgow was not unhealthy', industrialization and crowding had soon spelled disease:

> But while the expansion of industry followed the application of science to the processes of production, the increase of population, on a scale commensurate with the industrial requirements, introduced a new element into human affairs. Mankind, indeed, had embarked on a new adventure, and the massing of populations which it produced, on a scale hitherto unknown, was destined to teach its own lesson through many years of bitter experience.[16]

The fourth condition which determines whether infection occurs is the level of the host's resistance.

Knowing the portals of entry of various pathogenic organisms is of major importance in arresting the spread of disease. Even more important is it to be aware of the portals of exit. That discovery was not made until later research generated the germ theory of disease.

Five portals of exit are known: the first, of great importance in our study, is the lower alimentary system via the faeces. Faecal contamination spreads diseases like Salmonellosis (typhoid and paratyphoid fevers), the dysenteries (bacillary and protozoal), cholera, and the entero-viruses such as poliomyelitis. The second exit, the genito-urinary system via urine, may contain organisms such as *M. tuberculosis* when the genito-urinary tract is the site of tuberculosis. Patients with salmonella infections can discharge those organisms in the urine as well as in faeces. The organism of undulant fever (Brucellosis) also exits via the urine. Undulant fever is an unfamiliar and therefore often misunderstood and misdiagnosed disease. It cannot be disregarded as a cause of disease among Highlanders in Old and New Scotland, even in the twentieth century. (We will discuss undulant fever in detail in chapter 8.) From the third portal of exit, the nose and the mouth through respiratory discharges, come the organisms that cause tuberculosis, whooping cough (often reported in historical records as chincough), pneumonia, scarlet fever, and epidemic meningitis (meningococcaemia). The viruses of measles, smallpox, mumps, poliomyelitis and influenza are also discharged through this portal. The rabies virus is transmitted from a fourth portal of exit, the salivary glands via the saliva. In rabies, man and animals are usually infected by the contaminated bite of a rabid animal, but the virus has been found also in the saliva of infected humans.[17] Several other diseases may be transferred by an insect through a fifth portal, the blood of an infected person, as in malaria (a mosquito), typhus fever (a louse), and yellow fever (a mosquito).

IV

Modern microbiology teaches the role of these portals of exit in the spread of disease, particularly among the malnourished. For example, Sieber and Lippman found that the incidence of pneumonia among malnourished children was six times the average. Discussing the effects of malnutrition on immune function, they note the nutritional and immunological effects of an infectious respiratory disease such as pertussis [whooping cough]:

> In a three month old baby with a risk factor, such as prematurity and failure to thrive, the mechanical interference of paroxysmal coughing with eating decreases calorie and protein intake to the extent that frank malnutrition results. This has been shown to be associated with a change in immunological functioning and prolongation of the clinical disease, unresponsive to therapy other than nutritional reconstitution.[18]

And we know that chincough (whooping cough or pertussis) was common in the Western Isles.[19] Chalmers also confirmed the presence and the danger of whooping cough in Scotland from 1885 onwards:

In individual years now and then the deaths ascribed to measles may outnumber those arising from whooping cough, but when viewed in mass, as in the quinquennial periods of the tables, the latest (1921–25) is the only one of the series in which measles deaths exceed those caused by whooping cough.[20]

We know too that nutrition is linked to the mortality rate from measles. Mitchison makes that connection:

The contribution of measles to the death rate is a useful guide to poor nutrition, since the killing power of the disease has been shown in recent famines . . . [21]

Sieber and Lippman's research demonstrates unequivocally that malnutrition was one cause of the high morbidity and mortality rates among Highland children, particularly when their lifestyle was disturbed.[22]

V

Changes in Highlanders' domestic life hastened the spread of communicable diseases among them. Tracing the routine course of a common infectious disease helps demonstrate why that was so. Infectious disease normally proceeds through six distinct Periods, the first of which is a Period of Incubation, the interval between the moment of infection and the appearance of symptoms. It is during this period, when the patient is still fit, asymptomatic and mobile, that epidemics are spread.

This asymptomatic period is usually followed by a Period of Prodromal Symptoms, characterized by non-specific symptoms such as headache and malaise. At this time, patients are aware that they are ill. In the Highlands, this was the time that help would have been sought: from a member of the family or a neighbour with the gift of healing, from the local natural physician, or, if economy and geography permitted, from the surgeon/apothecary. Whoever administered it, the treatment was the same – phlebotomy (blood letting), or the administration of a clyster (enema), or both.

The specific pattern of the disease process is revealed during the third period, the Period of Invasion, when early diagnosis can be made. The disease becomes increasingly severe, finally reaching its Period of Acme, when signs and symptoms are fully developed. Should the patient survive this period and the concomitant treatment, the disease enters a fifth stage, the Period of Defervescence, and ultimately, a period of Convalescence, that state in which the body, much weakened, should start to regain its lost strength. Convalescence would have been impossible for destitute Highlanders. For them, full recovery depended solely on their general health, the efficacy of their immune system, and the calibre of nursing given during the earlier Periods of the disease pattern.

Germ theory has taught us much about how disease is transmitted. We now know that the causative agent of communicable disease may be transmitted from person to person by direct body contact, or by droplet infection from the respiratory tract or body fluids, as happens in many cases of smallpox, tuberculosis and streptococcal diseases. Transmission can also occur through indirect contact, the disease agent being conveyed by water, milk, food and fomites.

Infectious diseases can be vector-borne as well. The flies swarming around the middens and the food of the poor are classic examples of vector-borne tranmission. Epidemics of louse-borne typhus fever provide other examples: typhus accompanied famines, when hunger and cold drove people to huddle together to conserve body heat. In fact, wherever humanity has been crowded together, as in the crofting counties during the Clearances, in the newly constructed fishing villages and in the urban tenements and the emigrant ships of that period, communicable diseases became epidemic.[23]

It is obvious that for a disease to continue in a population, there must be a reservoir of infection. Human carriers were probably the most sinister cause of the spread of disease among Highlanders, particularly when their communities were exposed to outsiders who were apparently healthy, but who in fact carried the disease.

In his report on smallpox in the Orkney and Shetland Islands in the eighteenth century, Tudor noted that 'There is also said to have been an idea prevalent at the time, that an outbreak of smallpox always followed the Census being taken.'[24] It is indeed possible that on occasion a member of a census party, or a crewman on the ship that transported the census takers to those islands, was incubating smallpox on arrival or even that he was ill from smallpox, though that diagnosis of his illness had not been made.

Carriers keep diseases alive during interludes between epidemic outbreaks. Furthermore, an increase in the number of carriers, particularly in overcrowded living conditions, will give rise to epidemics.[25] The diseases most often spread by carriers are diphtheria, the enteric group of diseases, streptococcal infections (scarlet fever, acute rheumatic fever) and pneumonia, all of which were prevalent in the Highlands.

While air-conveyed outbreaks of infections like measles, scarlet fever and the like may occur even now at intervals, others, the squalor-engendered infections such as typhus and relapsing fever, also called famine fever, are almost unknown today. Normally, it is only in times of war or destitution, when water and sewage facilities are no longer available and when unwashed, starving people huddle together for shelter and warmth, that the free transmission is ensured among them of louse-borne or of other propinquity infections endemic in the area.[26]

The introduction of disease into an isolated Highland community frequently followed the return from the south of a relative who was incubating the disease, or one who was terminally ill, usually tubercular. This pattern was spotted by the parish ministers and was reported frequently in the *New Statistical Account*. New roads and steamer connections in the West Highlands and Islands had made a pathway for infection. The report of the minister from Kilbrandon and Kilchattan in Argyll makes that point:

> Typhus fever and small-pox are often conveyed from the south country by those young people who go thither in quest of employment. Their friends, from motives of mistaken kindness, insist on taking them home before they have fully recovered, which brings disease among the people. For some years past, owing chiefly to this cause, cases of fever have been very prevalent in the parish.[27]

Many young people back from the south were recuperating from smallpox or from typhus fever. If they or their friends or relatives at home were infested with lice, the transmission of typhus was assured. If they carried smallpox back, the absence of preventive inoculation in their home community would ensure an outbreak of that disease. And the minister of Duirinish on the Isle of Skye noted 'that a very loathsome disease, commonly called the *sevens or sibbens*, is very prevalent here', though he was not sure whether it was indigenous or imported.[28] This disease may have been syphilis, or a tropical disease known as yaws.[29] Both diseases are caused by a spirochaete and present similar signs and symptoms, although yaws is rarely fatal. Such diseases could have been introduced into the parish by local seamen returning from foreign service with the navy, or as the minister of Elgin believed,' by the military returning from Flanders.'[30]

The Duirinish minister went on to name as the most prevalent diseases in Skye dyspepsia, dysentery, slow fevers, and cutaneous diseases, all of which were confined to the humbler classes; all of which arose from poor diet and want of cleanliness. The dyspepsia and skin diseases he reported could have been manifestations of pellagra, caused by vitamin B deficiency. The early stages of this disease are characterised by debility, spinal pains, digestive disturbances and later, erythema, which causes drying and exfoliation of the skin. In severe cases of pellagra, mental disturbance and other neurological manifestations resembling a stroke or palsy are present.

Animals as well as people can account for the spread of disease. Mankind's close link with his domestic animals can spread disease in four ways: by direct contact with an infected animal; by contamination from animal discharges of food, air and water; by insect and rodent vectors; and by the consumption of infected animal products such as milk, eggs and meat.[31] We will examine this source of disease in detail in Chapter 8.

VI

To this point, we have examined the body's natural immune defence and the major classes of infectious disease, and we have discussed those advances in microbiology which help us understand how disease was transmitted in the Highlands. In the remainder of this chapter, we discuss a very different source of disease, prolonged stress, and its effects on the body's defence system.

In the eighteenth and nineteenth centuries, the term mental illness encompassed a wide range of 'diseases of the mind', ranging from retardation to psychopathy. Most mental disorders in childhood were regarded as congenital, and in adults as the terminal stages of somatic disease or as senile dementia. In the brutal world of the Highlanders, natural selection tended to limit the number of physically and mentally disadvantaged in a given community. In the second half of the nineteenth century, those who had not died from natural causes or from misadventure and had become an unacceptable burden to family, community or parish would be given asylum in an institution appropriate to their social status.

The notion that emotional and social stress were associated with mental problems was largely unknown in the eighteenth century, although by the end of the century, some parish ministers had become cognisant of this relationship. The minister of Craignish, for example, remarking 'the uncommon degree of bodily strength and mental vigour' of some of his older parishioners, foretells the evils of modern habits and attitudes:

> Being far removed from that intercourse which, though it polishes manners, yet undermines the constitution of man, it was their happiness to have led a simple and frugal life, strangers to those excesses, to which luxury leads, and thence unacquainted with the distempers which it generates.[32]

In fact, Highlanders' distinctive natural and social systems were intimately related to their psychobiology, as Figure 1 illustrates. Many Highlanders advanced the importance of that inter-relationship, as did this commentator:

That differing as the Celtic population do in their mother tongue, manners and habits of thought from their fellow countrymen, they require, when morbidly affected in mind to be particularly dealt with.[33]

By the mid-nineteenth century, a link between mental disorder and social conditions had been identified and acknowledged by the Lunacy Commission. The Commission saw the connection between mental problems and pauperism:

> . . . a population of 79,887 paupers yielded more than one-half of the whole number of the insane of the kingdom, showing the powerful affinity that exists between poverty and mental disease . . . The cares that attend poverty, in conjunction with the deteriorating agency of scanty innutritious food, have a powerful influence in weakening the mental powers, and inducing insanity.[34]

While the Lunacy Commissioners noted that they did not have sufficient information to institute any valid comparison between the proportional numbers of the insane in 'those counties which have most advanced in civilisation, and in those which have lagged behind', they were prepared to conclude that the number of insane was higher in the large cities; that is, in those 'Counties exposed to Influences that incite to Mental Activity' [Tables I and II]:

> For, in the first place, in large cities, where there is the greatest mental activity, there, also, is the greatest physical deterioration. The energies of the working population are wasted by continuous labour, while their physical condition is lowered by a residence in unwholesome dwellings, and by abuse of stimulating liquors to restore their exhausted powers. Experience shows that these combined influences constitute a prolific source of insanity among the crowded population of our towns. And, secondly, in those counties where thought most stagnates, a large proportion of the cases of mental disease is due to congenital causes. The population, unaffected by extraneous influences, intermarry among themselves, and the hereditary taint which is thus engendered, shows itself unmistakably in the large proportion of idiots and imbeciles . . . It thus appears [from tables I and II] that a Highland population contains more than three times the number of congenital cases of mental disease found in an equal lowland population.[35]

The association between mental disorders and environmental factors like social upheaval and poverty was being recognised, albeit slowly. We know today how poverty can impair intellectual health and development:

> New research shows that the human brain is vulnerable to the effects of malnutrition for much longer than was thought previously. Poor nutrition up to two years after birth can inflict permanent brain damage leading to intellectual and social defects.[36]

Here is that point put another way:

> First, we must recognize that health is highly political: social and environmental
> conditions are important determinants. Poverty and its unremitting effects can
> increase stress and leave many families and children isolated and subject to
> mental and physical disorders. Child poverty has a devastating effect on
> society . . . [37]

We know too that social upheaval can produce profound emotional and
psychological disturbances. For example, the connection between social
trauma and health has been described in recent Scottish studies. The authors
of one report argue that the cause of 'inequalities in health' lies not only in
the environment, but also in people's lifestyles, in the structural and cultural
factors which influence their lives, in the choices open to them, and in
their capacity to react to stress and other adverse influences. [38]

One historian, Jean-Pierre Peter, speculates on the connection between
social and cultural upheaval and 'nervous disorders':

> I have spoken of these examples [of 'hysteria'] in some detail only because it
> seems to me that they point to profound hysteroid tendency characteristic of
> the Old Regime, at least in the lower classes. A frightening encounter with
> disease, personal troubles, fear – all of these often evoked responses of the same
> type, namely, convulsions and even paralysis. These reactions had strong
> hysterical overtones . . . Thus in the last analysis, the permanence of hysterical
> components in the behaviour of the lower classes says something about the
> nature of a society which, in fact, gave rise to these tendencies. [39]

Peter's reference point was eighteenth-century France and the dramatic
cultural change which followed the French Revolution. Similar trauma
would surely have attended the cultural disruptions that shook the
Highlands and Islands: the Protestant Reformation, the Massacre of
Glencoe, the Battle of Culloden and the Clearances. And such trauma
could surely have accounted for the psychopathology being reported
among Highlanders during the period.

Notes

1. Dr H. Cameron Gillies quotes this Gaelic proverb in his article, 'Gaelic
   Names of Diseases and of Disease States', *Caledonian Medical Journal*, iii,
   1897–9, 105.

2. David Hamilton, *The Healers: A History of Medicine in Scotland*, Edinburgh,
   Canongate, 1987, 169.

3. *Control of Communicable Diseases in Man*, Abram S. Benenson,Ed., 16th edn., Washington, DC,The American Public Health Association,1995, 537.

4. While the part played by colostrum (the first milk from the mother's breasts after the birth of the child) in immunity is debatable, the role played by breast feeding cannot be understated in any discussion of infant nutrition and neonatal infection.'Infant feeding begins in the uterus' and if the mother is malnourished the prenatal development of the foetus will be at risk.The quality and quantity of breast milk will also reflect the malnutrition of the mother. Jelliffe and Jelliffe discuss the attitudes regarding colostrum in some societies, and the importance of breast feeding in poor societies if the baby is to survive. Artificial feeding in such circumstances gives rise not only to nutritional problems but almost guarantees some form of infection and death. For example, in 1660 in England, over half the 'hand reared' babies died in infancy, and their deaths were correctly labelled 'died from want of breast milk'. By contrast, only one-fifth of breast-fed babies died.

   For a more detailed discussion of this important subject see:

   Derrick B. Jelliffe and F.F. Patrice Jelliffe, 'Breast Feeding and Infant Nutrition in Developing Countries' in *Nutrition, Food and Man: An Interdisciplinary Perspective*, Eds., Paul B. Pearson and Richard Greenwell, Tucson,Arizona, Univ. of Arizona Press, 1980, 11–20.

5. Dr Alexander Monro Sen., *An Account of the Inoculation of Small Pox in Scotland*, Edinburgh, 1765, 4.

   He noted in this pamphlet that inoculation against smallpox was first practised in Scotland in 1726 by Mr Charles Maitland, surgeon. There is evidence that this technique in fact was much older, part of traditional Celtic culture used by the proto-Celtic nomadic tribes that streamed westward into Europe and the British Isles from the Russian Steppes during the first millennium BC.

   Ibid., 3, 20.

   See also:

   Mr. La Condamine, *A Discourse on Inoculation*, London, 1755, xi–xiv, 3.

6. Sir John Sinclair, *Analysis of the Statistical Account of Scotland*, in two parts, Edinburgh, 1825. (Hereafter *Analysis*), New York, Johnson Reprint Corporation, 1970, Part First, 110.

7. *Analysis*, Part First, 79.

   Logan also noted this finding but questions the veracity of many of these reports.

   James Logan, *The Scottish Gael*, 2 Vols., Edinburgh, Reprinted by John Donald, 1976, 182–4.

   Marx (1818–1883), writing a century later, did not support these observations and noted that the country labourers, in spite of the fresh air and the principle of natural selection that works so powerfully amongst them and only permits the survival of the strongest, was already beginning to die off:

They resemble in fact the 30,000 'Gallant Highlanders' whom Glasgow pigs together in its wynds and closes with prostitutes and thieves.

Karl Marx, *Capital*, New York, The Modern Library, Random House Inc., 1906, 296, n.2.

8. Martin Martin, *A Voyage to St. Kilda* 1697, 4th edn., James Thin, Edinburgh, 1986, 39–41.

Tom Steele, *The Life and Death of St Kilda*, Glasgow, Fontana/Collins, 1975, 149.

Charles Maclean, *Island on the Edge of the World*, Edinburgh, Canongate Classics, 1993, 41–2, 88–9.

The 'boat cough' in the twentieth century was still a feature of St Kildan life, according to the Revd D.J. Gillis (1901–1993), a Gaelic-speaking clergyman, who was born there and left the island before the evacuation of 1930. Gillis remembered as a boy on St Kilda that an epidemic of the 'cold' would follow the visit of any fishing boat from the mainland. Interview R. Mathieson/Revd D.J. Gillis, born St Kilda 1901; at Mira Ferry, Cape Breton. July, 1988.

9. Peter Ludwig Panum, *Iagttagelser, Anstillede Under Maeslinge-Epidemien Paa Faeroerne I Aaret* 1846, (Observations made during the epidemic of measles on the Faroe Islands in the year 1846), Translated by Mrs. A.S. Hatcher, Baltimore, Medical Classics, 1939, 3, 828–886.

This classic medical observation confirmed the vulnerability of a population to an infectious disease when its naturally acquired immunity had been lost due to a lack of subsequent 'booster' epidemics.

10. O.S.A., VIII (Glenorchay and Inishail), 341–2.

11. J.R. Currie and A.G. Mearns, *Hygiene*, 2nd edn., Edinburgh, E. & S. Livingstone Ltd., 1945, 275.

12. Calvin W. Schwabe, *Veterinary Medicine and Human Health*, 3rd edn., Baltimore, Williams & Wilkins, 1984, 194.

The Highland black house, in use in some remote areas until the early twentieth century, provided communal shelter for humans, domestic animals and fowls.

13. *Analysis*, Op cit., Part First, 138.

14. Ibid., Part First, 139.

15. Ibid., 138.

16. Dr A.K. Chalmers, *The Health of Glasgow* 1818–1925, Glasgow, Bell and Bain Ltd., 1930, 2,

After discussing the rising incidence of tuberculosis and other communicable diseases, Dr Chalmers came to the conclusion that:

It would thus seem that whatever prejudicial influence local conditions exert in reducing the resistance of the individual to particular forms of disease, variation in the virulence of the infecting organism, or in the susceptibility of the individual to its action, must also be taken into account. 91–5.

17. Benenson, Op cit., 384.

18. Otto F. Sieber Jn., and Glenn Lippman, 'Nutrition, Infection, and Immunity', in *Nutrition, Food, and Man: An Interdisciplinary Perspective*, Eds., Paul B. Pearson and Richard Greenwell, Tucson, Arizona, Univ. Press, 1980, 25–27.

    Sieber and Lippman also found that some rash-producing diseases, for example, measles, when associated with malnutrition, have a lowered frequency of rash. This, at the beginning of an epidemic, or in sporadic cases, would make diagnosis difficult and so delay the preventive measures required to contain the epidemic.

    See also: Mark Nathan Cohen, *Health & the Rise of Civilization*, New Haven Yale Univ. Press, 1989, 54.

19. Martin Martin, *A Description of the Western Islands of Scotland* (circa 1695), 2nd edn., Edinburgh, reprint, James Thin, 1970, 11.

20. Chalmers, Op cit., 338.

21. Rosalind Mitchison, 'Malnutrition in Scotland since 1700, and its Social Consequences', *The Society for the Social History of Medicine*, Bulletin No., 38, 1986, 17.

22. René Dubos acknowledges factors applicable to the 'Highland Problem' – those of the socio-economic component:

    Eradication is an unattainable goal, not only in the case of microbial diseases but also of other environmental threats. In fact, progress in disease control does not always go hand in hand with scientific progress, because social factors often interfere with the application of knowledge. Naturally, these social limiting factors are most in evidence among populations of low economic status.

    René Dubos, *Man Adapting*, New Haven, Yale Univ. Press, 1980, 382.

23. Lobban reports that by 1700 there might have been 70–80 Highlanders (6% of the population) living in the town of Greenock in Renfrewshire situated close to the south-west Lowland interface. After 1750 the Highland population increased and reached, by the 1790s, about 5,100 (20–30% of the population). He also states, however, that the Highlanders in Greenock were not set apart in a physical sense in a particular ghetto or district of the town. Certainly there were pockets of Highlanders living clustered together in different parts of the town, for Highland migrants liked to live close to their fellow countrymen and people from their own home areas . . . The Highlanders, too, were subject to all the diseases that struck down the populations living in the towns of the eighteenth and nineteenth centuries. Perhaps they were more prone to suffer from smallpox since many of them were not vaccinated, but there was little apparent difference between their

rates of mortality and disease and those of the general population.
R.D. Lobban,'The Migration of the Highlanders into Lowland Scotland
c 1750–1890.' Edinburgh, Unpublished PhD thesis, Univ. of Edinburgh, 2
Vols., 1969. I, 403, 408–9.

24. John R,Tudor, *The Orkneys and Shetland* (1883), Edinburgh, Reproduced by
John Dunlop, 1987, 173.

25. Currie and A.G. Mearns, Op cit., 272.

26. Ibid., 277.

27. N.S.A.,VII (Kilbrandon and Kilchattan), 73.
Similar observations were noted elsewhere:
Ibid., (Ardnamurchan), 133, and (Kilfinichen and Kilviceuen), 302.

28. N.S.A., XIV (Duirinish), 326.

29. For a fuller description of 'sibbens' and the opinion of contemporary
medical observers regarding its aetiology and prognosis see:
Guenter B. Risse, *Hospital Life in Enlightenment Scotland: Care and Teaching
at the Royal Infirmary, Edinburgh*, Cambridge, Univ. Press, 1986, 128–9.

30. Thomas Pennant, *A Tour of Scotland in 1769*, 3rd edn., Warrington, 1774,
Reprinted, Perth, Melven Press, 1979, 273.

31. Maxcy-Rosenau, Op cit., 71.
Currie and Mearns, Op cit., 154–173.

32. O.S.A.,VII (Craignish), 437.

33. 'Portion of a memorial submitted by the inhabitants of the town of
Inverness, N.B. on the subject of a proposed Lunatic Asylum'. British
Sessional Papers (Commons),1857, Session 2, XLII, 123.

34. *Scottish Lunacy Commission: Report of the Lunatic Asylums in Scotland*,
Edinburgh, 1857, 37.

35. Ibid., 38–40.

36. Dr Roger Lewin, 'The Poverty of Undernourished Brains', *New Scientist*,
24 Oct. 1974, 268.

37. "Canada's Poorest Citizens: Looking for Solutions for Children', Denice M.
Avard, PhD; Graham W. Chance, MB, FRCPC, FRCP., *Canadian Medical
Association Journal*, 1994; 151 (4) 421.

38. Vera Carstairs and Russell Morris, *Deprivation and Health in Scotland*,
Aberdeen, Univ. Press, 1991, 67–78, 214, 224–6.

39. Jean-Pierre Peter, 'Disease and the Sick at the End of the Eighteenth
Century', in *Biology of Man in History*, Ed., Robert Forster, Baltimore, Johns
Hopkins Univ. Press, 1975, 117–8.

7

The Most Prevalent Diseases

Ye shall know them by their fruits.[1]

IN THE LAST CHAPTER we discussed the aetiology of those communicable diseases most prevalent in the Highlands during the Clearances. For a graphic account of the signs and symptoms of those diseases, we turn to Sinclair's *Analysis of the Statistical Accounts*. Sinclair reported eight diseases as being most prevalent: smallpox, formerly the most fatal; rheumatism, then the most general; the ague [malaria]; fevers; consumptions; croup [most likely diphtheria]; scrofula [tuberculosis of the lymph nodes of the neck]; and last, a general group of other diseases of lesser importance.[2] To Sinclair's list we will add two other diseases that were almost certainly prevalent at the time, though they had not then been diagnosed. Throughout this analysis, we will use current medical knowledge to interpret the signs and symptoms that Sinclair reported.

I

Sinclair's last, general group were the 'new diseases', such as gout and palsy, then being introduced into Scotland. On the rise of such new diseases, Sinclair observed: 'It has been justly remarked that, in proportion as civilization advances in a state, the number of diseases is augmented.'[3] In fact, increased trade, military service abroad and seasonal migration for work had exposed Highlanders for the first time to several new diseases.[4]

Sinclair was not sure of the aetiology of the new diseases; further, he cautioned that because names for some had no Gaelic equivalent, names had to be borrowed from another source. Palsy was one such. Finding no name for this 'visitation of God' in the Gaelic translation of the Bible, Sinclair called the disease paralysis, from the Latin – actually, from the Greek words *parlyein*, *para*, beside, and *lyein*, to loose.

In affluent societies, paralysis, or palsy, is usually associated with a cerebrovascular accident or stroke. However, as we have observed in Chapter 5, the signs of palsy could in fact be the neurological complications of pellagra, a disease resulting not from high blood pressure but from malnutrition. Sinclair's palsy was almost certainly pellagra, the result of that more mundane pathology.

Pellagra is a vitamin deficiency disease, the direct result of severe malnutrition, an aetiology not understood until the nineteenth century. In the Highlands, the potato had become the dietary staple, and though the potato proved a good source of energy if consumed in large amounts, it is dangerously low in B vitamins. Indeed, any attempt to use potatoes to relieve famine in maize-consuming areas or, conversely, to use maize in potato-consuming countries (as was done in Ireland) does nothing to correct the vitamin(s) deficiency.[5]

Whenever it occurs, pellagra can be taken as an indicator of malnutrition. Deficiency in any member of the vitamin B complex group gives rise to various neurological, dermatological and digestive signs and symptoms. In its early stages pellagra is characterised by depression, insomnia, headaches and dizziness, followed by spinal pains and other neurological complaints similar to those from chronic alcoholism and the severe dietary deficiencies which accompany it.

Pellagra typically follows a chronic and relapsing course, with a peak incidence at the end of winter. In the Highlands, it may have represented, in part at least, the avitaminosis associated with much of the general ill-health common in the spring. Such ill-health was consistently reported by parish ministers at the end of winter.

In many cases, a deficiency of niacin is also linked with deficiencies of the other members of the vitamin B complex. Stewart Truswell gives the food sources of niacin as liver and kidney (the primary sources), as well as meat and poultry, fish, brewer's yeast and marmite, peanuts, bran and pulses, wholemeal wheat and coffee.[6] Even in the years of plenty, many Highlanders' intake of niacin would have been marginal. In any period, their main sources of niacin were fish, grain and possibly peas. Eventually, especially in the crowded kelping estates of the West Highlands and Islands, virtually no crop or vegetable other than the potato was grown. Furthermore, the arable land in the Highlands could seldom produce enough cereal to supply the needs of the local population. What grain was consumed was imported by the landlords. Failure of the supply of this grain, or of fish in those areas where fish was the only source of high quality food, would, therefore, have resulted in evidence of deficiency diseases among the poor and the elderly, either seasonally or periodically.

As with other diet-related diseases, it is difficult to extract and identify the presence of vitamin deficiency disease from among the descriptions of common diseases in the reports of the eighteenth century. The description of scurvy given by Dr Buchan in 1774 illustrates how a wrong diagnosis could have been made:

> This disease may be known by unusual weariness, heaviness, and difficulty of breathing, especially after motion; rottenness of the gums, which are apt to bleed on the slightest touch; a stinking breath; frequent bleeding of the nose; crackling of the joints; difficulty of walking; sometimes a swelling and sometimes a falling away of the legs, on which there are livid, yellow, or violet-coloured spots; the face is generally of a pale or leaden colour. As the disease advances, other symptoms come on; as rottenness of the teeth, haemorrhages, or discharges of blood from different parts of the body, foul obstinate ulcers, pains in various parts, especially about the breast, dry scaly eruptions all over the body, etc. At last a wasting or hectic fever comes on, and the miserable patient is often carried off by a dysentery, a diarrhoea, a dropsy, palsy, fainting fits, or a mortification of some of the bowels.[7]

Furthermore, dietary deficiency diseases would have been amenable to almost certain cure by natural healers or practitioners of Highland medicine. Nonetheless, it is reasonable to assume that uncertain, meagre and restricted diet, together with an ever-increasing addiction to alcohol, must have predisposed Highlanders to manifestations of vitamin-deficiency disease like pellagra.

Yet another form of paralysis or palsy, general paralysis of the insane, is a condition characterised by progressive loss of power and deterioration of the mental faculties, ending eventually in dementia and death. This paralysis is associated with the late stages of syphilis. Tabes dorsalis is another palsy which presents in the later stage of syphilis. Syphilis, and sibbans (sibbens), the latter endemic in the Highlands, were no newcomers to Europe and are in all countries traditionally associated with a reservoir of infection, particularly in ports and near military concentrations.[8] From such a nidus, they are spread to all ranks of sailors and soldiers until all social strata are eventually at risk. Service life is also commonly associated with chronic alcoholism and so the signs and symptoms of the two diseases generally appear concurrently.

Dropsy was another in Sinclair's group of 'new' diseases. If by dropsy he meant what dropsy means today, abdominal ascites (fluid rich in protein in the abdominal cavity), then this formerly 'very rare' complaint may have been the natural outcome of cirrhosis of the liver, linked to chronic alcoholism. This association is reasonable in view of Sinclair's contention that the principal alteration in diet and in the mode of living in the eighteenth century, when the new diseases began to appear, comprised the use of potatoes and tea and the greater abundance of spirituous liquors.

That alcoholism was chronic in the Highlands is also suggested by another of Sinclair's observations:

> Nay, the excessive use of spirituous liquors among the lower ranks of people, is justly considered a great cause of that deplorable evil insanity, to which they are liable, as well as to those bilious and dropsical complaints, formerly so little known.[9]

Alcohol consumption was an accepted part of Highland lifestyle. Martin Martin observed at the end of the seventeenth century that in Skye, 'scarlet fever, which appeared recently in this isle, is ordinarily cured by drinking now and then a glass of brandy.' What is of greater significance is his next observation: 'If an infant happens to be taken with it, the nurse drinks some brandy, which qualifies the milk, and proves a successful remedy.'[10] The comment suggests a connection between the blood–alcohol level of the wet nurse and that of the infant; that is, the intra–uterine transfer of maternal blood–alcohol to the foetus, a phenomenon that has since been confirmed. Chronic alcoholism does, we now know, make its début in the womb.

In the first quarter of the eighteenth century, Edward Burt reported the extent of alcohol consumption in Lewis:

> The Collector of the Customs at *Stornoway* in the Isle of *Lewis* told me, that about 120 Families drink yearly 4000 *English* Gallons of this Spirit, and Brandy together, although many of them are so poor they cannot afford to pay for much of either, which you know must increase the Quantity drank by the rest, and that they frequently gave to Children of six or seven Years old, as much at a time as an ordinary Wine-glass will hold.[11]

Dr Johnson, on his *Journey* to the Western Islands, commented on alcohol consumption there:

> A man of the Hebrides, for of the women's diet I can give no account, as soon as he appears in the morning, swallows a glass of whisky; yet they are not a drunken race, at least I was never present at much intemperance; but no man is so abstemious as to refuse the morning dram . . . [12]

The minister of Stornoway supplied what Dr Johnson could not, an account of 'the women's diet':

> . . . it is a curious circumstance, that time out of remembrance, their maidservants were in the habit of drinking, every morning, a wine glass full of whisky, which their mistress gave them; this barbarous custom became so well established by the length of time, that if the practice of it should happen to be neglected or forgotten in a family, even once, discontent and idleness

throughout the day, on the part of the maid or maids, would be the sure consequence.[13]

Johnson would have been shocked at the increase of alcoholism in the West Highlands and Islands half a century later, most of it a response to the pressures of changing social and dietary patterns.[14] Before the disintegration of the clan system, alcohol consumption was high but its effects were then moderated by a diet that was not predominantly potatoes.

Alcoholism was not, however, the only cause of the new disease of dropsy. Dropsy is associated also with an upset in the protein content of the blood and is related, therefore, to low protein intake, especially in infants and children. The resulting oedema is classically present in times of famine. It is a condition of long-continued underfeeding, commonplace in the daily life of poor Highlanders. The parish minister of Craignish in Argyll noted that dropsy had become much more common in the eighteenth century:

> Some instances of a dropsy of the belly occurs; and, it is affirmed by the aged, . . . that this complaint is much more prevalent through the whole country, than it was 50 or 60 years ago, and that it is becoming more general . . . The cause, however, which is commonly assigned, and which seems most obvious and plausible, is the immoderate use of the potato root.[15]

Woodham-Smith, writing about the Irish potato famines of the mid-nineteenth century, quoted William Bennett of the Society of Friends who, in 1847, identified the causal connection between famine and dropsy. Dropsy, Bennett said, was 'that horrid disease – the results of long continued famine and low living – in which the limbs and then the body swell most frightfully and finally burst.'[16] In fact, it is doubtful if the body actually burst in life, but in death decomposition would have been rapid and 'horrid.'

Another form of dropsy, cardiac dropsy or oedema, is the result of a failure of compensation of the cardiac output, commonly a result of valvular disease of the heart, itself most often caused by rheumatic fever, a form of 'rheumatism'. According to Sinclair's *Analysis*, rheumatism had become 'the most general' disease in Scotland. However, because of Sinclair's repeated reiteration of the increase in alcoholism and in view of the signs he described, particularly if by 'bilious' he meant jaundiced, then the dropsy and jaundice he reported were likely to be related not to rheumatism, but to alcoholic cirrhosis of the liver.[17] Sinclair's term 'bilious' also included the 'bilious fevers', diseases such as yellow fever, malaria and typhoid fever. At the time, these fevers were thought to be produced by putrefaction, and to become epidemic only by means of an impure atmosphere (miasma).[18]

II

Those then were the 'new' diseases in Sinclair's list. Let us turn now to the disease he named first, smallpox. In the eighteenth century, the major killer, especially of children, was infectious diseases. Of that group, smallpox (variola major), was the most lethal. Sinclair noted that smallpox ('the mortal pock') was believed to have destroyed one-fifth of the human race; that sometimes one-half of the children infected died; and that when the disease was associated with chincough (whooping cough), smallpox ravages were disastrous. Elsewhere he quoted the minister of Snizort, on the Isle of Skye, as saying that in the past when the disease had visited, 'it swept away almost whole families, leaving not above one, two or sometimes three in a house.'[19] Monro has supplied annual figures for burials in Edinburgh and its suburbs over the period 1744–1763, from which he compared deaths from smallpox against the total number of burials. He concluded that one death in ten had been the result of smallpox.[20] The impact of such a loss to a labour-intensive Highland township scratching a bare living from the land and sea was staggering. Moreover, smallpox, like measles and other viral diseases, may present crippling sequelae such as deafness, dumbness and blindness in those who survive the initial attack. To support survivors so crippled strained the meagre resources of family and community.[21]

But in the Lowlands and in England, inoculation was gaining ground, and the death rate from smallpox was in consequence drastically reduced. In Glasgow, during the period 1783 to 1812, vaccination reduced the death rate from smallpox considerably, as the figures below reveal:

	1783–1792	1793–1802	1803–1812
Total Deaths under 10 years	9,919	9,080	10,913
Smallpox under 10 years	3,466	2,849	1,013
Proportion of Smallpox	35%	32%	9.2%[22]

Sinclair quoted the minister of Fortingal in Perthshire on the effectiveness of vaccination:

> It has been remarked, that fewer children die in the Highlands than almost anywhere, and this has been particularly the case since inoculation has been so universally practised.[23]

In fact, prophylaxis against smallpox was conferred by two procedures, variolation and, later, vaccination. Variolation was an active immunity, conferred by passing the living virus of smallpox from the pocks of a patient to a healthy subject. The procedure was risky and the recipient had to be healthy. A sickly, undernourished child of the Highland poor would have had little resistance to variolation. Moreover, since a particularly virulent strain of the virus would invariably kill both the donor and recipient, both had to be carefully chosen. Consequently, variolation presented grave problems as a preventive or remedy among the urban poor.

Despite its risks, variolation had been practised successfully in the Highlands and Islands of Scotland by doctors and laity alike for decades. Monro reported that Mr Maitland, a surgeon in Aberdeenshire, had introduced into the north-east in 1726 the operation of inoculation.[24] Further, Monro reported that a questionnaire sent in the 1760s to doctors and surgeons all over Scotland showed that out of the 5625 inoculations reported, only 72 people had died.[25] Those deaths he attributed variously to the bad constitution of the patient and the improper timing of inoculation; to the bad management of the inoculated; to the natural, not the artificial infection; and to other supervening diseases.[26] It is noteworthy, however, that in the only questionnaire filed from the West Highlands and Islands, Mr John Maclean, surgeon on the Isle of Skye, reported that of the 198 inoculations he performed, 10 persons died, a figure 5 times the national death rate.[27] Either Mr Maclean's technique left much to be desired, or the resistance of some of his patients to fight even a 'good, mild small pox' was low. Nor was Maclean the only inoculator to report an above average death rate, a fact which probably reflected the destitution and thus low resistance in many of the catchment areas.

In the late eighteenth century, Edward Jenner (1749–1823) recognised the importance of dairymaids' discovery that infection with cowpox conferred a lengthy immunity to smallpox and that it did so with far fewer risks than variolation. That recognition revolutionised the prophylaxis of smallpox: vaccination quickly replaced the ancient preventive of variolation. In fact, Jenner fought for decades to have variolation banned, though the ban did not come into effect until 1840.[28]

That inoculation by either method was widely accepted in the Highlands was surprising, given the religious beliefs and superstitions of the people. Indeed, it was not approved in all quarters. An anonymous pamphlet published in London in 1756 summarised the superstitions that lingered in some areas:

> The two grand Objections to Inoculation, are, First, That it is an affront to the Almighty, or, as they term it, 'presumptuous' to infect wilfully and premeditatedly any Person with a loathsome Distemper, the View being to prevent a greater Severity of it, or death.
>   The second, That other Distempers, as the Scurvy, the Itch [scabies], Scrophulous Swellings, [enlarged tuberculous lymph nodes] hereditary Madness, Palsy, Etc., may be inoculated with the Small-pox, if the Matter be

taken from a Person infected with either of the above Distempers, or whose Blood was supposed to contain even the Seeds of the Palsy, or Madness by inheritance.[29]

And on the Island of Mull, a parish minister reported a prejudice to inoculation in isolated parishes:

> The havock made formerly by the small pox is now by inoculation mostly done away. The inhabitants of I [island of Iona], Ross, and Brolass, inoculate their children; but the people of Airdmeanach have not as yet got over their prejudices, which occasions the loss not only of many young children, but sometimes of grown persons.[30]

Overall, however, inoculation met little resistance. A few parish ministers reported that even where people could not afford the services of a surgeon, they accepted the procedure being performed by the minister of the parish, and that it achieved 'the greatest success.'[31] In fact, inoculation by variolation was widely and successfully practised by lay people, as this extract from a letter written in 1794 by Robert Burns to a Mrs Dunlop attested:

> I would without hesitation have crossed the country to wait on you, but for one circumstance – a week ago I gave my little James the smallpox and he is just beginning to sicken – .[32]

But variolation, and in turn vaccination, gave rise to an unexpected complication: it could, ironically, leave inoculated populations at greater risk from new outbreaks. We have seen that when donor and recipient were carefully screened, variolation virtually guaranteed lifelong immunity against smallpox. Indeed, in the isolated Highlands and Islands of Scotland, variolation may have in fact been an ancient Celtic custom:

> It is indeed by no means impossible, but that the Circassians are alone in possession of the secret, as the people of Wales are said to have it exclusive of any other part of this island. One may suspect that if the motive of our inoculating women sellers was to make the most of this their staple commodity, [the serum containing the virus that was removed from the lesions of a suitable donor] they had sufficient inducement to conceal this lucrative practice from their neighbours.[33]

From that comment, we may infer that inoculation could have been practised in the remote Highlands long before the procedure was introduced into lowland Scotland from England.[34] Assuming that inoculation was practised successfully by 'women sellers', family members, ministers, lay practitioners or surgeons, we can see that a district would eventually come to be populated by immune Highlanders and the disease would no longer be a threat. Two conditions would then prevail. First, the local supply of serum would disappear, and a resupply of serum would therefore have to be imported – an unlikely prospect since the immediate fear of the disease would naturally have lessened with time, and the practice of inoculation itself might well have died out. Second, offspring of this immune community would be protected against smallpox only by short-lived natural, passive immunity from their mothers. This second generation would then be vulnerable to infection imported from any case at any time.

Prophylaxis by the new method of vaccination was not without problems either. The first of these was that the smallpox vaccine, like all commercially-prepared vaccines, could lose its potency if it was not carefully prepared, stored, and its shelf life acknowledged. In isolated Highland communities, proper storage was impossible, and thus the efficacy of the artificial active immunity was often doubtful.[35] Furthermore, artificial immunity, unlike the longer-lasting immunity conferred by an attack of the disease or by variolation, was protective only if supplemented by re-vaccination. In the Highlands, the surviving population was usually so ruggedly healthy, the result of natural selection of the fittest, that even a single inoculation was often not thought necessary.

III

Sinclair's second disease group was rheumatism, in which he included acute rheumatic fever of the young. Sinclair noted that rheumatic diseases were common to all cold and moist climates and that these diseases were reported in all the parishes in Scotland. He also reported that the change from traditional flannel shirts to the newer linen shirts was blamed for the prevalence of rheumatic diseases in districts as far apart as Killbrandon in the south-west to Contin in the north. In fact, he cited eight reported causes for rheumatism, the adoption of linen shirts being the principal culprit.[36] There is substantiation for Sinclair's claims about the danger of the switch to linen. Woollen garments, especially those made from the wool of the small indigenous Highland sheep (*na caoraich bheaga*), were warm in winter, cool in the summer and always hard-wearing. The modern Harris tweed, although no longer made from the wool of the small sheep, illustrates those qualities. The traditional woollen garment of the Highlanders, the plaid, was perfect protection from the elements:

> . . . when the Highlanders are constrain'd to lie among the Hills, in cold dry windy Weather, they sometimes soak the Plaid in some river or Burne; and then holding up a Corner of it a little above their Heads, they turn themselves

round and round, 'till they are invelop'd by the whole mantle. Then they lay themselves down on the Heath, upon the Leeward side of some Hill, where the wet and the warmth of their Bodies make a Steam, like that of a boiling Kettle. The wet, they say, keeps 'em warm by thick'ning the Stuff, and keeping the Wind from penetrating.[37]

Yet the Scottish government had encouraged the switch to linen. An Act of 1686 went so far as to stipulate that

hereafter no Corps of any Person whatsoever shall be buried in any shirt, sheet or any thing else except in plaine linen made and spun within the Kingdom.[38]

Scantily clad, the malnourished could not maintain body heat. Whatever food they consumed was immediately metabolised for energy, at the expense of the body-building and maintenance that are vital to resisting rheumatics. This group of diseases, rheumatics, to which we now add gout, is as yet not fully understood, though we now know, of course, that it consists of joint pains (arthritis), muscle pains (myalgia) and pain related to ligaments (fibrositis).

We know more about another of the rheumatic diseases, rheumatic fever, which Sinclair did not specifically mention. Sinclair would have listed the disease we know as rheumatic fever under the inclusive heading of fevers. Rheumatic fever was extremely common among children in all regions of Scotland in the eighteenth and nineteenth centuries (as it was in the pre-antibiotic decades of the twentieth century). The disease is caused by a *Group A streptococcus*, which can produce a variety of diseases: strep throat; skin infections such as impetigo or pyoderma; scarlet fever; puerperal fever (child bed fever); septicaemia (blood poisoning); erysipelas; cellulitis; mastoiditis; otitis media (inner ear infection); pneumonia; peritonitis; and wound infections.[39] All were potentially fatal diseases. In each, the cause of death would be attributed to the most prominent symptom. In many instances, a simple sore throat, the result of a *Streptococcal type A* infection, would clear up, only to be followed in one to five weeks by acute rheumatic fever, an acute nephritis, or chorea. This latter illness 'is a distemper, called by the country people leaping "ague", and by the physicians "St Vitus' dance".'[40] A later and very common complication of this infection is rheumatic heart disease.[41]

Benenson states that the 3–15 year age group is most often affected, that the highest incidence of infection is during the late winter and early spring, and that military and school populations are often affected. There can be no doubt that in the crowded strips of poor, often marshy and unsheltered land that Highlanders were consigned to after the Clearances, simple sore throats led in alarming numbers to rheumatic fever.

IV

The disease that Sinclair named as third in prevalence was 'the ague'. This disease was probably what is now called malaria. Some of the diagnosed cases may also have represented other acute fevers, such as typhus fever (the spotted ague), or the common domestic flu. In his *Analysis*, Sinclair certainly described signs and symptoms which support the diagnosis of malaria. He noted, for instance, that the ague was an enfeebling disease which in the past had prevailed over a large proportion of Scotland, those afflicted being subject usually to annual attacks. He also noted that the ague had been banished from several districts of Scotland, a development he attributed to better agriculture; that is, better clearing and draining of the land.[42] That observation too suggests that Sinclair's ague may in fact have been malaria.

Malaria has man as its reservoir of infection and is transmitted by the bite of the female of a specific genus of mosquito, the *Anopheles*. The different types of this parasite give rise to four clinical types of malaria, each with its own incubation period and disease pattern.[43] One type, *Plasmodium vivax*, is the agent most likely to be responsible for English and Scottish malaria.

Without the anopheline mosquito, malaria cannot be transmitted. In Britain, land drainage and climate change brought that eradication, for, like all insects, the *anopheles* mosquito is sensitive to changes in climatic humidity and requires stagnant water in which to lay its eggs. Nevertheless, as O'Dell and Walton observe, climatic conditions vary according to the physical geography of a district, thus ague (malaria) remained endemic in the marshy districts of the warm south-east of Britain until the beginning of the twentieth century, the last case of English malaria being reported in 1911.[44] Similarly, the ague or malaria could have been 'common in Scotland in spring and autumn, and sometimes even in summer', as Sinclair reported.

V

Before the mid-nineteenth century, diseases had been diagnosed and treated symptomatically; that is, by their symptoms and syndromes, thus fevers were classified and sub-classified according to their type.[45]

Sinclair's *Analysis* states that the nature of fevers had changed over the thirty years that his study spanned. Three decades earlier, pleuritic and inflammatory fevers had prevailed. They had been replaced by the low, lingering and nervous type; that is, by the asthenic or weakening type of fever.[46]

The aetiology and classification of fevers occupied the most brilliant minds of the medical and scientific community during the nineteenth century. Papers were published and findings were debated in the learned societies as well as in both Houses of Parliament.[47] Meanwhile, fevers ravaged the poor throughout Britain and eventually threatened the upper class. Researchers slowly came to grips with this scourge: new preventive measures were introduced, measures that reflected concern and represented advances, even if they were not always successful. That they frequently failed was noted by Dr Gordon of the Aberdeen Dispensary. The Dispensary was instituted in 1781 to treat in their own homes patients who could not be admitted to the Infirmary. At the time of his report, Dr Gordon had been the physician in charge of the Dispensary for ten years. Under his direction it had acquired a reputation for successful treatment of acute diseases, especially fevers. Yet Dr Gordon cautioned that

> the method of treatment commonly practised, and recommended by the most celebrated *modern professors*, so frequently failed of success; and that many more recovered, when left to the efforts of unassisted nature, than when treated according to the most approved rules of art. He was therefore naturally led to entertain suspicions with respect to the propriety of those rules; and was soon convinced by observation and experience, that it was impossible for him to be successful in the treatment of fevers, without imitating the method by which nature cured them . . . This method is not new, though of late, too much neglected; for the same principle has been the guide of all great *practical physicians*, both of ancient and modern times.[48]

Victory in the battle against fevers had to await the acceptance of the germ theory of disease, the isolation of the causative agents, and the determination of their portals of entry and exit. With some fevers, like cholera, such was the calibre of the minds addressing the problem that these portals were identified before the pathogen itself was isolated.

VI

'Consumptions' constituted Sinclair's fifth disease group.[49] In this group, pulmonary tuberculosis was primary, though that designation may well have included many other terminal diseases, such as primary or secondary malignant tumours involving the lungs. Some pulmonary diseases associated with the industrial revolution were by the late eighteenth and early nineteenth centuries appearing in Scotland and must also have been represented in this group. Highlanders emigrating to urban centres in search of employment were at risk from these diseases, later to be classified as pneumoconiosis. Furthermore, many pulmonary diseases, once established in the lungs, are associated with a superimposed tubercular infection or cancer. As with others of Sinclair's diseases, his consumptions span a broad range. That such general diagnosis and labelling were common is attested by the Registrar-General of Scotland in his first *Report* in 1861. For example, on the diagnosis of consumption, the Registrar-General observed:

> In the Western Isles, it was ascertained that the word 'Consumption' was used as a common term to express any illness which reduced the strength and wasted the body, and, in fact, it was commonly applied to the decay produced by the infirmities of old age.[50]

Sinclair and the ministers who contributed to his *Analysis*, though limited by the generality of the medical information available to them, did attempt to identify the contributing causes of the consumptions. Most of their observations were sound. Often their analyses were correct. In some cases, their explanation for the aetiology of the disease, though it may have appeared far-fetched at the time, has been confirmed by subsequent medical advances. Sinclair's impressive summation of the causes of consumptions is typical:

> 1. the coldness and dampness of the houses. 2. the change of clothing, from the thick and warm Scotch plaiding, to the fine but thin and cold English cloth, now so prevalent. 3. the sedentary employment of manufacturers, particularly of linen weavers, who carry on their business in damp workshops, into which no fire is admitted. 4. Spinning also, which is the employment of the young women during the winter months, is justly reckoned the occasion of consumptions among them, by the waste of saliva requisite in that laborious employment. 5. Consumptions are sometimes owing to a radical weakness of constitution, and to the pernicious custom of persons exposing themselves, in a state of violent perspiration, to the sudden impression of cold. A large draft of cold water, in this state has often proved the beginning of consumptions and dropsies.[51]

His reference to the 'waste' in spinning clearly referred to the expectorating discharge from the respiratory tract. Sinclair had identified a portal of exit for *M. tuberculosis*, as well as the conditions conducive to the rapid spread of disease; that is, the presence of *fomites*, any substances capable of acting as the media for transmitting contagion. Airborne agents such as irritant dusts may also induce disease processes (such as pneumoconiosis). It has been established, for example, that in textile industries, dust from the processing of flax, cotton and silk can give rise to respiratory diseases such as byssinosis, a form of pneumoconiosis still found in some cotton-mill workers. These chronic respiratory conditions, coupled with poor working and living conditions, are usually followed by the onset of pulmonary tuberculosis.

Sinclair observed that since weaving silk had become the general employment in Paisley, consumptions had become much less frequent. On the other hand, the linen shops presented other risks, damp and poorly ventilated as they were. The minister of the Abbey Parish of Paisley noted that scrofula was greatly aggravated by the damp shops in which linen was manufactured.[52] In the parish of Louden, the minister contended that 'Scrofula or white swelling is frequent from poor living, and sedentary life, and bad air in weaver's shops, where they never have a fire.'[53]

The association of tuberculosis of the lymph glands of the neck with an airborne organism can, however, be misleading and can mask the much more serious underlying cause of scrofula; namely, bovine tuberculosis. This infection, arising from contaminated dairy produce and food in general, has the alimentary tract as the portal of entry. Non-bovine tuberculosis; that is, normally the human strain, can also enter the oral route by means of fomites and produce scrofula. But the much more likely source would be airborne bacilli, as a direct spread from a case of 'open' pulmonary tuberculosis in a fellow worker, or from the inhalation of dried contaminated sputa from such cases. The latter circumstance would explain the high incidence of consumption among weavers and like trades. In fact, the same conditions would have obtained as surely in Highland cottage industries as well as in the industrial south, and with the same results. Moreover, as Highlanders' resistance to disease declined, an attack of tuberculosis among them might have represented a reactivation of a previously 'cured' infection.

Sinclair ended his discussion of consumptions without dwelling on the supposition, then widely held, that where consumptions were most apt to appear, the ague had ceased to exist. In other words, consumptions were apt to replace ague. This *Doctrine of Replacement* was based on bitter experience with what generally happened where conditions were unsanitary and people malnourished: when one epidemic disease was rooted out, it was replaced by others.[54] The *Doctrine of Replacement* was rooted in two fundamental medical observations: that unhygienic living conditions play a part in disease process, and that organisms, like people, are basically opportunistic.'[55]

VII

The croup or *cynache trachealis* was sixth in Sinclair's list. It had become, he reported, 'the most fatal disorder to which children are liable'. He also noted that 'it often baffles every remedy.'[56] The term *cynache trachealis* literally means 'to strangle' and is the old name given to any acute affection of the throat, like diphtheria, croup and tonsillitis in which the patient struggles for breath. In most cases, the croup was diphtheria, a disease which usually killed in its early stages. Sinclair remarked that 'it in general proves fatal, unless the immediate aid of a physician be procured [to perform a tracheotomy].'

VIII

In Sinclair's taxonomy, the seventh most prevalent disease type is scrofula (also known as King's Evil and the White Swelling). It was said to be cured by touching the King's hand. Sinclair reported that 'the increasing prevalence of this disease is loudly lamented.'[57] He connected scrofula with consumption and attributed its cause to the diet of agricultural labourers, since it increased in all the parishes 'where the living of the inhabitants is poor and principally of the vegetable kind.'[58]

Dr Johnson acquired scrofula as a child. For him, touching the royal hand (in his case, Queen Anne's) failed to provide a cure and he suffered from the disease for the rest of his life. The superstition about the curative power of the royal touch was not confined to the Anglo-Saxon culture, as the minister of Logierait explained:

> There is a disease called *glacach* by the Highlanders, which, as it affects the chest and lungs, is evidently of a consumptive nature. It is also called, the Macdonald's 'disease', because there are particular tribes of Macdonalds, who are believed to cure it with the charms of their touch, and the use of a certain set of words. There must be no fee given of any kind. Their faith in the touch of a Macdonald is very great.[59]

As we have already noted, scrofula is tuberculosis of the lymphatic system, but besides involving the lymph glands of the neck which drain the throat, scrofula may also affect those lymph glands that drain the lower alimentary tract, giving rise to the equally common but then unrecognised *tabes mesenterica*; that is, tuberculous disease of the mesenteric lymph glands in children, a disease associated with progressive wasting. The portal of entry for scrofula is the mouth; the disease organism is commonly transported in dairy products taken from infected animals. Bovine tuberculosis was the common reservoir, and since milk and other dairy products were a mainstay of the Highland poor, an infected cow could readily spread the disease to other animals or to a Highland family, and so put an entire township or village at risk.

Tuberculosis is a classic example of that critical balance which exists between the resistance of the host and the invasive capacity of the pathogen.

Tuberculous lesions have been found in prehistoric skeletons, as well as among contemporary groups of hunter-gatherers, but the disease 'did not become common in Britain until Roman times and may have become a significant disease burden only in the middle ages.'[60] The prevalence of tuberculosis is an indication of a community's resistance and, therefore, of its socio-economic health.

IX

Sinclair's analysis makes clear how disease-ridden Highland communities were after the Clearances, exposed as they were to new diseases and made vulnerable to the return of old ones as well. Modern medical science enables us to interpret his descriptions of signs and symptoms and so more accurately diagnose the diseases he reported.

Notes

1. Bible, Authorised (King James) Version, Matthew 7:16.

    This quotation is appropriate here since before the Bacteriological Revolution of the late nineteenth century disease states were classified according to the predominant symptom. For example, fevers were known by duration and type and not by causal pathology.

2. *Analysis*, Part First, 126–140.

    For a broader view of the spectrum of disease and its treatment in Scotland during this period see:

    Guenter B. Risse, *Hospital Life in Enlightenment Scotland: Care and Teaching at the Royal Infirmary of Edinburgh*, Cambridge, Univ. Press, 1986.

3. Ibid., Part First, 139–40.

4. For a fuller discussion of this seasonal migration and its cause see;

    T.M. Devine, 'Temporary Migration and the Scottish Highlands in the Nineteenth Century', *The Economic History Review*, 2nd Ser., XXXII, 1979, No 3. 344–359.

    The reports of parish ministers also indicated that the attraction of voluntary service in the army or the navy varied from region to region.

    O.S.A., XVII (Small Isles),289.; XIX (Stornoway), 251.; IV (Duirinish), 137.

    But as already noted 'the military spirit' was apt to diminish as the economy of a region improved.

    O.S.A., XX (Thurso), 525n.

5. Cecil Woodham-Smith, *The Great Hunger* Ireland 1845–9, London, New English Library, pb edit., 1975, 48–51.

The occurrence of pellagra can be taken as an indicator of malnutrition. Interestingly, in the United States, maize meal is now fortified with niacin, and its use has been largely replaced by wheat.

A. Stewart Truswell, *A B C of Nutrition*, 2nd., edn., London, British Medical Association, 1992, 39–40.

6. Stewart Truswell, Op cit., 49.

7. William Buchan, *Domestic Medicine*, 3rd edn., London:, S. Strahan, T. Cadell, 1774, 428–9.

8. Sibbens or sibbans (from the Gaelic *subhan*, raspberries) is identified by some with syphilis, by others with yaws.

   Benenson identifies Yaws as *Frambesia tropica* and describes the classical raspberry-like skin lesions described by Sinclair. The infectious agent of both diseases is a spirochaete.

9. *Analysis*, Op cit., Part First, 141–2.

   The minister of the Small Isles noted that two of the most common diseases in the parish were dropsy of the belly, and jaundice. O.S.A., XVII (Small Isles), 279.

   See also; O.S.A., VII (Craignish), 437.; III (Applecross), 377.

   The minister of Reay reports: 'The dropsy sometimes makes its appearance here; in which cases it is supposed to be brought on by the excessive drinking of raw spirits.'

   O.S.A., VII (Reay), 571.

   Campbell makes an interesting point regarding alcoholism in Scotland: Drink and drunkenness were most commonly cited as the great evils of the industrial society. The alcoholic tradition had, however, been inherited from rural Scotland. The difference lay in the increased social disapproval, partly because of the emergence of different drinking habits among different groups and because drunkenness caused greater economic dislocation in an industrial society which could not accommodate the long periods of drinking possible in a rural society.

   R.H. Campbell, *Scotland Since 1707*, 2nd edn., Edinburgh, John Donald, 1985, 150.

10. Martin Martin, *A Description of the Western Islands of Scotland* (circa 1695), 2nd edn., Edinburgh. Reprint, James Thin, 1970, 177.

    Hippocrates (and therefore the Beatons) was reputed to have been aware of this connection: 'The effects of a mother's humours upon the embryo, and the mother's or nurse's milk upon the child, vary according to the circumstances.'

    Hippocrates, 6 Vols., translation of Vol., I by W.H.S. Jones, London, William Heinemann, 1923, I, Nutriment, xl, 357 and note 356.

11. Edward Burt, *Letters From a Gentleman in the North of Scotland to His Friend in London*, [c 1720–30], 2 vols., 2nd edn., London, 1754, II, 270.

12. Samuel Johnson, *A Journey to the Western Islands of Scotland*, in *A Tour to the Hebrides*, Johnson & Boswell, Ed., R.W. Chapman, London, Oxford Univ. Press, 1933, 49.

13. O.S.A., XIX (Stornoway), 158–9.

14. Many Highlanders and 'housemaids' of the eighteenth and nineteenth centuries would fit into the above categories and yet, as now, they would not admit to being alcoholics:

    The views of alcohol use are as diverse and emotional as those of good and evil . . . Like all drugs, alcohol has potential benefits, but it also has serious, undesirable side effects in short-term and long-term use. Hence, it merits the same respect as any other potent drug, regardless of its ancient and legendary reputation.

    William R. Jacyk, MD, FRCPC., 'Moderate drinking and health: proceedings of an international conference', *Canadian Medical Association Journal* 1994;151 (6), 748–9.

15. O.S.A., VII (Craignish), 437.

16. Woodham-Smith, Op cit., 1977, 188–9.

17. Malignant tumours (often recorded in the eighteenth and nineteenth centuries as consumption) which involved the organs and tissues of the abdomen, could also give rise to jaundice and ascites.

18. Charles-Edward Amory Winslow, *The Conquest of Epidemic Disease*, Wisconsin, Univ. Press, 1980, 205.

19. O.S.A., XVIII (Snizort), 183.

20. Alexander Monro Sen., *An Account of the Inoculation of the Smallpox in Scotland*. Edinburgh, 1765, 11–12.

21. O.S.A., VIII (Dundee), 215.

22. Dr A.K. Chalmers, *The Health Of Glasgow 1818–1925 – An Outline*, Glasgow, Bell and Bain, 1930, 351–2.

23. *Analysis*, Op cit., 129.

24. Monro, Op cit., 4.

25. Ibid., 26–9.

26. Ibid., 30–1.

27. Ibid., 29.

28. Indiscriminate inoculation may be consider'd as the grand source from which the Pestilence now draws its support. I have not been wanting in my endeavors to call the attention of the Legislature to the immense benefits the Empire would derive from their putting the present murderous System under due restriction.

    Letter, Jenner to Dr John Thomson, Halifax, England, 19 October 1809, in *Letters of Edward Jenner*, Ed., Genevieve Miller, Baltimore, The Johns Hopkins Univ, Press, 1983, 63.

29. *The Grand Objections to Inoculation Considered*, anon., London, 1756, 6.
    Analysis, Op cit., Part First, 127–8.

30. O.S.A., XIV (Kilfinichen and Kilviceuen), 173.

31. *Analysis*, Op cit., 128.
    One minister had this to say: 'The people entertain no prejudice against inoculation, but grudge the expense of it.'
    O.S.A. XII (Jura and Colonsay), 320.

32. This letter from Robert Burns to Mrs Dunlop dated 24th August, 1794, is located in the Burns Centre, Alloway, Scotland. Note that the incubation period of smallpox is 7–17 days.

33. Mr L.A. Condamine, *A Discourse on Inoculation*, Read before the Royal Academy of Sciences at Paris, the 24th of April 1754, London, 1755, Postscript, xiv.
    The Celtic peoples were credited with originating in the Russian Steppes at a period circa 8th century BC. At this time, the invading Sythians drove the nomadic Cimmerians from the Steppes; to the northwest into what is now Europe, and also southward across the Caucasus into Anatolia and Greece. The region of the Black Sea was the homeland of the Circassians and therefore it is not unreasonable to assume that the practice of inoculation known to them would also be part of Celtic folk medicine carried westward by the descendants of the Cimmerians and the Sythians and so into pre-Roman Britain. By the same reasoning it is tempting to speculate that in the remote areas of the Celtic fringe, barely touched by later cultures, the practice of variolation endured.

34. Monro, Op cit., 5.

35. Campbell, discussing the vaccination program of Glasgow in the early nineteenth century, remarks the high incidence of smallpox 'among the city's Highlanders, a group which tended to neglect vaccination or which had been vaccinated in the Highlands with impure lymph.'
    R.H. Campbell, *Scotland Since 1707*, Oxford, Basil Blackwell, 1965, 197.

36. *Analysis*, Op cit., Part First, 131–4.
    O.S.A., XIV (Killbrandon and Killchatan), 160.: I (Kiltearn), 263.: XII (Jura and Colonsay), 320.

37. Burt, Op cit., II, 108.

38. Acts of Parliament of Scotland, (A.P.S.), VIII, 598, c. 28.
    For further information on the economics of the new textile industries of Scotland see; Alastair J. Durie, *The Scottish Linen Industry in the Eighteenth Century*. Edinburgh, John Donald, 1979.

39. Benenson, op cit., 367.

40. O.S.A. IV (Lethnot), 5.

41. For further medical information on Group A streptococci and its diseases see; Benenson, Op cit., 367–373.

42. *Analysis*, Op cit., 135.
    Risse, Op cit., 133–5.

43. Richard H. Foots and David R. Cook, *Mosquitoes of Medical Importance*, Agricultural Handbook No. 152, U.S. Dept. of Agriculture, Washington D.C., 1959, 2.

44. G. Melvyn Howe, *Man, Environment and Disease in Britain: A Medical Geography Through the Ages*, New York, Barnes and Noble Books, 1972, 42–6, 90–91.

45. Risse, Op cit., 118.

46. Sinclair's frame of reference was the post-Culloden years, a period of marked cultural and economic change, a time when misfortunes were blamed on the 'new ways':

    > This alteration may arise, from our wanting the hardiness of our forefathers. Everything cold is in disuse. Clothing is warmer [?]. Warm liquors, as punch, tea, &c. are in fashion, even among the lower classes. On the whole, we are becoming more effeminate, and labour more severely, *by which the mind is depressed, from the anxieties of life, and the difficulty of procuring a subsistence* [italics are mine].
    > *Analysis*, Op cit., Part First, 136.

47. It is beyond the scope of this book to explore in depth the fascinating story of the escape of medicine from the inherited dogma of its past. The exciting evolutionary and revolutionary changes reached a climax in the second half of the nineteenth century but these changes had started earlier. Below are a few examples of early and modern observations which cover this subject.

    William Pulteney Alison, M.D., 'Observations on the Epidemic Fever now prevalent among the lower orders in Edinburgh', *The Edinburgh Medical and Surgical Journal*, 1 October 1827.

    The Fourth Annual Report of the Poor Law Commissioners for England and Wales, London, 1838, Appendix (A.) No. 1, Supplement, No. 1. 'Report as to the removal of some Causes of Disease by Sanitary Regulations.'

    Neil Arnot, M.D. and James Phillips Kay, M.D.: Supplement, No. 2. 'Report on the cause of Sickness and Mortality among the Poor', Southwood Smith, M.D..

    The Fifth Annual Report, 1839, Appendix (C.) No. 2. 'Report on the Prevalence of Fever in the Metropolis', Southwood Smith, M.D..

    Reports on the Sanitary Conditions of the Labouring Population of Scotland, B.P.P., XXVIII (Lords), 1842

William Budd, *On the Causes of Fevers* (1839), Ed. Dale Smith, Baltimore, The Johns Hopkins Univ. Press, 1984.

Idem, *Typhoid Fever: Its Nature, Mode of Spreading and Prevention*, London, Longmans, Green, and Co., 1873.

John Snow, *On the Mode of Communication of Cholera*, 2nd enlarged edn., London, J. Churchill, 1855; reprinted Oxford Univ. Press, 1936.

William Farr, *Vital Statistics*, Ed. N.A. Humphreys, Sanitary Institute of Great Britain, 1885.

See also: *Vital Statistics: A Memorial Volume of Selections from the Reports and Writings of William Farr,* Introduction by Mervyn Susser and Abraham Adelstein, Metuchen, N.J., The Scarecrow Press, Inc., 1975.

Report of the Committee for Scientific Inquiries in Relation to the Cholera Epidemic of 1854. London, 1855, submitted by N. Arnot, William Baly, William Farr, Richard Owen and John Simon.

Report on the Last Two Cholera Epidemics of London as Affected by the Consumption of Impure Water, by the Medical Officer of Health of the General Board of Health, [John Simon] 1856, British Sessional Papers, House of Commons, 1856, LII, 300–399.

The following historians review this period of medical history in great detail:

James C. Riley, *The Eighteenth-Century Campaign to Avoid Disease*, New York, St Martin's Press, 1987.

Margaret DeLacy, 'Puerperal Fever in Eighteenth-Century Britain', *Bull Hist. Med*, 1989, 63, 521–556.

Margaret Pelling, *Cholera, Fever and English Medicine 1825– 1865,* Oxford Univ. Press, 1978.

R.J. Morris, *Cholera 1832: The Social Response to An Epidemic*, New York, Holmes & Meier Pubs., 1976.

Guenter B. Risse, *Hospital Life in Enlightenment Scotland: Care and Teaching at the Royal Infirmary of Edinburgh*, Cambridge, Univ. Press, 1986.

E.P. Hennock, 'Urban Sanitary Reform a Generation before Chadwick?' *The Economic History Review*, 2nd Ser., Vol. X, 113–120

R.A. Lewis, *Edwin Chadwick and the Public Health Movement 1832–1854*, London, Longmans, Green and Co., 1952.

48. O.S.A., XIX (Aberdeen), 193–5.

49. *Analysis*, Op cit., 138.

50. *First Detailed Annual Report of the Registrar General of Births Deaths and Marriages In Scotland,* B.P.P., 1861, XVIII. 257, xlii.
    This report reflects conditions present in 1855.

51. If by 'radical weakness' is implied a tubercular diathesis, or any other state or condition of a normal body, whereby it was especially liable to certain diseases, for example, as a result of a constitutional inability to resist tuberculous infection, the suggestion is contrary to the theme of this book

and the views of the author. Such an explanation for the cause of a disease process belongs to an age when ignorance was masked by pseudo-science. There is always a scientific explanation for disease, though it may as yet not have been discovered and confirmed. Disease, in the context of this book and of the conditions prevalent in the Highland lifestyle under study, was the result of faulty nutrition, a subsequently lowered resistance to pathogenic and opportunistic organisms and a flagrant disregard, that amounted at times to contempt, for the fundamentals of preventive medicine, especially as applied to the health of common people.

52. O.S.A.,VII (Abbey parish of Paisley), 76.

53. O.S.A., III (Loudoun), 107.

54. Thomas Ferguson, Op cit., 133.

55. The validity of that observation was driven home to the medical community when, in the first flush of the great antibiotic era, a type of penicillin was produced that would be selectively secreted in the respiratory system. This was an immediate success in helping to eradicate in the lungs pathogenic organisms that were hitherto resistant to treatment. Unfortunately, the profession had forgotten that the respiratory passages were also the home of some normal commensals; that is, agents which normally cause no trouble because they are kept in check by the dominant normal flora. Thus with the demise of the penicillin-sensitive pathogens, which most pathogenic organisms and normal commensals were when penicillin was first used, any penicillin-resistant organism present, particularly some of the fungi, would be allowed to flourish unchecked and possibly invade the host. This takeover presented a medical problem much greater than the original disease process. At that time, there existed no alternative antibiotics or other effective therapy against the dominant and resistant commensals other than the patient's own resistance to disease, which would be greatly weakened by the underlying primary disease.

56. *Analysis*, Op cit., 138–9.

57. *Analysis*, Op cit., 139.

58. Ibid., 139.

59. O.S.A.,V (Logierait), 84.

60. Mark Nathan Cohen, *Health & The Rise of Civilization*, Yale Univ. Press, New Haven, 1989, 108, 86, 123–4.

8

Eviction and Its Aftermath I

A physician is obligated to consider more than a diseased organ, more than the
whole man — he must view the man in his world.

— Harvey Cushing.[1]

MODERN MEDICAL SCIENCE allows us to interpret Sinclair's signs and
symptoms of disease as evidence of particular disease processes. It also
enables us to classify the diseases he reported as to general cause. In fact,
his seven most prevalent diseases, we now appreciate, fall under one or other
of the three principal classes of disease: Zoonotic, those caused by infected
animals or vermin; Nosocomial, those transported by infected persons; and
Iatrogenic, those induced by physicians or other care-givers. This chapter
revisits Sinclair's diseases, examining them as examples of one or other of
these classes. In our discussion of iatrogenic diseases, we will examine the
debate then current between advocates of therapeutic medicine and the
more radical proponents of the new preventive medicine.

I

We now appreciate that many of the diseases reported in the *Statistical
Accounts* as being the deadliest and most prevalent would have been
transmitted by infected animals and vermin, both of them commonplace
in post-eviction settlements.[2] Today, we classify those diseases as Zoonotic
diseases (the Zoonoses).[3]

Relocation to poorer agricultural land had a marked effect on the
nutrition and immunity of animals no less than of humans. The loss of
access to spring and summer pastures meant that inbye grazing was
insufficient and of such poor quality that by late autumn the livestock were
in no condition to withstand a Highland winter:

> They have many large Parcels of Ground never yet manur'd, which if cultivated,
> would maintain double the Number of the present Inhabitants, and increase
> and preserve their Cattle; many of which, for the want of Hay or Straw, die in
> the winter and Spring: so that I have known particular Persons Lose above one
> hundred Cows at a time, meerly by want of Fodder and had to be protected in
> the shelter.[4]

By springtime, the cattle that survived were standing in their own dung up to their udders. Contamination of cattle by their dung, coupled with their poor physical condition, soon led to a bovine mastitis, usually streptococcal in origin, which produced infected milk and put at risk any person imbibing it, especially those who had not acquired a natural immunity to the streptococcal organism.

As conditions worsened, Highland families were forced to take further nourishment from their cows by bleeding them and mixing the nutritious blood with meal to produce a *marag dhubh*, a blood or black pudding. The practice had long been resorted to in times of want, as Hugh Miller has noted:

> The practice was an ancient, and by no means unphilosophic one. In summer and early autumn there is plenty of grass in the Highlands; but, of old at least, there used to be very little grain in it before the beginning of October; and as the cattle could, in consequence, provide themselves with a competent supply of blood from the grass, when their masters, who could not eat grass and had little else that they could eat, were able to acquire very little, it was opportunely discovered that, by making a division in this way of the all-essential fluid, accumulated as a common stock, the circumstances of the cattle and owners could be in some way equalized.[5]

But bleeding cows further weakened them.[6] In some lean years, the cattle that survived were so weak that they had to be carried out to spring pasture.[7] Thus weakened, they were prey to disease. Tuberculous cows produced contaminated milk, which at a time when pasteurisation was still unknown, led to diseases such as scrofula and 'consumption' and put the health of other animals and the household at risk.[8]

Dairy produce could also be infected by disease-carrying milkers and food handlers. As early as the mid-eighteenth century, Dr Tobias Smollett (1721–71) vividly described in his *Humphry Clinker* some of the possible contaminants of milk.[9] The ingestion of raw, unpasteurised milk and dairy products made from such milk exposed Highlanders to a number of other diseases as well. Typhoid and para-typhoid fevers, bacillary dysentery, scarlet fever, and septic sore throat are all milk-borne and were all reported as being present in the Highlands.[10] Raw milk has also been linked to the spread of diphtheria (Sinclair's croup or *cynanche trachealis*).[11]

The organism of undulant fever (brucellosis) is likewise transmitted by ingestion of raw milk and dairy products. In the Highlands, the main reservoir of this disease was cattle and swine, but we now know that sheep and goats can also be infected. Before the introduction of the large sheep walks, cattle and goat rearing had played a large part in the economy of the Highlands.[12] It is reasonable to assume, therefore, that some animals would have been infected with brucellosis. In fact, brucellosis would have become, as it is today, an occupational disease for those working with infected animals, and with their hides, tissues, blood and urine, vaginal discharges, aborted foetuses and placentas. Infection could have occurred through breaks in the skin – in Highlanders, and in Southern drovers, slaughter-house workers, butchers and tanners. Animals in pens, stables and abattoirs may also have become infected as a result of airborne infection.[13]

Because diseases were classified according to their salient symptoms, cases of what we now know to be brucellosis might well have been treated and reported variously as fever, consumption, rheums, influenza or the ague. For example, in April 1881, an outbreak of epidemic disease occurred in Aberdeen in north-east Scotland which was apparently milk-borne. Many of the signs and symptoms reported in that incident are similar to those of undulant fever, or brucellosis.[14]

In overcrowded settlements, shelters were generally shared with other animals.[15] Poultry were fed off the earth floor; they roosted wherever they could; and they spread their droppings everywhere. The earth floor of the Highland shelter was, therefore, well inoculated with a variety of organisms from the discharges of all the occupants and, depending on the drainage of the site, from the discharge of adjacent houses as well. Some of these organisms would not remain alive for long. Others could survive the most adverse conditions. It was on this same earth floor, or very near it, that Highlanders were born. One killing disease known as 'fifth night epilepsy' or 'eighth day fever' was caused by the spore-bearing tetanus bacillus, a normal commensal of the intestinal tract of man and animals ubiquitous in all manured soils – including the floor of a Highland house. The spores were transmitted during the ritual dressing of the umbilical stump of a newborn with soil from the floor or with other dressings equally contaminated, such as butter or fulmar oil.[16] What is more, Pennant recorded that in the Highlands, 'Midwives give newborn babes a small spoonful of earth and whisky, as the first food they taste.'[17] When those practices were banned or declined naturally, the mortality rate decreased.

We reiterate that these conditions had obtained in Highlanders' traditional settlements as well. There, however, families and their animals were better nourished and more naturally immune to disease. After the Clearances, subsistence was threatened, immunity weakened and over-crowding made more severe. Thus contamination was much more often fatal.

Another disease of farm animals, anthrax, is caused by the *Bacillus anthracis* and is spread to humans through contact with the tissues of diseased animals or by the inhalation of spores from diseased tissue. The disease is also known as malignant pustule, malignant oedema, woolsorters' disease, and ragpickers' disease. Benenson describes how anthrax is spread:

> Infection of the skin is by contact with tissues of animals (cattle, sheep, goats, horses, pigs and others) dying of the disease and possibly by biting flies which had partially fed on such animals; or contaminated hair, wool, hides, or products made from them such as drums, brushes, etc; and soil associated with infected animals. Inhalation anthrax arises from ingestion of contaminated undercooked meat; there is no evidence that milk from infected animals transmits anthrax.[18]

From what we now know about the mode of transmission, the lesions and the symptomatology of anthrax, we must suspect that anthrax too occurred in the Highlands. Without immediate and specific treatment of man and animal, and without efficient disposal of the infected carcass and fomites, an epidemic with many fatalities can develop. Since neither treatment nor disposal were possible in the nineteenth century, many of the epidemics of rapidly fatal cutaneous and systemic diseases and malignant fevers reported in the Highlands could well have been cases of anthrax.[19]

Animal products, animal handling and animal droppings were all sources of contamination and disease for Highlanders. Animal parasites were another source. In fact, animal parasites figure inevitably in zoonosis since they are to be found in every animal, including man. The occurrence of parasites among Highlanders is well documented in the accounts of travellers and parish ministers. Worm infestation, for instance, was common.[20] The practice in the Highlands of collecting the excrement produced by all occupants of the black house for use as spring fertiliser would ensure infestation. Martin Martin and Thomas Tennant recorded the Highland practice of removing 'worms' from under the skin.[21] It is difficult to classify those worms from the writers' descriptions, but their presence probably represented some form of myiasis, a condition in which certain flies deposit their eggs on wounds or on the mucous membranes of cattle, sheep and man. The larval stage, the maggot, crawls under the skin, eating the subcutaneous tissue and causing discomfort and eventual suppuration of the site.[22]

Donaldson's description of the worm infestation in man suggests that the worms which Martin Martin and others referred to were indeed a form of myiasis:

> In cattle an upward migration [of the worm] brings it to the back, but in man may bring it into the head. A warble forming on the shoulders or head external to the skull is unpleasant enough, but a larva trapped in the skull cavities can cause death.[23]

Another animal parasite, the sheep tick or ked, commonly attaches itself to the skin of dogs and shepherds, though that attachment is not followed by any serious symptomatology. In 1982, however, a spirochaete, *Borrelia burgdorferi*, was first identified as the causal agent of Lyme disease. The disease is a tick-borne zoonotic disease found in Europe and Great Britain. This finding means that ticks may also have been a source of many diseases reported a century or more ago in the Highlands. In Lyme disease, the tick is carried on wild deer, the deer being the reservoir of the parasite. Anyone walking in a deer habitat that is also the area of distribution of the tick is at risk of becoming infected during the summer months.[24]

Besides Lyme disease, Highlanders would have been exposed to various skin diseases, such as the different forms of ringworm, caused by fungi. These diseases can also be transferred from livestock to humans.

Overcrowding and poor sanitation exposed Highlanders to diseases from another group of animals, the vermin that over-ran their settlements. The vermin most commonly associated with the human population of the eighteenth and nineteenth centuries, and by inference with their domestic animals, were mites, lice, fleas, bed bugs and flies. The larger vermin, rats and mice, besides transmitting disease, also competed with the human population for food.

Among the diseases that affect human migrations, typhus fever is prominent. And in typhus fever, vermin are the cause. Typhus is caused by the organism *Rickettsia prowazekii*, which is transmitted by a typhus-infected louse. When the louse bites the new host, it defaecates. The germ-carrying faeces are rubbed into the wound when the host scratches the bite. Benenson notes that infected lice tended to leave abnormally hot or cold bodies in search of a normothermic, clothed body, a finding particularly significant in the crowded huts and slums that Highlanders occupied at home and in the crowded holds of many of the emigrant ships they sailed in overseas. The infected lice would in these conditions spread typhus by moving from febrile sick to healthy and better-clothed humans.

The fatality rate from typhus fever increased with age, the mortality among adults varying from ten to forty per cent.[25] In short, in an age when smallpox was the primary killer of children, typhus was the principal killer of their parents.[26] (This fact stimulated the interest of the Establishment, since the number of orphans that typhus produced increased their Poor Law contributions.)

One attack of typhus usually confers a lasting, active immunity but mild infection may occur without the classical skin eruption, especially in children and in persons protected by partial immunity.[27] In other words, the disease may be present in a community or be carried into it as an undiagnosed or wrongly diagnosed subclinical infection. This fact is of great significance in understanding the cause of the many epidemics that raged through the catchment areas for Highland migration, and through many emigrant ships. Classical or louse-borne typhus fever is one of a group of Rickettsial diseases. In some diseases of this group, the organism is borne by fleas, in others by mites. Louse-borne typhus was once diagnosed as spotted typhus, common fever, continued fever, jail-fever, ship-fever, *enteric fever*, and, wrongly, as relapsing fever. (Relapsing fever can be tick or louse borne, although among Highlanders, the vector was more likely to have been the louse and the infectious agent to be the spirochaete *Borrelia recurrentis.*[28]) In all forms of the Rickettsial fevers, overcrowding is the common causal factor.

Other vermin, mites, were responsible for various skin diseases among Highlanders. The association between skin diseases and poor personal hygiene was noted by observers in Scotland in the eighteenth and nineteenth centuries.[29] Skin infections, particularly erysipelas (a streptococcal infection), were common.[30] The 'itch' or scabies was also widespread, infecting the well-to-do as well as the poor.[31] Scabies is caused by the mite *Sarcoptes scabiei.*[32] Burt commented on the prevalence of this disease among Highland children:

> But what seems to be the worst of all, is, they are over-run with the Itch, which continues upon them from Year to Year, without any Care taken to free them from that loathsome Distemper. Nor indeed is it possible to keep them long from it, except all could agree, it is so universal among them. And as the Children of People in better Circumstances are not nice in the Choice of their Companions and Play-fellows, they are most of them likewise infected with this disease.[33]

The minister of Kilmalie presented an interesting explanation for the 'itch':

> The *itch*, which has been computed, as a disgrace, to this quarter of the island, is but rarely seen now, even among the lower classes of the people. This, doubtless, is owing to their living in a more cleanly manner than their forefathers. But this distemper is not peculiar to a Highlander, – nor to a Scotch-man. It is a *plant* which grows in countries south of the Tweed, else there would be no word to express it in the *English* tongue; and it is well known to have been one of the plagues incident to the Egyptians.[Deut. xxviii][34]

II

The zoonotic diseases, those transferred to Highlanders from their animals, particularly during the overcrowding caused by the Clearances, overlap with a second group of diseases, the nosocomial, to which Highlanders were also increasingly subject after their relocation:

> Nosocomial infection is an infection occurring in a patient in a hospital or *other health care facility* [italics are mine] and in whom it was not present or incubating at the time of admission, or the residual of an infection acquired during a previous admission. [The nosocomial group] includes infections acquired in the hospital but appearing after discharge, and also such infections among the staff and visitors of the facility.[35]

The principle of nosocomial infection was clearly recognized by many reporters in the *Statistical Accounts*. They noted two major causes for the spread of disease. The first was the common habit of visiting the sick on a Sunday – the Sabbath and therefore a day when no work was done – to 'administer comfort to the distressed'.[36] Hospitals were then unknown in the Highlands and Islands: the primary care facilities were Highlanders' houses. In them, an unfortunate patient had to compete with his well-wishers for the oxygen that was always in short supply in smoke-filled shelters.[37] What is more, if a visitor was in the infective stage of an infectious disease or was a carrier of such a disease, cross-infection to the already weakened patient often proved fatal, especially if the patient was young or elderly. A typical example of cross-infection was smallpox aggravated by a superimposed chin cough in a child.[38]

The second and more obvious cause for the spread of nosocomial disease was from infection by the patient of the other inmates of the house. The outcome of this nosocomial infection depended on whether the disease was endemic, or one recently brought in to the locality, one to which the community had developed little or no resistance. In other words, it depended on the strength and pattern of the herd immunity of the contacts. There was danger too during the Sunday visitation from the free exchange of vermin among the inmates and visitors, a factor that Sinclair does not stress.[39]

In settings like the Sunday visits, nosocomial diseases gave rise to many epidemics of infectious diseases, particularly in children and the weak. Such epidemics were triggered by 'alien' visitors. After the battle of Culloden, the rate of acculturation increased, thus so did the number of visitors and the incidence of new disease. As it did among Highlanders who left the Highlands and Islands for the towns and cities of the south. Among them, the morbidity and mortality rates of communicable diseases soared. In 1861, in his *First Detailed Annual Report*, the Registrar-General of Scotland noted 'that of the classes of disease . . . the most fatal in Scotland was the Zymotic, or Epidemic and Contagious, Class.' Of this class, the diseases causing most deaths were typhus fever, scarlatina, whooping cough, diarrhoea, smallpox and measles.[40] The zymotic diseases include many that Sinclair had grouped as 'fevers' and identified as the fourth most prevalent group of disease. By 1885, they had displaced smallpox as the most prevalent disease. In his *First Report*, the Registrar noted too that diarrhoea had killed 1320 persons in that year, an incidence that implicated the overcrowding and poor sanitation that had become so common by that date.

III

A third kind of disease, iatrogenic, or physician-induced disease, also contributed to the prevalence of many diseases in Sinclair's index. Traditionally, Highland medicine was folk medicine administered by the people themselves.[41] In many districts, however (and later in the Highland settlements of Cape Breton Island), the services of a 'specialist' folk-healer or natural physician were also used when they were available.[42] In fact, in traditional Celtic culture, such specialisation was common and the healer's skills and appointments were hereditary. The Beaton family were a case in point. By the eighteenth century, however, most educated families and most clergymen, particularly in the Lowlands, had a well-thumbed copy of some popular home medical guide.[43] One very popular guide book was *Domestic Medicine* by Dr William Buchan. First published in 1769, it ran for twenty-one editions.[44] It had a large circulation, not only in Britain but on the European continent and in North America as well. The numerous recommendations of contributors to the *Statistical Accounts*, such as that lay people, specifically the clergy, be instructed in the methods of inoculation against smallpox, imply that *Domestic Medicine* or a similar guidebook was a prominent feature of many manses throughout Scotland.[45] Buchan recognised the role played by what we now term nosocomial diseases and warned against the danger of visiting the sick and attending wakes.[46] He also recognized that simple sanitation, like ensuring that every house had a dry floor, was apt to be more effective than much of the medical treatment then available. One writer recalled Buchan's practicality:

> Dr Buchan, author of the *Family Physician*, had occasion to be in this part of the country some years ago, when he very judiciously remarked, that every man's house was built upon a rock, meaning, that every man had a dry gravellish

stance whereon to found his house; which, the Doctor observed, is more conducive to health, than all the benefits that result from medicine.[47]

Buchan noted too that in the eighteenth century, 'almost one half of the human species perished in infancy, by improper management or neglect.' Appropriately, he devoted the first part of his book to discussing the diseases of children.[48] Elsewhere, he gave valuable and timely advice regarding the regulation of lifestyles and personal hygiene.[49] For instance, he vigorously denounced alcoholism, which by the eighteenth century had become a disease of major social and economic proportions.[50]

With his emphasis on hygiene and sanitation, Buchan typified the new medical radicals and free thinkers. Unlike Establishment physicians, who sought simply to treat disease, Buchan and other radicals wanted also to prevent disease. Buchan's insight into the importance of preventive medicine was uncanny:

> The cure of disease is doubtless a matter of great importance; but the preservation of health is still greater. This is the concern of every man, . . . it is not to be supposed, that men can be sufficiently upon their guard against diseases, who are totally ignorant of their causes. Neither can the legislature, in whose power it is to do much more for preserving the public health than can ever be done by the Faculty, exert that power with propriety and to the greatest advantage without some degree of medical knowledge.[51]

Again, observing that prevention is better than cure, Buchan made this plea:

> To guard the poor against the inference of these prejudices, and to instill into their minds some just ideas of the importance of proper food, fresh air, cleanliness, and other pieces of regimen necessary in disease, would be a work of great merit, and productive of many happy consequences.[52]

Guided by medical manuals like Buchan's, much lay medicine, though not scientific, was at least for the most part innocuous. Not so the medicine of the licensed practitioners of the eighteenth and early nineteenth centuries. The profession's treatment of uninoculated cases of smallpox, for example, contributed to the high mortality rate among children:

> Much mischief is done at this period [the eruptive fever stage] by confining the patient too soon to his bed, and plying him with warm cordials or sudorific medicines [the common medical treatments]. Everything that heats and inflames the blood increases the fever, and pushes out the pustules prematurely. This has a number of ill effects . . . Sweating never relieves unless where it comes spontaneously, or is the effect of drinking weak diluting liquors.[53]

And because their hands and clothes were often contaminated, physicians themselves contributed to the spread of disease.[54] Not surprisingly, records of the period express a general preference for the services of the natural physician or quack over those of the 'qualified' doctor.[55] Even where their action did not actually cause disease, Establishment physicians intimidated others from offering simple but effective care of the sick. Here is Buchan again, this time on the mystique cultivated by qualified physicians:

> The benefits of Medicine as a trade, will ever be confined to those who are able to pay for them, and of course the far greater part of mankind will be every where deprived of them. Physicians, like other people must live by their employment, and the poor must either want advice altogether, or take up with that which is worse than none. There are not, however, any where wanting well-disposed people, of better sense; who are willing to supply the defect of medical advice to the poor, did not their fear of doing ill often suppress their inclination to do good. Such people are often deterred from the most noble and praise-worthy actions, by the foolish alarms sounded in their ears by a set of men, who, to raise their own importance, magnify the difficulties of doing good, find fault with what is truly commendable, and sleer at every attempt to relieve the sick which is not conducted by the precise rules of medicine.[56]

Indeed, Establishment practice, self-serving and convention-bound as it was, did contribute to disease among evicted Highlanders. Just as surely, it delayed medical reform. During the eighteenth century, the medical Establishment in Scotland, England and elsewhere was dominated by the medical school of the University of Edinburgh and the personality and teachings of its Professor of Medicine, William Cullen (1710–1790).[57] Cullen, a brilliant teacher and experimenter, had held the Chair of Chemistry at Edinburgh before becoming professor of the Institutes of Medicine. His new 'heroic medicine' shaped the practice of medicine not only in Scotland and Britain; it became the standard as well in Nova Scotia because of the presence there of graduates of Scottish and Irish medical schools. Graduates from American schools practising in Nova Scotia were influenced by the teachings of Cullen's North American pupil and friend, Dr Benjamin Rush (1745–1813).[58]

Cullen's 'heroic' approach to medicine was aggressively interventionist. Particularly pertinent to our discussion was his disregard for the curative power of nature, one of the fundamentals of 'unqualified' Highland medical practice. His treatment consisted instead of aggressive therapeutic assault on the disease process, by medical procedures and by heavy, if not toxic, doses of the medicines then commonly used, particularly mercury in all its forms:

> Remedies such as calomel, antimony, emetics, purgatives, opiates as well as bleeding, etc., although previously employed with some restriction, suddenly became more frequently used, and with more abandon.[59]

Cullen urged that medical and surgical procedures be pursued fearlessly. If a patient required to be bled, then he or she should be bled frequently. This fearless, 'heroic' approach catapulted late eighteenth-century medicine out of an era of folk medicine into the modern period of allopathic medicine.

But heroic therapy probably killed more patients than had the initial disease.[60] William Cobbett called heroic medicine, 'one of the greatest discoveries . . . which have contributed to the depopulation of the earth.'[61] And a Cape Breton doctor, writing about the medical pioneers of nineteenth-century Cape Breton Island, saw a connection between the practice of established medicine and the incidence of disease:

> It is a remarkable fact that the more doctors that exist in any community, the more their services are in demand, and the more people seem to suffer the ills that flesh is heir to.[62]

Nonetheless, among Establishment physicians, the therapeutic approach reigned supreme. They knew what it would take to alleviate the distress of the poor, yet very few echoed Buchan's plea for prevention. Establishment physicians, no less than parish ministers, were in effect 'lairds' men.' In fact, during the British cholera epidemics of the nineteenth century, it was not uncommon for Establishment doctors to falsify the cause of death, or 'to have areas declared safe before the epidemic had actually ended.'[63]

IV

To this point, we have used the three primary classifications of diseases in order to examine the underlying causes of the diseases in Sinclair's index. One other condition prevalent at the time, diarrhoea, defies assignment to any of those three classes. Diarrhoea is not a disease; rather it is simply a sign of several disease processes and it may, therefore, be associated with zoonotic, nosocomial and iatrogenic infections. By the 1850s, the number of deaths caused by diarrhoea had risen dramatically. The Registrar-General of Scotland wrote that 'No disease exhibited more strongly the influence of site on [its] prevalence and fatality than diarrhoea.'[64] During the second quarter of the nineteenth century, the most feared of the diarrhoeas was cholera. In fact, cholera focused the British Establishment's attention on the conditions of the poor and forced it to adopt poor law reform and public health legislation. Those topics we will take up in the next chapter. Here we will examine the aetiology of cholera. We should say that Sinclair does not mention cholera, but only because his *Analysis* was not published until 1825, seven years before the outbreak of the cholera morbus epidemic.

When it descended, cholera was one of the most feared diseases of the century. Cholera is an acute bacterial enteric infection with a sudden onset. The portals of entry and exit are respectively the upper and lower alimentary tract. With cholera, as with all communicable disease, the clinical response depends on the virulence of the organism and the resistance of the host. Clinically, this can translate into a mortality rate of 50 per cent or greater within a few hours of infection, or merely to a mild diarrhoea followed by full recovery. It is the degree of this intestinal hurry or diarrhoea, the so-called rice water stools of the severe cases, that kills or endangers the patient's life. The rapid loss of body fluid and the accompanying loss of minerals and other nutrients lead to dehydration and circulatory collapse.

As with other infectious diseases, the carrier state of cholera presents most danger to a community. Asymptomatic carriers excrete the organisms in their faeces. During this period of faecal excretion, which lasts for a few days until the recovery stage, sufferers are highly contagious, and their vomitus as well as their faeces can contaminate water, food and hands.

The cholera epidemics in South Britain terrified the Highlands. William MacGregor reported, 28th February, 1832, the preparations made on the Isle of Lewis to offset the ravages of the expected cholera epidemic. His report noted the poverty and disease among the people and their want of clothes and bedding:

> I am sorry to say, when I examined their houses that I find the one half of the people from Caroloway to Eoropie are all ill for want of Blankets as the few I mentioned in the list, so that it is impossible to supply their wants. In most of their houses, there is nothing in the shape of bedding to be seen except one old Blanket and an old Covering, and 5 or 6 of a Family lying under that in one bed, and some of them have none at all, but the generality of them might have been better off if they had an inclination to be so; they were ever careless regarding any sort of cleanliness, so that it is to be feared if the cholera comes among us that it will make a sad sweep on this coast, so far from medical aid or any other assistance, but the Lord is merciful and may show his kindness to the poor people here and not visit them with such an awful Visitation.
>
> We had some meetings in the Parish for the purpose of promoting Cleanliness among the people. We got them all to build partitions between themselves and the Cattle.[65]

Mr MacGregor's prayers were answered. Cholera did not visit the West Highlands and Islands, largely because of their remoteness. Cholera did, however, reach the towns of Helmsdale and Thurso (25th and 30th July, 1832 respectively) on the extreme north-east coast of Scotland, probably initially via a vessel carrying coal or lime from Sunderland in the north-east of England to Dingwall.[66]

The Highlands and Islands were indeed blessed. Historical documents do not record a cholera epidemic there, although several writers, perhaps to dramatise the suffering of the people during the potato famines and the Clearances, describe devastation by what they call cholera. Had the disease indeed reached the area, the mortality rate would have been staggering, given Highlanders' destitution and their defencelessness against alien disease.

Although cholera was not its cause, diarrhoea was nonetheless widespread in the Highlands. Diarrhoea can kill, not only by the action of the pathogen but because of dehydration and the loss of salts and other nutrients. Among the starving rural poor of the potato famines, the mortality rate from diarrhoea; that is, from loss of fluid and nutriment, climbed inexorably. Diarrhoea killed 1320 persons in 1855 alone:

> This was very nearly the same mortality as that of Small-pox; being in the proportion of 48 Deaths in every hundred thousand persons. No disease exhibited more strongly the influence of site on its prevalence and fatality than Diarrhoea; for, while the Insular Districts only furnished 17 Deaths in every hundred thousand persons, the Mainland Districts yielded 34 Deaths, and the Town Districts 75 Deaths, in like populations.[67]

Diarrhoea can result when the alimentary tract ingests something that does not agree with it. During periods of starvation, such as the Clearances made common, Highlanders searched the seashores and land for anything thought to be edible – seaweed and shellfish, plants, roots and rotten potatoes. Diarrhoea and its complications would certainly have been the products of such a diet.[68]

Modern medical knowledge allows us to classify Sinclair's most prevalent diseases as Zoonotic, Nosocomial or Iatrogenic. Whatever their classification, Highlanders' diseases were the direct result of the poverty and malnutrition that the Clearances brought, and in some instances, of Establishment medical practice itself.

Notes

1. Quoted by René Dubos in *Man Adapting*, enlarged edition, New Haven, Yale University Press, 1980, 342.

2. O.S.A.,V (Logierait), 82–5.
    N.S.A., XIV (Kilmuir), 252, 254.: (Duirinish), 348.
    William MacKenzie, *Gaelic Incantations, Charms and Blessings of the Hebrides*, Inverness, The Northern Counties Newspaper & Printing, 1895, 53–86.
    Alexander Polson, *Our Highland Folklore Heritage*, Dingwall, George Souter, 1926, 25–144.

3. John C. Bell, Stephen R. Palmer, and Jack M. Payne, *The Zoonoses: Infections Transmitted from Animals to Man,* London, Edward Arnold, 1988, ix.
    This book provides the reader with the current zoonoses with which the modern crofter has to contend and it suggests the cause of many of the diseases reported during the eighteenth and nineteenth centuries.

4. Martin Martin, *A Description of the Western Islands of Scotland* (circa 1695), 2nd edn., reprinted Edinburgh, James Thin, 1970, 337.

5. Hugh Miller, *My Schools and Schoolmasters*, Edinburgh, W.P. Nimmo, Hay & Mitchell, 1886, 104.

6. O.S.A., XIII (North Uist), 306.
    N.S.A., XIV (Kilmuir), 271.

7. Edward Burt, *Letters From a Gentleman in the North of Scotland to His Friend in London* (circa 1720–30), 2 vols., 2nd edn., London, II, 123.

8. Charles-Edward Amory Winslow, *The Conquest Of Epidemic Disease*, Wisconsin, Univ. Press, 1980, 309–10.

9. Tobias Smollett, *Humphry Clinker*, New York, Signet Classics, 1960, 128.

10. These diseases and at times their association with the ingestion of milk, were reported throughout Scotland:
    O.S.A., III (Durness), 582.;VI (North Knapdale), 259.;
    V (Cruden), 434.; X (Tiry), 403.; XVII (Small Isles), 279.;V (Inveraray), 289–290.

11. Abram Benenson, Ed., *Control of Communicable Diseases In Man*, 16th edn., Washington, D.C., The American public Health Association, 1995, 153.
    Raw milk was cited as a source of infection for bovine tuberculosis in twentieth-century Toronto:
    . . . where 99.8 percent of the milk used in this city was pasteurised, 300 children were examined for evidence of bovine tuberculosis; 45, all from outside the city, were found to be suffering from the disease; the remaining 255 were free, being Toronto bred.

J.R. Currie and A.G. Mearns, *Hygiene*, 2nd, edn., Edinburgh, Livingstone, 1945, 161.

12. Malcolm Gray, *The Highland Economy 1750–1850*, Edinburgh, Oliver and Boyd, 1957, 36–7.

13. Benenson, Op cit., 71–4.

    Benenson also states that the reported incidence of brucellosis in the USA is less than 120 cases annually but that, world wide, the disease is often unrecognised and unreported.

    In the Highlands today, a control scheme, often with a slaughter policy, especially for cattle suspected of infection, is in place.

14. Thomas Ferguson, *Scottish Social Welfare 1864–1914*, Edinburgh, E. & S. Livingstone, 1958, 398–9.

    This epidemic resembled influenza in some of its features. The patient usually had been in good health and the first marked symptoms were related to the upper alimentary tract and were suggestive of poisoning. Later the temperature would rise to 105 degrees and was associated with a fullness of the throat attended by pain and stiffness at the angle of the jaw. The lymph glands of the neck showed a marked enlargement and many suppurated. In severe cases delirium accompanied the fever. The attack lasted 24 to 48 hours. Then after a period of apparent recovery, the weakened patient was stricken by a series of similar episodes, often five or six in number. In other cases, scattered abscesses were observed in the neighbourhood of the joints.

15. As late as 1905, a reporter noted that in a district in Lewis, which included the township of Arnol, 'cattle-housing was the almost invariable rule': and when, as usual, the houses were built side by side, the fluid from the heaped manure in the byre of one house percolated into the sleeping quarters of the next . . . In one house, which was just one large room, they found nine people – of whom one, the wage earner, was dying of phthisis – three cows standing above their knees in about four to five feet of manure, a sheep that had evidently just lambed, and a number of fowls.

    The Report of the Sanitary Conditions of the Lews, 1905, B.P.P., XXXIV, 767.

16. O.S.A., VI (Kilchrenan and Dalavich), 272. Idem., VIII (Kilbride in Arran), 579. IX (Kilmory), 166. XIV (Killbrandon and Killchattan), 160,–1. XIX (Stornoway), 250.; (Barray), 265.; (Uig), 281.

    Tom Steele, *The Life and Death of St Kilda*, Glasgow, Fontana Books, 1975, 50–5.

17. Thomas Pennant, *A Tour of Scotland in 1769*, 3rd edn., 1774, Reprinted, Perth, Melven Press, 1979, 101.

    This custom may have had some merit. In certain cases the brandy would act as a stimulant. The earth would, during the first few weeks of life, also enhance the accumulation in the alimentary tract of a variety of organisms (commensals) essential for the proper functioning of the digestive system of the infant.

18. Benenson, Op cit., 18–22.

19. Anthrax, along with other virulent pathogens, was developed in the mid-
    twentieth century as an agent for biological warfare. A small island lying off
    Gairloch, on the West coast of Scotland, was experimentally seeded with
    anthrax spores after World War II. Only in the late 1980s was the island
    considered safe enough to be re-opened to humans and animals.

20. Martin Martin, Op cit., 175, 179.
    O.S.A. IX (Dron), 468 n.

21. Martin Martin, Op cit., 41, 186, 191–2.
    Thomas Pennant, *A Tour in Scotland and Voyage to the Hebrides* 1772, 2 Vols.,
    Chester, 1774, I, 215.
    Walker also reported that:
    > in the Island of Jura, the Cripples are remarkably numerous; owing to
    > a very singular Disease with which this Island is peculiarly infected.
    > This disease arises from a Worm lodged under the Skin, that penetrates
    > with exquisite pain, the interior parts of the Limbs. It is termed in
    > the Galic Language, Fillun [Fillean, Fiollan fionn], and is Generally
    > lodged either in the Knees or Ancles.
    The Revd John Walker's *Report on the Hebrides of 1764 and 1771*, Ed.,
    Margaret M. McKay, Edinburgh, John Donald, 1980, 115–6, 238.

22. In Britain, the Ministry of Agriculture, Fisheries and Food (MAFF) are now
    conducting an intensive campaign against the warble fly. They have issued
    an URGENT!! WARBLE ALERT pamphlet advising cattle owners of a possible
    resurgence of warble fly infestation and cattle importers to be especially
    vigilant for signs of the disease. The six stages of the life cycle of the warble
    fly are:

    Stage 1. During the months of May to September, each female lays up to
    600 eggs on the leg hairs of cattle.
    Stage 2. Larvae hatch from the eggs within four to five days.
    Stage 3. They burrow through the animal's body to reach the gullet wall
    where they lie dormant from December to February.
    Stage 4. February to July — The larvae burrow further to reach the
    animal's back where they remain under the skin for about 10 weeks and
    form increasingly obvious swellings.
    Stage 5. March to July — The larvae emerge and fall to the ground where
    they pupate.
    Stage 6. The pupae remain on the ground from three to five weeks, after
    which the adult fly emerges to begin the cycle again.
    MAFF, 1995, PB 2164.
    While the above warning is concerned with warble fly infestation in
    animals, myiases can occur in humans:
    > Human myiases occur among rural populations, especially where and
    > when there is a great abundance of *C. hominivorax* flies, whose reproduction

depends mainly on domestic animal hosts. As a result, when myiases are abundant in animals, many cases can occur in man. Human myiasis is clinically similar to that of animals. In addition to the invasion of wounds and ulcers (varicose ulcers of the legs), myiasis also occurs in a furuncular form, characterized by a nonmigratory cutaneous nodule. Most myiasis of the natural cavities are also due to larvae of *C. hominivorax*. Invasion of the nasal fossae (rhinomyiasis) is the most frequent . . . To prevent invasion by *C. hominivorax* larvae — the principal myiasis in the Americas — parturition in domestic animals should not coincide with the season when flies are abundant. The navel of animals born during the hot season should be treated with repellant preparations. During such seasons, castration, dehorning, docking, branding, or other operations that leave tegumentary lesions should be avoided. All accidental wounds, whether affected by myiases or not, should be cleaned and adequately treated as soon as possible and covered with an insecticidal preparation.

Pedro N. Acha, Boris Szyfres, *Zoonoses and Communicable Diseases Common to Man and Animals*, 2nd edn., Scientific Pub., No. 503, WHO, Washington D.C., 1987, 867–8.

23. R.J. Donaldson, Ed., *Parasites in Western Man*, London, M.T.P. Press Ltd., 1979, 28.

24. Benenson, Op cit., 275-9.

25. Ibid., 508–9.

26. J.H.F. Brotherston, *Observations on the Early Public Health Movement in Scotland*, London, H. K. Lewis, 1952, 42.

27. Benenson, Op cit., 508.
28. Benenson, Ibid., 392-5.

Thomas Ferguson,(1948), Op cit., 122. See also: Hans Zinsser, *Rats, Lice And History*, New York, Blue Ribbon Books Inc., 1935, 233–5. For further information on the differentiation of the two diseases in the first half of the nineteenth century, and particularly on the work of the Glasgow school see: Archibald L. Goodall. 'Glasgow's Place in the Distinction Between Typhoid and Typhus Fevers', *Bulletin of the History of Medicine*, 1954, xxviii, 140–153.

It is noteworthy that in America in the first decade of the twentieth century, the true aetiology of typhus fever was unknown:

It is not positively known at the present time whether there is an infecting organism. The contagion is conveyed by inhalation of the breath, of exhalations from the skin, or infected dust from arm or of the infection from fomites. [but see Benenson, 426. on the viability of the organism in the body of the dead louse.]

'Typhus Fever', *The Encyclopedia Americana*, New York, The American Co., 1904, XV.

A preceding entry, however, under Typhoid Fever was more enlightened. Not only did it identify the causal organism, but acknowledged the association of the disease with poor sanitation and personal habits.

In Britain, the two diseases were reported for statistical purposes as one disease until 1929.

Michael Flinn et al., *Scottish Population History From the 17th Century to the 1930s*, Cambridge, Univ. Press, 1977, 388.

29. N.S.A., XIV (Duirinish), 326.

William Buchan, *Domestic Medicine*, 3rd edn., London, Printed for W. Strahan, T. Cadell, 1774, 107.

30. O.S.A., XIX (Uig), 181.; XVII (Small Isles), 279.

N.S.A., VII (Ardnamurchan), 132.; XIV (Kilmuir), 244, 254.; (Duirinish), 326.

Guenter B. Risse, *Hospital Life in Enlightenment Scotland*, Cambridge Univ. press., 1986, 159–162.

The *WHO's International Classification of Disease* (I.C.D.) now groups as 'Streptococcal Diseases' streptococcal sore throat, scarlet fever, impetigo, erysipelas (St Anthony's fire) and puerperal fever (metria or child bed fever).

31. George Low, *A Tour Through the Islands of Orkney and Shetland*, Kirkwall, William Peace and Son, 1879, 194.

David Hamilton, *The Healers, A History of Medicine in Scotland*, Edinburgh, Cannongate, 1987, 34–5.

See also: John I. Chalmers. 'Notice of Patrick Chalmers, M.D., of Haselhead and Fedderat, Professor of Medicine in Aberdeen . . .', *Proceedings of the Society of Antiquaries of Scotland*, 1863, 138, 161.

32. Benenson, Op cit., 415.

33. Burt, Op cit., I, 110.

34. O.S.A., VIII (Kilmalie), 409–410.

35. Benenson, Op cit., 541.

36. O.S.A., XIV (Kilfinan), 234–5. Idem., IV (Dunbarton) 21–2. Idem., X (Saline), 314.

Buchan, Op cit., 114–7.

37. N.S.A., XIV (Snizort), 292.

38. Analysis, 127.

39. Writing during the same period, Robert Burns was aware of the ubiquitous louse:

Ye ugly, creeping, blastit wonner,

Detested, shunn'd by saunt an' sinner,

'To A Louse: On seeing one on a lady's bonnet at church'.

Poetic Works of Robert Burns, Edinburgh, W.R. Chambers, Ltd., 1908, 150–1.

40. *First Detailed Report of the Registrar General of Births Deaths and Marriages in Scotland*, 1861 (hereafter First Report of the Registrar General), B.P.P., 1861, XVIII.257, xxxii–xxxviii.

This Report is compiled from statistics collected in 1855.

41. Hamilton, Op cit., 34–5.

Pennant, Op cit., 27 293.

George Menary, *Duncan Forbes of Culloden*, London, Alexander Maclehose & Co., 1936, 186.

42. M.D. Morrison, 'The Medical Pioneers of Cape Breton', *Nova Scotia Medical Bulletin*, III, No. 5, (1924), 6–8.

43. O.S.A., VIII (Cromdale), 253.

Revd Donald Sage, *Memorabilia Domestica*, Edinburgh, John Menzie & Co., 1889. 179.

Sir James Balfour Paul, Ed., *Diary of George Redpath, Minister of Stitchel, 1755–1761*, Edinburgh, Scottish Historical Society, 1922.

The numerous entries in this diary showed that the minister was well-read in popular medicine and was frequently consulted on medical matters by his parishioners.

Marjorie Plant, *The Domestic Life of Scotland in the Eighteenth Century*, Edinburgh Univ. Press, 1952, 222–3.

44. Another very popular book of the early eighteenth century, though not of the same calibre as Buchan's, was *The Poor Man's Physician; or, Receits of The Famous John Moncrieff of Tippermalloch*, [in Perthshire] — *being a choice collection of simple and easy remedies for most distempers, very useful to all persons, especially those of a poorer condition.*

One reviewer of this book was of the opinion that Moncrieff was insane. See: Charles Rogers, *Social Life in Scotland*, 3 Vols., Edinburgh, The Grampian Club, 1884–86, II, 314.

Another reviewer noted that many of the 'Receits' were 'recommended far on in the century by country practitioners, even after they were being discredited by the more enlightened men of the profession.' An example of Moncrieff's art was a remedy for 'falling sickness' [Epilepsy]:

Take a little black sucking puppy (but for a girl take a bitch whelp), choke it, open it, take out the gall, put it all to the child in the time of the fit with a little tile-tree flower water, and you shall see him cured as it were by a miracle presently.

H.G. Graham, *Social Life in Scotland in the 18th Century*, 2 Vols., London, Adam & Charles Black, 1899. I, 51–2.

45. Buchan, Op cit., 249, 252–3, 256.

O.S.A., IV (Kirkpatrick-Irongray), 527. :II (Newabbey), 126.

46. Ibid., 113–5.

47. O.S.A., VIII (Cromdale), 253.: II (Eaglesham), 118.

48. Buchan, Op cit., Chapter VI.

49. Ibid., Chapter VIII.

50. Ibid., 106–7.

51. Ibid., XXIV.

52. Ibid., XXVII–XXVIII.

53. Ibid., 234–5.
    For a description of the 'hot' treatment of smallpox see also:
    O.S.A., XX(Thurso), 504–6.:VIII(Glenorchy and Inishail), 341.

54. Ibid., 117.

55. Ibid., XX–XXII. See also:
    Revd James Hall, *Troubles in Scotland* Etc., 2 vols., London, J. Johnson, 1807, II, 589.
    J.G. Kohl, *Travels in Scotland*, 3 Vols., London, Bruce & Wild, 1844, 205–210.
    Charles Rogers, *Social Life in Scotland,* 3 Vols., Edinburgh, Printed for the Grampian Club, 1884–86, 330–1.

56. Ibid., Intro., xxvi–xxvii.

57. Hamilton, Op cit., 125, 135–6.

58. Ibid., 126–8.
    Alex Berman, 'The Heroic Approach in 19th Century Therapeutics' in *Sickness and Health in America; Readings in the History of Medicine and Public Health*, Ed., Judith Walzer Leavitt and Ronald L. Numbers, Wisconsin, Univ. Press, 1978, 77.
    For further information on Cullen's contribution to medical science see:
    Rosalie Stott, 'Health and Virtue: Or, How to Keep out of Harm's Way. Lectures on Pathology and Therapeutics by William Cullen c. 1770', *Medical History*, 1987, 31: 123–142.
    By 1830, there were 76 physicians and surgeons in the province of Nova Scotia, twenty-one of whom were native-born Nova Scotians. Of the 76 doctors, Halifax (the capital city) accounted for only eighteen, which reflects the increase in the population of the rural areas due mainly to Scottish immigration. Of the twelve doctors holding university degrees, six were graduates of Edinburgh and two were educated at the New York College of Physicians and Surgeons. The remaining four were graduates of Dublin, Glasgow, Marischall (Aberdeen) and Guy's Hospital, London respectively. At least twelve other doctors were licensed by one of the Royal Colleges. See: A.E. Marble, 'A History of Medicine in Nova Scotia, 1784–1854', *Collections of the Royal Nova Scotia Historical Society*, XLI, 1982.

59. Berman, Op cit., 77.

60. Buchan, Op cit., VIII–XI.
    W.W. Buchanan, W.F. Keen, 'Robert Burn's Illness Revisited', *Scottish Medical Journal*, XXVII, 1982, 75–88.

The authors suggest that Burns died as a result of the heroic treatments prescribed by his doctor. Burns was aware of the dangers of the new therapy, dangers that inspired his poem, 'Death and Dr Hornbook.'

61. Cited by Berman, Op cit., 77.

62. M.D. Morrison, Op cit., 6.

63. A.Allan MacLaren, Ed., *Social Class in Scotland: Past and Present*, Edinburgh, John Donald, 1976, 41.

64. *First Report of the Registrar-General*. Op cit., xxxvii.

65. Letter from W. MacGregor to J. M. Stewart MacKenzie, 28th February, 1832. Scottish Record Office, Seaforth Manuscripts, GD 46/13/185/1.
    The minister of Bracadale on the Isle of Skye, when contemplating the arrival of cholera, had made a similar discovery regarding the clothing of his parishioners. N.S.A., XIV (Bracadale), 297.

66. Ferguson (1948), 128, 126–7.
    Cholera again visited Scotland in 1848–49 and 'was at its worse in areas where overcrowding was most serious and sanitation most primitive, as in the mining areas.'
    Ibid., 128.

67. *First Report of the Registrar-General*, Op cit., xxxvii.

68. David Balfour, the hero of Stevenson's *Kidnapped*, suffered greatly after the ingestion of raw shellfish when he was shipwrecked on Mull.
    Robert Louis Stevenson, *Kidnapped*, New York, Charles Scribner's Sons, 1911, 113–118.
    The minister of Torryburn related that during the seven year famine of the late sixteenth century, a great number of fish are said to have been thrown in upon the coast; and these the people eat immediately from the want of other food, and thereby became the prey of dysenteries, and other putrid disorders.
    O.S.A., VIII (Torryburn), 445.
    The minister of Inveraray made a similar observation.
    O.S.A., V (Inveraray), 289–290.

9

Eviction and Its Aftermath II

Storm-Clouds in the Highlands[1]

AFTER THE CLEARANCES Gaeldom was in a state of upheaval. Confused and demoralised, Highlanders awaited reorganisation and leadership. Leaders came, not bearing a fiery cross to rouse the clans to battle, but beckoning them purposefully into the Highland Uprising of the nineteenth century. The regeneration of Gaeldom was the product of two movements. One was religious, its leaders the representatives of a new evangelicalism, and of a radical Presbyterianism. The second was political, a call for the State to take responsibility for the care of the Highland poor.

I

Ironically, Gaeldom's religious reform was ignited in the Lowlands. By the sixteenth and seventeenth centuries, Christianity had all but disappeared in the Highlands, even in the 'catholic corridor', that bulwark of the old culture that stretches from South Uist and Barra across the Minch on to the Mainland and as far east as Lochaber. The remote Highlands and Islands had reverted to paganism or to a mixture of Christianity, superstition and the parent Druidism:

> Superstition . . . grew up side by side with the most austere belief of orthodox religion, like flowers and weeds springing up in an ill-kept garden. Each was held with equal tenacity in the same mind, unconscious of any incongruity. Trust in charms, omens, incantations, were rife amongst them all. Every incident of daily life — a baptism, a death, the illness of a cow, the churning of milk, the setting forth on a journey — each was associated with some mysterious sign which foretold it, or some strange rite which infallibly caused or hindered it. Those notions and these practices were guarded from the Kirk . . . Most deeply rooted were superstitions among the peasantry in remote districts separated by moor, and hill, and loch from contact with towns — regions where schoolmasters were scarce and kirks were powerless.[2]

John Knox had foreseen the danger of such chaos. He knew that acculturation would eventually mean conversion to and education by

Establishment religion. And so it had happened. By the eighteenth century, acculturation had brought Establishment Christianity to the Highlands, and soon various strata of Establishment religion, principally Anglicanism and Scottish Presbyterianism, overlaid the bedrock of paganism and early Christianity. In fact, the Revd John Kennedy, writing about the Parish of Killearnan on the northern shore of the Beauly Firth, remarked upon that layering:

> At the time of my father's induction [1813], there were upwards of 300 Episcopalians [Anglicans] in the parish, in whom were found surviving all the changes that had transformed the whole country around them, much of the ignorance of Scotland's old heathenism, much of the superstition of its Popery, and much of the disaffection of its Jacobitism.[3]

During the eighteenth century however, Establishment Presbyterianism came to supplant all other religious influences. By the last quarter of the century it ruled supreme, temporally and spiritually, even though it was sparsely represented in the remoter areas of the West Highlands and Islands. But supremacy soon made the Church complacent and corrupt. John Macleod reveals the extent of that corruption:

> The landlord's creatures frequently led lives of farcical sloth, even immorality. Others spent their days in pleasant pursuits: farming, entertaining, private hobbies. Congregations dwindled to nothing. In the outer Isles especially, a lazy and often drunken minister might have charge of a vast parish containing thousands of souls, most of whom never set eyes on the one with the cure of their souls.[4]

Little wonder that to many Highlanders, Establishment Christianity, whether Anglican or Presbyterian, was the religion of the landowners. From it, they had learned, they could expect little empathy, guidance or relief, spiritual or physical.[5]

Corrupt and despised, its end was near, and by the end of the eighteenth century, the evangelical movement had all but replaced it as the religion of the common people, sweeping throughout Lowland Scotland and into the North-east. By 1798, the evangelical revival spirit had reached even the remote West Highlands and Islands and in 1798 the Society for Propagating the Gospel at Home was founded in Edinburgh. The Society was eventually dominated by two brothers, Robert and James Haldane, whose missionary zeal and congregationalism guaranteed the movement's immediate popularity among oppressed Highlanders. From the Lowlands, many other lay preachers and missionaries took the Message into the Highlands. Highlanders embraced evangelicalism enthusiastically – for its purity and fervour, and because its fellowship made it a religion of the common people:

> . . . the new Gospel was water for the thirsty souls of the crushed people of the Highlands . . . many saw in the Scriptures a picture of their own sufferings, a vindication of their plight. And the Moderate ministers [of the Established Presbyterian Church of Scotland] who had said nothing, not a word against the evil of that day were abandoned by their people.[6]

Lowland missionaries soon learned that the further west they travelled into the Highlands, the more Gaelic-speaking and Highland was the population. They realized that the Message had to be preached in Gaelic by a Gael and that the Bible had to be printed in Gaelic as well. In 1811, the Gaelic School Society was founded in Edinburgh to teach Highlanders to read and write Gaelic and so to introduce them to the Bible. The Society in Scotland for Propagating Christian Knowledge (SSPCK), founded much earlier in Lowland Scotland, helped distribute thousands of Gaelic Bibles and New Testaments.

Those lay evangelical preachers, respected throughout Gaeldom as *na daoine*, 'the men', had an inestimable impact on the daily life of Highlanders. Wherever they preached, change followed.[7] Evangelism drew the people of a parish together, at Sabbath services, in fellowship and prayer meetings, in 'diets of catechising' and in the popular communion services which might last a week:

> As the appointed time draws nigh, special meetings for prayer are held, and, with holy solicitude, all the preparatory arrangements are made. The *Fast-Day* is come. Eminent ministers have arrived to take part in the solemn services. Many of the Lord's people are gathering. From as many as forty parishes they come; but lodgings they will easily procure, as the parish people are striving for the pleasure of entertaining them.[8]

Evangelicalism did much more than entertain Highlanders; it reunited them and gave them the leadership and sense of common cause they had so long lacked. In particular, it bound them together against the landlords. Despite its quickening of Highland spirit and its practical support of parishioners, Highland evangelicalism was generally accounted as gloomier, less tolerant and less energising than the Lowland evangelicalism from which it had sprung – a difference attributed to the character of its Highland adherents:

> There are certain peculiarities which distinguish it from the type assumed by the religious feeling in the Lowlands, the Southrons have been anxious to make out that the difference is owing to some defect or excess that may be charged against the north . . . To the radical peculiarity thus indicated, whether it be

accounted a defect or an advantage, may be traced all the developments of the religious spirit in the Highlands that form its distinctive character, as compared with the Christianity of the Lowlands . . . A Highland Christian is, therefore, in their esteem, a gloomy bigot, as compared with the more cheerful and liberal Christians of the South . . . The Christian Highlander, they say, is employed in determining whether he is a true servant of Christ or not, when he should be proving that he is so by being 'up and doing.' The same amount of religious principle, because of this subjective tendency, is thought to throw off a less amount of work than otherwise it would. It is to the same source the peculiar order and position of 'the men' is ultimately traced. It is an excessive self-suspiciousness, say they of the south, that has originated the fellowship meeting, and there 'the Men' acquired their position and influence. The same peculiarity finds another development in the paucity of communicants in the Highlands. It is affirmed that they frighten themselves by an exaggerated standard of fitness, and are guided by their feelings rather than by the written Word. Thus all the peculiarities of the type of religion prevalent in the Highlands are traced to one source; and would be designated by those unfriendly the gloominess, the bigotry, and the closetism of Highland Christians.[9]

Such criticisms of Highland communicants did not go unchallenged:

If that man's state of feeling is not to be regarded with respect, let it not at least be treated with rudeness. And can we wonder that he, accustomed to see the southern practice followed by the moderates around him, whom he regarded as ungodly men, never looking for guidance from on high, should have imagined that what he had originally derived from a study of the Word of God was confirmed to him by experience, that he should therefore have held his own views very firmly, and have looked with grave suspicion on the state of mind and feeling that differed from his own.[10]

The fact is that evangelicalism, whether more or less cheerfully practised in the Highlands, proved a truly humanitarian and culturally therapeutic force there in the eighteenth and nineteenth centuries. Hunter remarks on its importance:

In this process [crofters' control of their own destiny], it is clear, a large part was played by evangelical presbyterianism — still [1976] an important element in crofting life and in the past one of its vital components.[11]

Nor was evangelical Presbyterianism the only revivalist religious force at work among Highlanders during those centuries. By the middle of the eighteenth century, a schism within the Established Church itself produced a separatist brand of Presbyterianism that was, like Evangelicalism, congregationalist and politically activist. That reform of the Established Church was in the making even as Evangelicalism was sweeping across the Highlands. We have said that by the end of the 1800s, the Established

Church of Scotland had grown corrupt and was almost universally regarded as an instrument of the landlords. Indeed, Established Church ministers were 'lairds' men', appointed and maintained by their patrons since 1712, under the authority of the Patronage Act. And many Establishment ministers relished their status:

> More ambitious of being popular as a 'country gentleman' than of being acceptable as a Gospel minister, he courted the favour and society of the lairds rather than the love and fellowship of the saints.[12]

Highlanders knew that their ministers' interests and sympathies lay with their colleagues in the Highland Establishment:

> The proprietor, the minister, the schoolmaster, and the large tacksmen – all who used to act as the leaders of the people, and to manage the public business of the parish – are ranged together on one side and on one cause; while the people are as unanimously and determinedly united on another side and in an entirely opposite cause.[13]

Self-serving most Church of Scotland ministers certainly were, and deserving of Highlanders' contempt. Some, however, chafed at their landlords' patronage, even though that was, in many estates, sorely inadequate. In many estates, landlords did not worship in the parishes they controlled. Thus the religious and social requirements of a parish were rarely their priority. In consequence, some ministers had no church in which to preach. They assembled their flock in a field. Some had no manse or glebe. Their stipend minimal, most had to work a small farm to feed and educate their usually large families. In fact, most parish ministers were no more than sub-tenants, as reliant as their parishioners on the goodwill of a local tenant farmer, proprietor or landlord. What is more, some ministers, like this one Sinclair quotes, openly blamed landlords for the people's distress:

> All the plans that have been hitherto proposed for the relief of these unfortunate people, will be of little avail towards ameliorating their condition, while the landed proprietors enjoy an unlimited power of raising their rents. Would a statute, regulating the rent of lands, be a greater infringement on the rights of the subject, than the regulation of the assizes of bread, or the rate of interest?[14]

Resentment at the precariousness and iniquity of landlords' patronage had simmered for decades within the Established Church.[15] It came to the boil during a period of unrest known as the 'Ten years' conflict'. In 1834 the General Assembly of the Established Church of Scotland, which included all its ministers as well as representatives of the laity, passed the Veto Act, an act which empowered congregations to reject their patrons' choice of minister. Establishment patrons shortly sued presbyteries for violation of their rights. In 1842, the General Assembly responded by presenting to the government its 'Claim of Rights and its Protest', formally grieving intrusion of the civil courts into what they considered an ecclesiastical sphere. By the time of the 1843 General Assembly, the government had still not replied to this submission, a snub which moved 475 'radical' ministers to demit their charges in the Established Church and to form The Church of Scotland Free. Among Highland Presbyterians, support for their action was almost unanimous.

With the Disruption of 1843, most of the 'moderate' Highland pulpits had been filled by separatist preachers. Moreover, because many Free Church ministers did not speak Gaelic, many charges were often initially filled by lay preachers. Highlanders had now in their preachers, ordained or lay, resident and compassionate leaders.

In time, the Free Church was able to fill its Highland pulpits with ordained ministers who would speak, preach and teach in Gaelic and who would thus have first-hand knowledge of the Highland agricultural quandary, and of the poverty which followed the Clearances. Above all, the Church would be pro-Highlander.[16] Thus did the Free Church provide from within its ranks the same kind of leadership that Evangelicalism had brought decades earlier.

The Free Church's new autonomy and power among the people were fiercely opposed by the landlords. The Revd Mr William McKenzie, an aged and venerable minister of the parish of Tongue and himself a Separatist, reported his own landlord's threat of reprisal against ministers who proposed to operate independently:

> I write to intimate my adherence, as minister of Tongue, to all the resolutions of the late Convocation at Edinburgh [the 1842 Claim of Rights and Protests]. I resolved this from the first communication to me, but immediately thereafter, *being assured by local authority that no separatist would be permitted to remain as officiating minister within the bounds of the Presbytery, all the property of the Duke of Sutherland* [italics are mine]: . . . At length with a clear light and a good conscience, I said, Come what will, and whatever the sacrifice I must render, that no proposed good can sanction doing evil to attain it, that nothing can warrant my remaining in an Erastian Church, and allying myself with ministers who would consent to make the Church of Christ a creature of the State . . . and its servants only to be slaves of a worldly tyranny . . .[17]

As always, there were exceptions, landlord-patrons who, like the 8th Duke of Argyll and his father before him, came to accept the logic of separating ministers from a laird's patronage:

My father, as Duke of Argyll, was one of the very largest holders of patronage in Scotland. He did not naturally sympathize at first with a movement which would damage, if it did not abolish, this right in the disposal of parochial livings, however little he might value it personally. The current of feeling, therefore, by which I was surrounded was leading me, so long as my mind was merely passive, in the direction which was adverse to the course and to the claims of the Church Assemblies, and in that current *I might easily have drifted to wrong conclusions, as so many of my class unfortunately did* [italics are mine] . . . in the very first year after his succession to the dukedom in 1840 he [his father] became more and more favourably disposed to the action of the Church.[18]

In fact, so persuaded did the younger Argyll become that he argued publicly the propriety of the separation, not missing a chance in the process to point to it as yet one more piece of evidence of Scotland's superiority over England in matters of sense and experience:

When the question had been referred on appeal to the House of Lords, one other influence, even more fatal than professional and official self-assertion, was added to the courses operating in that supreme tribunal. That influence was Anglicanism. I have never yet met an Englishman who could understand, or even conceive, that idea of the relations between Church and State which was embedded and embodied in the Constitution of Scotland. John Bull, with all his great qualities, is a very parochial creature. What he has never seen in his own experience, within his own part of the kingdom south of the Tweed, he cannot see elsewhere, even when it may stare him in the face.[19]

Exceptions like Argyll aside, the Establishment did not relinquish control easily. At every turn, they blocked or impeded Separatists' efforts to find sites for churches, manses and schools.

It is an interesting aside that the Presbyterian Synod of Canada was not sympathetic to the Disruption. A motion to unite with the Free Church was defeated by a majority of 39 to 21. The 21 separated from the Synod, 'taking the original name, The Presbyterian Church of Canada and placing themselves in fellowship with the Free Church of Scotland.' In Nova Scotia, however, a two-thirds majority sided with the Separatists and that Synod set 'itself free from its connection with the Established Church of Scotland.'[20] However their Synod voted, many ministers left Canada to take up Highland parishes that the dissenters had vacated:

The news of the Disruption had acted on them like a charm. Hundreds of pulpits were vacant in Scotland, and, in hot haste, men left their Canadian congregations, and started across the sea eager to have a share of the spoil . . . 'Satan took them up to an exceedingly high mountain and showed them, across the Atlantic, empty manses, good stipends, and comfortable glebes in Scotland, and – they fled from us.'[21]

II

Whatever the reaction abroad, however, and whatever the opposition from the Establishment at home, congregationalism, whether evangelical Presbyterian or Free Church, reshaped Highland lifestyle. Much of that reshaping is attributable to the clergy's success in educating ordinary Highlanders. As we have said, most of the Highland upper classes had been acculturated. Most of the Highland middle class had been driven away by the Clearances. The Highlands had been effectively emptied of all but its lowest class. That class was neither the noble savage, the *primus inter pares* of the early historians, nor the warrior clansman of romantic writers. It consisted rather of ignorant, illiterate peasants, the scallags or cottars.

The task of educating that population would have been enormous even with an army of clerics. Yet it was accomplished by a handful only, and that representing a variety of sects. The following observations, although made in the first quarter of the nineteenth century, illustrate the mix of religious representation typical in the Highlands for decades:

> There were only 264 clergy in the Establishment (including 40 missionaries) for a population of 416,000 persons, embraced in the counties of Argyll, Inverness, Nairn, Ross and Cromarty, Sutherland, Caithness, Orkney, and Shetland, with the Gaelic districts of Moray, and of Dunkeld, in Perthshire. In the same wide region there were at that time only thirty-five ministers of 'every denomination of dissenters', and six or eight Roman Catholic priests . . . Within the Established Church [Presbyterian] the two parties known as Moderate and Evangelical had conflicts between themselves but they co-operated for the improvement of the people. *Though a large part of the population was unable to read* [italics are mine], they all entertained great respect for religious ordinances.[22]

The extent of illiteracy in the Highlands was assessed by a three-man deputation sent by the General Assembly of the Church of Scotland. One deputy, Dr Norman Macleod (known as the 'Friend of the Highlanders'), was a Gaelic-speaking Highland minister. Of the investigators' work, James Barron tells us:

> In 1828 they reported that they had travelled upwards of 1600 miles, having spent two months on their journey. The visit established the melancholy fact that 90,000 persons, between the ages of six and twenty years, could read neither English or Gaelic . . . In the eighteenth century schools the reading and even the speaking of Gaelic was forbidden, but this led to a mechanical kind of teaching which did little good to the learner . . . 'Our schoolbooks were in English and not a sentence could we understand.'[23]

Another report on illiteracy put the number of schools in Lewis, in the parish of Stornoway, at thirteen in 1833. In that parish, 586 children between the ages of six and fifteen years, and 1265 persons above the age of fifteen could not read. In Barvas, there were three schools in 1836, and in Uig, five schools in 1833. In the same year, Lochs had a newly erected Parish school and four schools maintained by the Gaelic School Society; yet of a total population there of 3067, only twelve persons could write. By 1865, a 'Report on the State of Education in all the Western Islands' showed that in the Eye district of the Parish of Stornoway (population 2159), of persons above school age, only 403 men and 463 women could read Gaelic, while only 208 men and 46 women could read English. The number who could write was 170 men and 26 women. In the district of Back in the same parish (population 2017), most adults could read Gaelic, but only 111 men and 13 women could read English; 'and out of all this large population only 75 men and 4 women could write.'[24]

Highlanders were not easily persuaded of the value of education, so suspicious had they become of changes said to be for their own good. Among their worries about any scheme for general education was their fear that their children, if educated, would leave them: 'the country people are not fond of their children being taught the English language; they think if they were taught to read the English language, they would leave the island.'[25]

But the clerical improvers persisted. By the end of the century, they had achieved their goal. In the Island of Lewis in the twenty-year period 1881 to 1901, the population increased by 13.5 percent while the 'number of scholars in average attendance increased by 108.2 percent.' The energetic and dedicated HM Inspector of Schools observed:

> Moreover school attendance has been greatly aided and facilitated by the construction of roads and footpaths to schools . . . Above all, the abolition of school fees has removed every excuse on the part of parents for neglecting the education of their children, and the school attendance may now be regarded as regular.

Furthermore, on the subject of higher education, the Inspector noted:

> The Nicolson Institute [Stornoway] is the recognised secondary centre for the whole island and is accessible to the best of the outlying pupils by a system of small bursaries . . . The Institute is very well staffed, and sends annually to the University direct a number of its pupils.[26]

III

Religious reform reunited Highlanders, furnished leaders they could admire, and began the monumental task of general education. Political reform was to achieve a second victory in the rejuvenation of Gaeldom: the state was made to recognise the causal link between poverty and disease and to assume responsibility for care of the destitute. In that political battle, one of the most influential antagonists was a Separatist minister. The Revd Thomas Chalmers (1780–1847), born in Anstruther in the Kingdom of Fife, was an academic cum divine and a dynamic preacher and activist who drew large congregations wherever he preached. Chalmers called for 'the diffusion of sufficiency and comfort throughout the mass of the population, by a multiplication of the enlargement of the outward means and materials of human enjoyment.' He also argued that labourers' wages be increased in order that 'workmen will share more equally than they do at present, with capitalists and proprietors of the soil, in the comforts and even the elegances of life.'[27]

Yet Chalmers opposed any form of charity except for the neediest, a stand undoubtedly influenced by his earlier ministry in a rural Scottish parish. The proud independence of the poor in that parish and the social responsibility of its heritors were, he maintained, the model of responsible behaviour for both groups. That model, he was convinced, made pauperism 'a decreasing quantity.'[28] His service later among the poor of Glasgow only strengthened his opinion: for Chalmers the solution to the problem of destitution lay in encouraging among the poor a spirit of independence, 'prudence and virtue.'[29] The State-subsidised poor relief then being proposed was, for Chalmers, no solution. In fact, Chalmers argued strenuously against it.[30] Poor relief would, he believed, perpetuate pauperism and so 'induce a great relaxation on the frugality and providential habits of our labouring classes.' Moreover, 'it would shut off the kindness of relatives . . . and the sympathy of the wealthy for the poorer classes; turning a matter of love into a matter of litigation and set up a barrier to the sympathy of the poor for one another.'[31]

Since the money for greater relief of the poor was to be collected from ratepayers, Chalmers soon found that he had much support among that group: conservative physicians, businessmen, industrialists and landlords, ratepayers all, championed Chalmers's program. In fact, Chalmers's view, though essentially humanitarian and activist, was taken up by the anti-reform forces as their religious script. An Establishmentarian, Edwin Chadwick, supplied their medical rationale. From London, Chadwick led a medical school of thought called Miasmatology. Simply put, miasmatists believed that disease was caused by floating microbic life or noxious effluvia, especially those generated in marshes. The miasmatists, and the middle class as a whole, argued a 'doctrine of predisposing causes' for disease:

> It was confidently believed that certain lifestyles or behavioural patterns predisposed one to contract epidemic disease and these predispositions were rooted in an irreligious proletarian culture.[32]

But then, Chadwick was a lawyer, not a doctor. His analysis of the conditions of the 'labouring poor' was certain to be radically different from that of a physician in practice in a working-class neighbourhood. His conviction that poor sanitation was a major cause of disease was not wrong, but it was limited. It assigned the blame and the responsibility for remedy to the poor themselves, and left unexamined the reasons for the poverty which engendered the unsanitary miasma where they lived.

In the debate about the cause of disease, Chalmers and Chadwick had a formidable opponent in Dr William Pulteney Alison (1790–1859), a Tory, the son of an Episcopalian manse, and Professor of Medicine at the University of Edinburgh. Alison was a tireless worker, researcher, teacher and writer who, during the period 1832–40, had become interested in the fevers which raged amongst the poor. As chairman of the committee representing the Scottish medical profession, he made it clear that there was a considerable distance between the Scottish medical profession's conception of the causes of epidemic diseases and that held by their English counterparts, the miasmatists.[33]

Alison and his committee were Contagionists, or Germ Theorists, who held that specific diseases were transferred from person to person, either by direct contact or by means of an intermediate agent.[34] On the basis of their clinical experience among the fever-ridden and destitute population of the Scottish urban centres, Alison and his colleagues were convinced that the prime cause of infectious disease was the destitution of the lower classes. For them, the remedy lay in redesigning the Scottish poor-law system to bring it into line with that operating in England. On the subject of the removal of the 'disease-causing miasma', Alison had this to say:

> I am confident that experience teaches that their [the miasmatists] labours will be in vain; and in Edinburgh in particular, I am convinced from ample observation that a great deal of money might be expended in removing various nuisances, such as irrigated meadows in the neighbourhood, and dunghills in various parts of the town, — all of which would be perfectly ineffectual in preventing the recurrence of epidemic fever, as long as the condition and habits

of the poorest of the people, and their resources when reduced by any cause to destitution, in this city and in the other parts of Scotland, continue as at present.[35]

It was well known in Scotland, by the medical profession and reformers alike, that disease among the poor was a product of the destitution and unsanitary conditions in which they lived. Yet recommendations for improving those conditions were blocked by conservative physicians, and by businessmen and industrialists who foresaw the high cost of preventive measures.

Debate between Miasmatists and Contagionists raged, although by the second half of the century the tide had turned in favour of the Contagionists. It was not until the end of the century, however, that the miasmatic theory was finally laid to rest. Debate about the cause of disease reflected the larger regional conflict between Scotland and England about the cause of ill-health generally and about the most appropriate approach to the care of the poor. That debate was evident in the treatment of most diseases. For example, it influenced treatment for childbed or puerperal fever. In her paper on puerperal fever in Britain, Margaret DeLacy notes that at the end of the eighteenth century, the Scottish and the English medical professions differed radically in their analysis of the disease:

> Dissenters such as the Quakers Fothergill and Lettsom, and the Scots like Alexander Gordon or professors of midwifery at Edinburgh Thomas Young [professor from 1756 to 1780] and Alexander Hamilton [professor from 1780 to 1800] differed from their English and Anglican colleagues in that they placed less emphasis on the importance of the climate – what Sydenham had called 'the epidemic constitution of the atmosphere' – and more emphasis on the possibility of specific local contagions, which were spread by contact or fomites and could be transmitted only over a short distance by air.[36]

However, though the Scottish Contagionists would eventually prevail, Scotland lagged behind England by more than a generation in tackling the problems of destitution and epidemic disease. One reason, McLaren claims, was administrative inadequacy and regional jealousy:

> When Scotland underwent the first and worst onslaught of the second cholera epidemic she had neither effective Boards of Guardians nor a General Board of Health [as had England]. When attempts were made by London to establish a central Board of Health in Edinburgh the resistance from other areas in Scotland was such that the idea was dropped.[37]

McLaren blames the lag on the inability of the Scottish medical profession to act as a united pressure group. As a result, the impetus for sanitary reform lapsed between epidemics.

The battle between Miasmatists and Germ Theorists, and between the conservatives and reformers they represented, peaked during the cholera epidemics of 1832 and 1848, when national concern amounted almost to panic, especially in England. When in the end Germ Theory and the impetus for reform prevailed, a Royal Commission was convened to study the question of poor law relief, and in 1845 the Poor Law Amendment Act was passed. The relief of the poor was to be obtained through legal assessment of their needs and compulsory contribution to their relief.

Traditionally, the relief of the Highland poor had been a voluntary parish effort. Parishes had looked after their own poor through contributions from the church poor box, augmented as required by donations from the patron, chief or landlord, donations solicited usually by the parish minister, or by bequests from successful businessmen who had local roots.[38] And voluntary effort had for generations been sufficient:

> . . . people of all ranks, particularly the small tenants, are hospitable, humane, and charitable to the poor, according to their ability; from them they experience real sympathy in their distress.[39]

In some cases, the minister's judgement of who needed relief was accepted without question and his request satisfied by the heritor or his factor.

The custom of a parish caring for its own poor is well documented in both *Statistical Accounts*. The report from the parish of Small Isles, which sent many Highlanders to Cape Breton, is typical. The parish consisted of the small islands of Muck, Eigg, Rum and Canna and in the 1790s had a population of 1339, of whom

> The number of the poor, on the kirk session roll, of the reformed religion, is 19, and those of the Roman Catholic, 20. They indiscriminately travel, and receive alms through the parish. There is no fixed fund, except about 30s. a year given by Mr M'Lean of Coll [the landlord], for the poor in Rum. The session fund consists only of a little money collected on Sabbaths, and of fines paid by delinquents. This money is, once a year, distributed among the poor of the reformed. The priest is left at liberty to uplift fines from delinquents of his own persuasion, and to apply them in similar manner.[40]

On many other estates, however, landlords did nothing to support the poor and increasingly, parish charity proved insufficient. In Culross on the Firth of Forth, the minister's report bluntly expressed the growing feeling among parishioners, themselves little better off than the poor, that the destitute of a parish were the heritor's responsibility:

> in times of scarcity or dearth, the heritors have voluntarily affected themselves to supply the extraordinary demands of the poor; – and a proposal was lately

made and agreed to, that such heritors as did not reside, or were of a different communion from the established Church, or did not attend the church regularly, should send a certain proportion weekly for the support of the poor; a mean of supporting the poor equally proper and just, especially in country parishes.[41]

In one north-eastern parish, the minister daringly observed that it 'was a duty incumbent upon them [the heritors] to remember the poor since heritors draw a great part of the produce of their estates, to spend where they will, . . . '[42]

In fact, relief of the poor had been legislated centuries before in Scotland. But that law, and landowners' delinquency in respect of it, had been conveniently hidden or forgotten, as the following explanation makes clear:

> Though poor rates were not generally imposed in Scotland, yet a law involving a compulsory assessment for the support of the impotent poor, was passed as early as the year 1576 by the Scotch Parliament, which Statute formed, until lately, the basis of the poor law code. The very existence of such a Statute seemed, however, nearly unknown till the middle of last century [the eighteenth]. Legal assessments were reluctantly resorted to, the resources of the kirk-sessions being in general deemed sufficient.[43]

IV

Passage of the Scottish Poor Law dictated that care of the poor was no longer to be left to voluntary aid: it was to be assigned as the legal responsibility of those who could afford to pay for it. In parishes where the money raised by traditional sources was insufficient, the remedy would be

> to take immediate steps for raising the required sum by an assessment, regularly imposed, and leviable from the parties liable by law to contribute.[44]

Unfortunately, the Act's promulgation by Parliament did not ensure its prompt execution or its universality. Practical problems and opposition spelled delay. For example, unlike English Poor Law, the Scottish Law was to be administered at parish level only, and determining how much relief a parish required was no easy task. Furthermore, topography, climate and landlords' sense of responsibility for their estates made for wide variation in the conditions of the poor, all of which complicated the assessment process.

More than practical detail impeded implementation of the Act, however. Landlords' opposition stalled it. Even in England, which had the resources of a larger taxation base to draw from, Poor Law reform had met resistance. In Scotland, with its fewer landlords to foot the bill, resistance was magnified. The Scottish Lunacy Commissioners, in their 1857 Report, addressed the Poor Law taxation issue:

> . . . it follows that any legal provision, which shall be levied on districts individually, and not on the community as a whole, must act unequally, and, to a certain extent, oppressively; for the burden will fall lightest on those communities which are most able to bear it, and most heavily on those which are least able. In such a case, injustice, also, would in so far be committed, that emigrants from a stationary county would escape the heavier rates that would there be levied, to share the lighter burdens of their adopted county; leaving the care of the insane poor of their native district to fall upon a community deprived of its most active and useful members.[45]

Moreover, whereas in England, the problem was how to curb excessive relief to able-bodied paupers, in Scotland, the problem was to raise enough money to give adequate relief even to the aged and the infirm.[46] Nicolls confirms that 'the relief given in the western Highlands is, the commissioners say, so small, as not to be of any material assistance in providing for the support of the poor.'[47] Jean Lindsay observes that three-quarters of a century would pass before the Scottish Poor Law came into general operation. That delay, Lindsay comments, was rooted in self-righteous opposition to state-subsidised poor relief:

> The case for the voluntary system is cast, as always, in ethical terms; and, as always, the system of morality assumed is one in which happiness and suffering are of little importance. This is the self-deceiving fanaticism which led to the division of the poor into the 'deserving' and the 'undeserving', and to the denial of relief to the unemployed. This is the attitude which prompted the *Aberdeen Journal* to praise those who would rather starve than ask assistance.[48]

In fact, delay was virtually assured by the mechanism set up to implement the law. A Board of Supervision was to oversee the provisions of the Act and to establish parochial boards to levy rates for poor relief. But the composition and rulings of the local boards were suspect from the outset:

> A great reform was immediately resolved upon. None but respectable men – men well-to-do in the world – were, from that time, to have seats in the committee [the parish relief committee]; and accordingly, every poor man, and, as a necessary consequence, every Free-Churchman, except one or two very harmless individuals of that species, were expelled from the Board, and the entire sway handed over to the upper and anti-popular party. The effect was deplorable.[49]

Ratepayers opposed Poor Law assessment because it cost them money. Highlanders themselves resisted the public health legislation that attended Poor Law reform because it cost them, they believed, their independence.

The influence of the Calvinist doctrine of predestination, the Will of Providence, strengthened Highlanders' resistance against reformers who would improve their health and living conditions. In the southern Highlands, however, the minister of the Argyll parish of Kilfinan commented on the Highlanders' awareness of a changing sense of individual responsibility:

> In those days [some time ago], the universal belief of the lower ranks of people, appears to have been, that there was a fatality in all circumstances in life, that the most trivial circumstances had been foreordained, and that consequently, no person could either accelerate, or escape his fated death. In proportion as they have dropped that idea, and begin to be sensible, that man is left, at least in many things, to the freedom of his own will, and that, as a free agent, he may be instrumental in promoting his own temporal happiness, or multiplying his misfortunes, they become more cautious in approaching any contagion which seems to them to be connected with danger.[50]

Against the reformers' calls for better sanitation, for example, the Highland poor staunchly defended their refuse heaps. Their middens contained organic material like dung, fish and meat offal and other bio-degradable by-products from domestic and industrial sources, all indispensable to the success of each year's crop. Like any garden compost heap, this refuse had to be stockpiled and allowed to mature. The heap, always stinking and verminous, might be adjacent to a black house or an urban tenement, or it might be an adjunct to urban industry, like a slaughter-house or a fish-processing plant. The refuse pile was in fact an integral part of the Highland niche: it supplied manure for the family's crops; its sale provided money for the household. Any legislation designed to remove it was fiercely resisted. Poor Law relief could hardly compensate for its loss.

Opposition to Poor Law reforms came from other quarters in Scotland as well. For example, when Chadwick proposed centralisation of the administration of health measures in Edinburgh during the cholera emergency, parochial jealousies among physicians and lay commentators flared up in Glasgow, Aberdeen and Dumfries. In December 1849, Chadwick sent his best man, Dr John Sutherland, to 'talk some sense into the benighted parochialists.' After one day in Dumfries, Sutherland wrote to Chadwick:

> My very spirit is crushed at the want of action of the people, In all my experience I have met nothing like it. Fair to look at and full of promises but no talk can be more empty. Anything but doing. The regulations of the Board appear to be so much waste paper.[51]

V

Notwithstanding Highlanders' opposition to improvements like those that would deprive them of their middens, people were becoming increasingly aware of the requirements for good health and of the connection between destitution and ill-health. Among the newly-enlightened were the migrant workers living in urban areas, and the commoners living in parishes at the Highland/Lowland cultural interfaces. In London, for example, commoners welcomed improvements in sanitation:

> The working classes – who, according to all the medical visitors, were well aware of the connection between their unsanitary dwellings and the diseases which afflicted them – revealed a touching gratitude, not unmingled with astonishment, at receiving visits from the bustling, efficient officers of the Board [of Health].[52]

The enlightened included as well members of the few remaining noble Highland families still in residence in their clan seats. Likewise, many Scottish physicians and lay practitioners showed amazing insight, particularly in the field of preventive medicine.

The Establishment as a whole, however, acted only belatedly and then grudgingly. Usually, only fear of the consequences of disease – for themselves – prompted them to legislate preventive measures:

> The transitory fears of the majority had been the force which drove the public health measures through Parliament; the permanent and implacable interests of minorities now opposed their application and extension . . .[53]

Traditionally, it had been the privilege, even the duty of the ruling Establishment to legislate change for the betterment of those classes that supported and protected them. In Scotland, this duty had been inherent in the clan system. In England, it fell to the traditional Tory lords of the manor. The new rulers of the Highlands, the Whigs, did not discharge that duty, a dereliction that troubled the minority among them who were close to their people. One member of the Highland nobility, Jane, Duchess of Gordon, in a letter (circa 1806–7) to the Lord Advocate, the Hon. Henry Erskine, expressed her concern for the welfare of her people:

> My dear Lord, – It has been often suggested by the benevolent and wise that some mark of His Majestie's bounty should be given to that part of the Kingdom which gave birth to the brave 42nd and 92nd Regts . . . .The Duke of Gordon has laid out 000 [*sic*] to build a town; and for years I have given premiums for all kinds of domestic industry – spinning, dyeing, &c . . . But

there is an evil I cannot remedy without a sum of money. The children are totally neglected in body and mind: cold, hunger, and dirt carries off hundreds . . . They say they may be better off in a foreign land; they cannot be more wretched . . . These horrors still exist in the utmost extent, – lands raised, and no knowledge of agriculture; of course, worse than slaves; no principle of action; no care of their morals or health . . . I wish to add to the comforts of the aged, and take the children – teach them to think right, raise food for themselves, and to prepare them to succeed to their fathers' farms with knowledge of all the branches of farming. Why Lady Stafford [the future Duchess of Sutherland] with 80,000 a year, should get money to build harbours where there is no ships, I cannot say. Much money has gone to Scotland for fishing towns, harbours. &c. All might as well been thrown into the sea. A healthy, well regulated people must be the proud riches of this country: by them we can alone be defended.[54]

The Duchess recognized the social problems in the Highlands and accepted the responsibility incumbent on her as a member of a privileged Establishment to attempt to alleviate them. The Duchess was, as we have said, one of a minority of landowners to do so.

By the late nineteenth century the Establishment was hotly divided on subjects such as social justice and health, in particular sanitation, around which the new concepts of disease and its prevention revolved.[55] By the end of the century the working classes in Lowland Scotland had begun to take an active, at times militant interest in the conditions in which they lived. The French Revolution sparked a spirit of change in all of Europe that eventually touched England and Scotland. The spirit of insurrection it engendered spread throughout the working classes and the intelligentsia of Britain. In Scotland, the evils of class inequality were openly exposed by popular writers such as Robert Burns, and a new radicalism became synonymous with Liberal politics and its drive for land reform.

Notes

1. This is the title of an article published in 1884 which reviewed many of the political and economic factors that had given rise to this 'climatic' change in the Highlands.

   J.A. Cameron, 'Storm-clouds in the Highlands.' *The Nineteenth Century*, XIV, 1884, 379–395.

2. H.G. Graham, *The Social Life of Scotland in the 18th Century*, 2 vols., London, Adam & Charles Black, 1899, I, 190–1.

3. John Kennedy D.D., *The Days of the Fathers in Ross-Shire*, (1861), Inverness, reprint, Christian Focus Publications Ltd., 1979, 156.

4. John Macleod, *No Great Mischief If You Fall: The Highland Experience*, Edinburgh, Mainstream, 1993, 53.

5. In the course of time these gad-flies were removed; and the only traces of 'black prelacy' left in the country were a very few Episcopal chapels, the resorts of Jacobite lairds and their underlings, and of fugitives from Presbyterian discipline . . . Before the middle of the century [the eighteenth] the great revival of religion began, which spread its blessed influence alike over Highlands and Lowlands.
    Kennedy, Op cit., 25–6.

6. John Macleod, Op cit., 53–4.

7. Carmichael described the phenomenon which was to significantly influence the personality of the Highlanders and Islanders:
    A blessed change came over the place and the people and the good men and the good ministers who arose did away with the songs and the stories, the music and the dancing, the sport and the games, that were perverting the minds and ruining the souls of the people, leading them to folly and stumbling . . . They made the people break and burn their pipes and fiddles. If there was a foolish man here and there who demurred, the good ministers and the good elders themselves broke and burned their instruments.
    Alexander Carmichael, *Carmina Gadelica* Hymns and Incantations, etc., 6 vols., (Vols., I and II only edited by Carmichael) Edinburgh, T. and A. Constable, 1900, I, xxx.
    See also: James Hunter, *The Making of the Crofting Community*, Edinburgh, John Donald, 1976, 99–102.
    Kennedy, Op cit., '*The Men' Of Ross-Shire*, 74–97. This chapter gives an account of *The Men* as assessed by a parish minister.

8. Kennedy, Op cit., 100.

9. Kennedy, op cit., 102–3.

10. Ibid., 124–5.
    But the Revd John Kennedy, while prepared to acknowledge the role played by 'the men', predicted further ecclesiastical conflict:
    There have been in the north, for half a century at least [eighteenth century], a few cliques of Separatists, quite distinct from the order of 'the men.' Specimens of the former have often been taken as if fairly representing the latter. Among these Separatists were men of eminent piety, and some of eminent gifts. Disgusted by the ungodliness, or driven off by the tyranny, of moderate ministers, they separated from the Church, and assumed an almost distinct position to themselves. Having begun to be leaders, in the first consciousness of power, they were unduly elated, and became the censors of some of whom they should have been the disciples . . . Extreme specimens of this section of the Separatists might be found, . . . But these were no specimens at all of 'the men.'

11. Hunter, 1976, Op cit., 94.

12. Kennedy, Op cit., 175–6.

13. Robert Somers, *Letters from the Highlands on the Famine of 1846*, (1848), Perth, reprint, Melven Press, 1985, 66.

14. O.S.A., X (Kilcalmonnell and Kilberry). 63.

15. Many ministers' observations about their rural parishes, no matter how sympathetic to Establishment policy they sometimes appeared, did at least reflect privation that many themselves shared with their parishioners. For the minister in most Highland parishes during the eighteenth century, the physical extent of some parishes, the remoteness of their boundaries and the lack of roads and bridges soon eroded the initial missionary zeal of all but an undaunted few. The *bête noire* was, therefore, not always the patron, though some ministers did have to sue their patron in order to obtain the basic necessities for the conduct of their ministry. The minister of South Knapdale [Argyll], for example, when he came to his parish had neither a church, a proper place to worship, a manse or a glebe. In 1772, he had to sue his 'heritors at law before he could prevail upon them to build a kirk.' For six years he had to preach in the fields.

    O.S.A., XIX (S. Knapdale), 321–2.

    The minister of Glassary [Argyll] had a manse but it was old and poorly built: 'It was twice partially repaired within these 30 years, and stands now in need of a thorough one, owing to the economy of the heritors upon these occasions.'

    O.S.A., XIII (Glassary), 660–1n.

    On Lord Macdonald's land on the Isle of Skye, the Sleat parish church had been built in 1681 and was the 'largest structure of that sort in the island' but there was no manse or designed glebe, 'the present incumbent being accommodated with a farm and tolerable mansion-house.'

    O.S.A., XVI (Sleat), 538–9.

16. The potato famine of 1846 revealed the Free Church's bond with the Highland poor. In a spirit of ecumenism, the Argyll Synod began to collect funds and supplies to distribute to all starving West Highlanders and Islanders. Their efforts and example prompted the rapid formation of the Free Church Destitution Committee which extended this aid to the whole of Scotland.

17. Revd Thomas Brown, *Annals Of The Disruption*, New edn., Edinburgh, Macniven & Wallace, 1893, 155–6.

18. J.G. Fyfe, *Scottish Diaries and Memoirs 1746–1843*, 2 vols., Stirling, Eneas Mackay, 1942, II, 578–9.

19. Ibid., 581.

20. Brown, op cit., 561–2.

21. Ibid., 560.

22. James Barron, *The Northern Highlands tn the Nineteenth Century,* Newspaper Index and Annals, 3 vols., Inverness, Robt. Carruthers & Sons, 1907, II (1825–1841), xix–xx.

23. Ibid., xxi–xxii.

24. *Report by the Crofters Commission on the Social Condition of the People of Lewis In 1901 As Compared With Twenty Years Ago.* B.P.P., 1902, LXXXIII, xxiv–xxv.

25. Ibid., xxiv.

26. Ibid., xxviii–xxx, xxxvii.

27. W.M. Mackay, *Thomas Chalmers: A Short Appreciation*, Edinburgh, Knox Press, 1980, 37.

28. Ibid., 39.

29. Ibid., 37.

30. In his belief that this would create a harmful dependence on charity, Chalmers was not alone. Many reports submitted to the Highland Famine Relief Committee supported his reasoning:

> I would also humbly suggest an opinion, that no relief ought to be eleemosynary, except to such as are incapable of earning it by bodily labour. Even in regard to charitable contributions, let the able-bodied do something for their allowances, by which they will benefit themselves and their country, and by which, above all, they will preserve that spirit of independence for which the Highlanders have always been proverbial.

Revd M. MacGregor, in *Extracts of Letters to the Revd Dr Mcleod, Glasgow, Regarding the Famine and Destitution in the Highlands and Islands of Scotland.* Glasgow, John Smith and Sons, 1847, 7.

> The Revd Archibald Clerk of the parish of Kilmallie also noted that:
> having so frequently expressed his dread of the evils of the ruinous effects of giving gratuitous aid to the able bodied, or of dealing with the Highlands in any impartial or sectarian spirit, [the Highlanders] if deprived of their cows and crofts, they sink into irretrievable pauperism, and become a fearful burden on the land. I am afraid that all these would require an immediate, and nearly gratuitous supply of food to keep them from utter wretchedness.

Ibid., 66–7.

> The Revd Clerk further reported that during the famines of 1836–37:
> Relief was given without exacting work for it; was given *gratuitously*; and the degrading effects were most visible on the character and conduct of the people for the following years. I speak not of what I have heard, but of what I have *seen*, when I say, that in 1838, '39, and

'40, able-bodied men frequently loitered for days around the houses of their superiors, entreating of them to petition for fresh supplies of meal.

Ibid., 69.

31. Ibid., 38.

32. A.Allan McLaren, 'Bourgeois Ideology and Victorian Philanthropy : The Contradictions of Cholera', in *Social Class in Scotland;Past And Present*, A. Allan McLaren Ed., Edinburgh, John Donald, 1976, 47.

33. M.W. Flinn, Ed., *Report on the Sanitary Condition of the Labouring Population of Great. Britain* by Edwin Chadwick, 1842, Edinburgh, reprint, Univ, Press, 1965, Introduction 1, 72–3.

34. Thomas Ferguson, *The Dawn of Scottish Social Welfare*, Edinburgh, Thomas Nelson and Sons Ltd., 1948. 147–8.

35. *Report on the Sanitary Conditions of the Labouring Population of Great Britain*, 1842, Local reports relating to Scotland, London, 1842, 13–4.

36. Margaret DeLacy, 'Puerperal Fever in Eighteenth-Century Britain', *Bulletin of the History of Medicine*, 1989, 63, 549.

37. McLaren, Op cit., 41.

38. In many other cases, however, requests for aid were ignored. For a detailed review of the state of the Highland poor see: *Poor Law Inquiry (Scotland)*, Appendix, Part II, 1844, B.P.P. XXVII–XXXVI.

The evidence taken included that from the Synods of Argyll and Glenelg. Invariably, on the Argyll estates, this request for assistance was forthcoming. Idem., 123, 124–5,128, 153.

However, on Lord Macdonald's estates, assistance appears to have been restricted mainly to those on the Outer Isles. He was not so generous to the poor on his Skye estate. Idem., 366–8.

Macleod of Macleod accepted his responsibility towards the maintenance of his estate's poor. Idem., 389.

The minister of Kintail petitioned the three heritors of his parish, none of whom were resident, and received contributions from two and no answer from the third.Idem., 434.

No support for the upkeep of the poor was received from the proprietors on Barra, South Uist and Ullapool.

As always, social relationships were based on individual personalities and identities, and some parish ministers were more fortunate in their source of relief.

Donald Macdonald, *Lewis: A History of the Island*, Edinburgh, Gordon Wright, 1990, 51, 127.

O.S.A.,VIII (Kilmalie), 435.

39. O.S.A., XIII (Glassary), 662.

40. O.S.A., XVII (Small Isles), 284.

41. O.S.A., X (Culross), 140.

42. O.S.A., XI (Wattin), 262.

43. James Hooper Dawson, *New Issue of the abridged Statistical History of Scotland*, Edinburgh, 1854, lviii, Poor Laws.

   Dawson noted that in 1579, the Scotch Parliament passed Statute 12 James VI. c. 74, which formed the basis of the existing code of poor laws. Furthermore, he noted that this Statute was, in several parts, literally copied from the English Statute, 14 Elizabeth, c. 5, passed about seven years previously. In the Scotch Statute, however, there was not a word about providing for any unemployed person, though this formed a prominent feature in the English Act.

44. Sir George Nicholls, *A History of the Scotch Poor Law* [London, 1856], Reprints of Economic Classics, New York, Augustus M. Kelley, 1967, 138.

   But the Report of the Poor Law Inquiry Commission for Scotland delivered in 1844 also added that

   a strong feeling in opposition to a legal assessment has existed in Scotland, and the clergy in general have strenuously exerted their influence, to prevent recourse being had to any compulsory mode of raising funds for the relief of the poor.

   Idem., 138–9.

   This observation suggests that during the period of the Committee's inquires many of the parish ministers were still 'lairds' men'.

45. *Scottish Lunacy Commission, Report of Lunatic Asylums in Scotland*, Edinburgh, 1857, 44–5.

46. The able-bodied Scottish poor would not become eligible for relief until the early twentieth century.

47. Op cit., 140.

48. Jean Lindsay, *The Scottish Poor Law: Its Operation in the North East from 1745 to 1845*, Ilfracombe Devon, Arthur H. Stockwell Ltd., 1975, 229.

49. Somers, Op cit., 67 and Appendix No. I.

50. O.S.A., XIV (Kilfinan), 234n.

51. R.A. Lewis, *Edwin Chadwick and the Public Health Movement 1832–1854*, London, Longmans, Green and Co., 1952, 199–200.

52. Ibid., 214–5.

53. Ibid., 215.

54. *Report to the Secretary for Scotland by the Crofters Commission*, 1902, Op cit.,

xlvi.

55. 'A Society For The Enforcement Of Sanitary Laws And The Improvement Of Dwellings'. A public notice printed in *The Nineteenth Century*, 1884, XV, No. 85, 361–2.

The object of the notice was to make known the existence of the Society, and it invited information regarding any particular cases of hardship or misery (in London) which were traceable to evasion or neglect of the existing law. Its committee of eleven contained one Baroness, two Earls, four Members of Parliament and one clergyman.

10

Gaeldom's Magna Carta

> Where some possess much, and the others nothing, there may arise an extreme
> democracy, or a pure oligarchy; or a tyranny may grow out of either extreme.[1]

IN THE LAST THREE CHAPTERS of this account, we continue our discussion
of health and land reform, and of the differences in class and ideology that
underlay the struggle for those reforms. In this chapter, we discuss those
events that led to land reform – that demand of radical preachers and
physicians and of enlightened Establishmentarians no less than of ordinary
Highlanders themselves.

Primary among those events was the appointment of the Royal
Commission of Inquiry into the Conditions of the Crofters and Cottars
in the Highlands and Islands of Scotland (1884), popularly referred to as
the Napier Commission, for its Chairman, Francis Baron Napier. Just as
the potato famines of the nineteenth century rank as a watershed in the
nutritional history of Gaeldom, the Napier Commission stands as a turning
point in its social history. Indeed, that the Commission was appointed itself
demonstrates that the Government had finally acknowledged the plight of
the Highland poor. Further, the Crofters Holding Act of 1886, the outcome
of the Commission's deliberations, though it did not order the restoration
of traditional farm land, was nonetheless regarded as the Highland Magna
Carta. Even as the original Magna Carta of 1215 was for Anglo-Saxons a
sacred symbol of English liberty and the rights of man, so the Highland
Magna Carta, the Crofters Holding Act, enunciated the basic principles of
liberty and the rights of Highlanders in the second half of the nineteenth
century. The truth is that neither document really protected commoners
from the policies or practices of the English or Scottish Establishment.
Indeed, it served Establishment interests in both countries to encourage
the myth that came to enshrine those documents. Nonetheless, the Crofters
Holding Act was a victory in the battle to have Highlanders' oppression
recognised and in the struggle to redress that oppression.

I

The warrant dated 22 March, 1883 appointing the Commissioners 'deemed
it expedient that [they] should forthwith issue to inquire into the condition

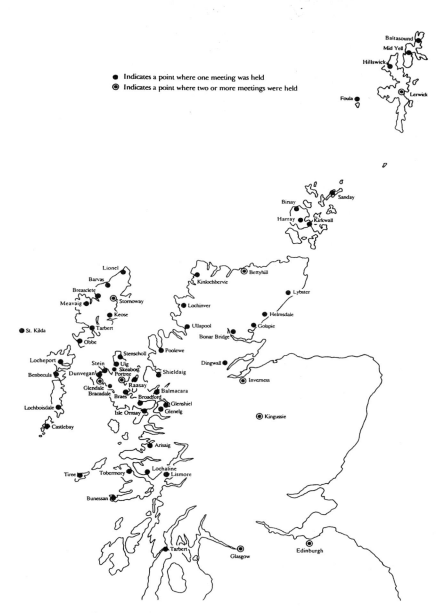

Figure 4. Map showing the points at which the Commission held meetings for the examination of witnesses.

of the Crofters and Cottars in the Highlands and Islands of Scotland, and all matters affecting the same, or relating thereto.'[2] The Chair of the Commission was Francis Baron Napier KT (Lord Napier and Ettrick), Lowland landowner, member of a famous Scottish family, retired from a distinguished diplomatic career as Governor of Madras, and Viceroy of India (*pro tempore*). Four other prominent Scots served on the Commission: Sir Kenneth Smith Mackenzie Bart., a Highland landowner and Lord Lieutenant of Ross and Cromarty from 1881; Donald Cameron of Locheil, a career diplomat, MP for Inverness-shire and proprietor of an extensive Highland estate; Charles Fraser-Mackintosh, a lawyer with known pro-crofter sympathies, a Gaelic scholar and Liberal MP (Inverness Burghs 1874–85, and Inverness-shire, 1885–92); Alexander Nicolson LLD, (a native of Skye), advocate, Sheriff-Substitute of the Stewarty of Kirkcudbright (south-east Lowlands), and also a Gaelic scholar who collected Gaelic proverbs and had revised the Gaelic Bible; Professor Donald Mackinnon MA, born on the Isle of Colonsay, the first holder of the Chair of Celtic, University of Edinburgh (1882–1914). Despite the fact that at least three Commissioners were Gaelic-speaking Gaels, they were clearly, by our definition, members of the Establishment, a fact not lost on Highland paupers and their leaders. In fact, the Commissioners were generally regarded as emissaries of the very class responsible for the distress they purported to investigate and relieve. In consequence, the Commission was ' . . . universally condemned by every Association, every individual, and by almost every newspaper throughout the country . . . ' The Celtic Magazine's derision was typical:

> Are [landowners] at all likely to recommend the modification of their present rights of property, or the abolition or material curtailment of deer forests, from which they and their class derive a great portion of their revenues? If they do so they will prove themselves more than human.[3]

The condemnation was ill-founded, as the contents of the Commission's *Report* were to reveal. The Commissioners solicited and recorded massive evidence of the plight of the poor, hearing testimony throughout the Highlands, questioning speakers candidly and helpfully. Their analysis of that evidence was meticulous and fair. Furthermore, the Commissioners made it plain that they were prepared to accept people's depositions, though many submissions contained allegations and grievances impossible to research or prove. Their task, they said, was to document the extent of the people's distress, as the people themselves gauged that distress:

> In judging of the validity of much of this evidence, we shall do well to remember that these depositions, regarding acts and incidents often obscure

and remote, are in many cases delivered by illiterate persons speaking from early memory, or from hearsay, or from popular tradition, fleeting and fallacious sources even when not tinged by ancient regrets and resentments, or by the passions of the hour. But here, in addition to causes of infirmity which would apply to miscellaneous testimony offered anywhere, not on oath, and not in the face of a court of justice, we have the fact that the progress of the Commission was anticipated by agents enlisted in the popular cause. Intervention from without of this character was to be expected in a free country, and it may not have been without justification, and even utility, among a population in a dependent and precarious condition, *unused to combination for a public purpose* [italics are mine] . . . Many of the allegations of oppression and suffering with which these pages are painfully loaded would not bear a searching analysis . . . It does not follow, however, these narratives are incorrect in detail, [or] they are incorrect in colour or in kind. The history of the economical transformation which a great portion of the Highlands and Islands has during the past century undergone does not repose on the loose and legendary tales that pass from mouth to mouth: it rests on the solid basis of contemporary records, and if these are wanting, it is written in indelible characters on the surface of the soil. Changes of this nature, going to the very foundation of social and domestic life, are not anywhere accomplished without some constraint, resistance, and distress, and if the instances produced are not specifically and literally true, they are akin to truth . . . On a general review of the positive information which we are enabled to supply, we are constrained to avow that it is not commensurate to the importance and complexity of the subject-matter of our Commission, and our conclusions are in no small measure founded on impressions derived from personal observation, from the opinion of men of competent authority, from books, and from previous familiarity with the interests at issue.[4]

That the Commission was as good as its word is evident throughout its record of proceedings. As illustration, we have furnished from its *Report* the Commission's questioning of the Revd Alexander Davidson, Free Church Minister, Harris. (Appendix B) The Revd Davidson's testimony is indicative of the Commission's sympathetic handling of witnesses. It is also especially informative of Highlanders' circumstances. The Reverend knew whereof he spoke. He was an educated Highlander 'from near Inverness', and he had been minister of South Harris since 1848. As a young man, he was one of the first ordained Gaelic-speaking ministers of the post-Disruption Free Church. More to the point, he had witnessed first-hand the suffering that accompanied the potato famines of 1846 and 1847. He was a good witness: forthcoming but not belligerent, not rehearsed for his submission. His presentation was, however, though candid, rather bland overall. Skilful cross examination, particularly by the lawyer, Mr. Fraser-

Mackintosh, extracted from him, however, a fuller description of the life
of the crofters and cottars in his parish.

Significant also was the Commissioners' use of a political tactic intended
to strengthen the 'people's cause': in their questioning of Reverend
Davidson, as of other presenters, they sought information that would
strengthen their argument that the welfare of the Highlands and of its
crofters and cottars was important to, among other national concerns, the
defence of the country:

> [The area provides] a natural basis for the naval defence of the country . . . It
> may be added, that most of the men incorporated in the corps of militia and
> volunteers would be able to serve ashore and afloat with equal efficiency.[5]

Their inquiry completed, the Commissioners submitted six 'suggestions
for the diminution and removal of the numerous causes of depression and
discontent' under the headings, *Land, Fisheries and Communications,
Education, Justice, Deer Forests and Game, and Emigration*. (Appendix C
presents the conclusion of the Commission's *Report*.) Their observations
identified many of the same causes of ill-health and disease that we have
discussed in previous chapters. In their comments about *Land*, for example,
they diagnosed the overcrowding on near barren plots as a tragic outcome
of free-held land tenure and as a certain cause of destitution and disease:

> The social problem in the Highlands and Islands is complicated by the
> prevalence of subtenancy and squatting. Where this practice is least injurious it
> takes the form of cottars' holdings, in which the occupiers pay a stipulated rent
> to the farmer in money or service, and may be regarded as occasional farm
> servants. A more unhappy case is where the offspring of the recognised
> occupiers of township holdings remain and multiply on the ground, either
> sharing the narrow dwellings of the family, or putting up habitations in defiance
> of estate regulations. But the evil assumes its darkest complexion in the Long
> Island, where in some places, in the waste, there are crowds of squatters who
> construct hovels, appropriate land, and possess and pasture stock, but pay no
> rent, obey no control, and scarcely recognise any allegiance or authority. These
> poor people [the cottars] support themselves by casual labour in the country,
> by the simpler kinds of fishing, and by wandering elsewhere in quest of work.
> It is needless to say that they are a burden to the crofter and the proprietor, and
> that they are in a chronic state of poverty, degenerating in bad seasons to
> absolute destitution . . .
>
> All persons, of whatever condition, living on lands occupied by the
> proprietor, and rendering him any covenanted service, or labour, or payment
> in kind, should have the right to commute such obligation for money payment
> by arbitration.[6]

The Commissioners concluded that whatever its merits or defects, the crofting system would continue for the foreseeable future. They therefore set themselves the task of ascertaining

what, in the opinion of the ordinary crofter, would be for him a comfortable holding. There was some difficulty in arriving at a just conclusion on this point, from the fact that every one, whatever the extent of his occupancy, professed to need more than he had.

Their inquiry was complicated by the great variations in Highland topography and climate:

The extent of land required for a sheep's grass in the mountain pastures of the north varies from three to six acres. In the Northern Hebrides, and on the adjacent parts of the mainland, the grazing cannot certainly be said to be above average quality, and though parts of Skye may be classed as superior, much of the Long Island is so poor that over the whole island it is safe to say not less than 4½ acres would be necessary for each sheep. But as this calculation refers to the sheep of the large farmer, it must be modified for those of the crofter, which are generally of inferior size, and from figures before us we think not more than three acres of pasture apiece should be allowed for them.[7]

Nonetheless, the Commission did recommend that crofters and cottars be granted more land:

We have now to state that in our judgement these provisions [for the improvement of townships] should be supplemented by others pointing to the expansions of townships . . . The occupiers in an existing township should have the right to claim from the proprietor an enlargement of the existing township in regard to arable land and common pasture, in virtue of a resolution adopted by not less than two thirds of the occupiers, . . . In case the proprietor should not . . . come to a voluntary settlement with the occupiers . . . the Sheriff-Substitute should [if he finds the claim well founded] record the claim as a reasonable claim.

In this case the proprietor should be held liable to grant to the existing township an increase of arable ground, or hill pasture, or both . . .[8]

In their comments about another aspect of crofting life, – *Dwellings* – we find no contempt for the traditional black house; in fact, the Commissioners recognised it as a reasonable adaptation to locale, even though they recommended improvements to effect better sanitation and comfort:

It is difficult to say how far the crofter or cottar is sensible of the disadvantages attached to the darkness and privations of his primitive habitation, or how far this feature in his life is actually prejudicial to his happiness and welfare. In the main his house does not make him unhappy, for he does not complain; it does not make him immoral, for he is above the average standard of morality in his country; it does not make him unhealthy, for he enjoys an uncommon share of vigour and longevity. Yet no one concerned for the elevation of the Highland people can fail to desire an improvement in this particular; no one can doubt that if they are well-conducted and robust, it is in spite of their lodging and in consequence of counteracting causes, and that if they enjoyed the benefit of purer and brighter homes they would prosper more . . . There is even in the remoter and least advanced parts of the country an unmistakable movement in the direction of improved accommodation, stimulated partly by the encouragements afforded by liberal proprietors, partly owing to increased intelligence and emulation among the people . . . *Public authority, which is powerless to create by any peremptory proceeding a higher order of dwellings for the Highland poor, is competent to correct abuses which are offensive to the first principles of decency and health* [italics are mine].[9]

The state of *Education* in the Highlands received considerable attention from the Commission as well. Of particular interest is their unequivocal endorsement of public instruction in Gaelic and of fluency in Gaelic as a requirement for all education officials:

> We think that the discouragement and neglect of the native language in the education of Gaelic speaking children, which have hitherto so largely influenced the system practised in the Highlands ought to cease, and a knowledge of that language ought to be considered one of the primary qualifications of every person engaged in the carrying out of the national system of education in Gaelic-speaking districts, whether as school inspectors, teachers, or compulsory officers.[10]

Under *Justice*, the Commissioners observed that the rights of the illiterate poor were often misunderstood or ignored, because officials were ignorant of the area they worked in, and because they were preoccupied by other responsibilities:

> The office of Sheriff-substitute in the Highlands and Islands is not always deemed a desirable one, and this circumstance has the effect of limiting selection at the seats of legal patronage, so that the choice of the responsible authorities may often fall on parties altogether unacquainted with the peculiar conditions of life in the districts referred to, and ignorant of the habitual language of the people . . . It is also expedient that the important qualification of a knowledge of Gaelic should not be lost sight of, and the same qualification is as desirable in the case of procurators-fiscal [Crown Attorneys] as in that of sheriffs. The representatives of public justice in the secluded situations to which we allude are placed under many disadvantages with reference to society and residence. There might possibly be in some cases an unconscious admission of external

influences, and in other cases the existence of such influences might be expected where it does not operate . . . There is a natural tendency, in the poor and remote localities to which we are adverting, towards a concentration of offices, partly consequent on the inadequate remuneration of public functionaries, partly on the paucity of qualified persons, and partly, it may be, on the desire of local power which is attached to the cumulative possession of positions of this nature . . . We are of the opinion that these functionaries, so closely identified with administration of the law, should be prohibited from doing any professional work or any business for profit other than their proper business respectively, either by themselves, or their partners, deputies, or others, and that this restriction should contemplate functions performed in other counties, as well as the counties in which they hold their appointments.[11]

Though supportive of cottars and crofters generally, the Commission did not take their side on all issues. On the question of land rents, for example, the Commission found for the landlords. The Commission did not accept that rents had become prohibitive. In fact, they maintained that most rents were fair, and that many landlords had acted benevolently in keeping rents at rates lower than market value:

Rents are commonly found to be most moderate on the larger estates transmitted in the old families of the country, and on those that have been purchased by great capitalists more, it may be, with a view to pleasure, local association, or social position, than to profit. They may probably be higher on smaller properties acquired with a distinct purpose of advantageous pecuniary investment. In most cases a considerable degree of indulgence, often amounting to benevolence, may be discovered in the rents of small holdings; they are rarely disposed of, when vacant, on a purely commercial principle, or by public competition in any form, and are almost invariably held on easier terms than might be obtained in the open market by the inconsiderate rivalry of people aspiring to the occupancy of land. The grievance of increased rent has been submitted to our notice in many instances, but in most, we think, *with much less force and earnestness than the complaint respecting restricted areas* [italics are mine] . . . We hope that Government may find in our proposals a basis for useful legislation, and that when the prevailing agitation has been stilled by reflection and the lapse of time, the crofter and the cottar may recognise in our action and advice an earnest desire for their welfare.[12]

The subject of *Deer Forests and Game* evoked some of the bitterest depositions the Commission heard. The Commissioners recognised the social and economic ramifications of landlords' practice of excluding people from those private domains and thereby depriving them of an important food supply. They acknowledged, too, people's deep resentment of the practice:

The social and economical aspects of the question have presented themselves at every turn, and have formed the basis of almost every answer given under examination, the effect of forests on the general subject of our inquiry, *viz.*, crofters and cottars.

The principal objections advanced against deer forests, as presented to us, are the following:

1. That they have been created to a great extent by the eviction of or removal of the inhabitants, and have been the cause of depopulation.

2. That land now cleared for deer might be made available for profitable occupation by crofters.

3. That it might at all events be occupied by sheep farmers, and that a great loss of mutton and wool to the nation might thus be avoided.

4. That in some places, where deer forests are contiguous to arable land in the occupation of crofters, damage is done to the crops of the latter by the deer.

5. That deer deteriorate the pasture.

6. That the temporary employment of gillies [a sportsman's attendant, from the Gaelic *gille* a lad or servant] and others in connection with deer forests has a demoralizing effect.

Nonetheless, the Commissioners stopped short of recommending that crofters have access to game reserves. In fact, they argued that for landlords to open the reserves to unrestricted hunting would be an unreasonable sacrifice since 'valuable interests have thus grown up, which could not be set aside without imposing on the proprietor greater sacrifices than he could be justly required to undergo.'[13] To appreciate the Commissions's stand on this matter, we must remember that most estates had by the time of the Commission's hearings, been converted from sheep walks to sporting estates in landlords' attempts to survive economically. Under the then-current economic structure of the Highlands and Islands, crofters and cottars depended on that survival. Forcing landlords to forfeit their sporting estates might well have bankrupted them and so consigned crofters and cottars to even greater poverty and misery.

On the particular question of destruction of crops by ground and flying game, however, the Commissioners found for the crofters:

> There seems to be no reason why, in cases of injury or destruction of crop, compensation should not be awarded to the sufferer in a manner more summary than has hitherto been used . . . to the amount in which the adjacent proprietor is liable.[14]

Another complaint which the Commission deliberated was 'the alleged demoralizing effect of sporting employment on the character of the people brought into contact with it', an allegation made in a 'Statement to the

Commission' by Revd Roderick Morison, minister of the Established Church, Kintail, Ross shire. On that issue, however, the Commission concluded that the minister's complaint could not be substantiated.[15]

Finally, on the thorny question of *Emigration*, the Commissioners openly encouraged emigration as one solution for the Highland Problem. In fact, they declared that in some areas it was the only solution:

> But it is principally in the Northern Hebrides, and to some extent on the adjacent coasts of Ross, and perhaps even Sutherland, that we think it should be resorted to. The destitution that called for charity last spring was in the main limited to those districts, and there too, more emphatically than elsewhere, the crofters' complaints turn on the smallness of their holdings. No doubt extraneous relief was given last year in Glenelg and in some parishes of the Southern Hebrides, but there is reason to hope that in these last the great evil of too small holdings is being gradually extinguished, and on the coast of Inverness-shire it might be questioned whether overcrowding is due to an actual want of land in the neighbourhood. Our remarks then on emigration will relate to the districts we have named . . . It has been repeatedly stated in evidence that there is no need for emigration, as there is plenty of land in the Highlands and Islands for all the people they contain, were it only divided among them. Even if this were so, it is clear that such a division would involve the exclusion of the whole wealthy and wage-paying class, a result which no one acquainted with the Highlands could contemplate without concern. But those who thus hold emigration to be unnecessary, have not, we think, given sufficient attention to the statistics bearing on the subject.[16]

In fact, after carefully calculating the acreage that the average crofter would require to run a subsistence farm, the Commission concluded that the land mass was patently inadequate for the population of people and their animals:

> If the average crofter were to keep a stock of 92 sheep he would . . . require 227½ acres of pasture land. He would also require nine or ten acres of arable ground, or 287 acres in all . . .

Nor could other occupations, like fishing or industrial work, provide enough money to compensate people for the shortfall in crofting land. The Commission saw *emigration* as the only way to relieve the pressure of over-population:

> It may possibly be replied that the Hebrideans do not rely solely on farming, that they are to a large extent fishermen and take their living out of the sea, . . . and after making every allowance for the number of people who may be expected to derive the whole or the greater portion of their livelihood from the sea, we are of the opinion that a resort to emigration is unavoidable. Were

trade more flourishing, a move to the great seats of industry might provide a natural outlet for the surplus population, but our overcrowded towns are themselves crying out for State-aided or State-directed emigration, and while individuals may still find openings in them, no great stream of migration can at present with advantage flow towards our industrial centres.

... Now, emigration from the Highlands and Islands, mainly consequent on want of employment at home, has been more or less continuous for the last hundred and fifty years.[17]

Moreover, the Commissioners argued that earlier emigration had been unplanned and wasteful: many of the Highland emigrants had been unprepared for conditions abroad; many had been encouraged to go to relieve impoverished Highland parishes, though they were as unable to support themselves elsewhere as they had been at home. The state must begin to control and support emigration, the Commission maintained:

The advantages of State direction which the Government Agency would confer should not be limited to emigrants requiring aid in the way of advances. Strangers in the colonies, without local guidance, waste both time and means in the selection of land and the search for employment, and, ignorant now to supply the requirements of their new position, they frequently make needless sacrifice of their small capital in providing for their earlier wants.

The State agency, if fitly equipped at home and abroad, could make arrangements beforehand which would save the crofter emigrants from these sources of loss.

We think it important that assisted emigration should be placed under the immediate direction of officers of the Imperial Government rather than under the control of local authorities. It would be the interest of the latter to shift poverty from their own locality, irrespective of the prospects of the poor who were removed, and almost inevitably this interest would to a greater or less extent prejudice the careful selection of emigrants. If emigration by families is to be conducted successfully, the proportion of dependants to bread-winners must not be lost sight of.[18]

On all matters, the Commissioners adhered rigorously to their terms of reference. And in general, their *Report* was pro-crofter and cottar. Their recommendations recognised the injustice of generations. On its publication in 1884, the Commission's *Report*, together with the volumes of *Evidence* upon which it was based, was studied as closely by the Establishment as by pro-crofter lobbyists. In the Highlands and Islands, landowners no less than paupers waited expectantly for the Government's reaction. Two years later, the Government responded with the Crofters Holding (Scotland) Act of 1886.

II

The Government that enacted the Crofters Act was the same one that had appointed the Napier Commission. The man behind both initiatives was the then Prime Minister, William Ewart Gladstone. Educated at Eton and Oxford, Gladstone was the son of a Liverpool merchant. He was first elected as a Tory MP in 1832, but by mid-century he had left the Tories for the Liberal party. Mindful of the unrest that had followed the French Revolution and the militancy that had accompanied the Irish land troubles, he recognised the danger of the turmoil that had surfaced in the Highlands and Islands. Besides, as a Liberal statesman he had gained a reputation as an 'ardent defender of the oppressed'. As such, he knew that Highlanders' needs had been shamefully ignored since the rebellion of 1745. And he knew that the 'Highland problem', like the 'Irish question', could explode into widespread violence and anarchy. Gladstone had ameliorated much of the Irish land problem by passing the Irish Land Acts of 1870 and 1881 and at that time he had recorded his belief that

> 'without the Land League (an agricultural tenants' movement) the act of 1881 would not now be upon the statute book.' He did not mean that the league had changed his own conception of what was desirable, but that its influence on British opinion had made it politically possible for him to carry that conception into effect.[19]

Solving the Highland problem, Gladstone reasoned, would require a vehicle similar to the Irish Land League to investigate, record and politicise commoners' complaints. The Napier Commission was to be that vehicle.

But his Liberal government was not strong enough to 'carry his conception' *in toto* through parliament. Highland estates and their proprietors' interests were too much part of the English Establishment for that Establishment to endorse the Commission's main recommendation – more land for crofters and cottars.

III

Despite that glaring omission, the Crofters Act did redress many grievances: it made tenure of land secure; it fixed rents; it ordered that crofters be compensated for any improvement they made; and it gave crofters the right to inherit, bequeath or assign their crofts. A Crofters' Commission was rapidly convened to implement the Act's recommendations and to protect the rights it conferred. At least one member of this Commission had by law to be a Gaelic speaker. (In 1911, this Commission would be superseded by the Scottish Land Court.)

In 1892 Gladstone appointed a further Royal Commission (Highlands and Islands, 1892).[20] Its *Report* showed that 1.7 million acres of Highland land was suitable for land re-settlement. But two years later Gladstone resigned, and in 1895 under his replacement, Lord Rosbery, an Anglicised Scottish peer, the Liberal government fell. With that fall went any hope of the resettlement that the Highlands and Islands Commission had recommended. As James Hunter notes, the Liberal collapse

> destroyed the credibility – in the Highlands at least – of both the Liberal party and the Land League which had nailed its colours firmly to the Liberal mast. In the ensuing election, therefore, Liberal and Land League fortunes suffered a decisive reverse – the latter organisation now a tattered remnant of its former self, being finally and completely swept from the political scene. The field was thus left open to Conservative and Unionist candidates who based their campaign on their advocacy of land reforms similar to those carried out by the Conservatives in Ireland between 1886 and 1892.[21]

We should say that the Unionism to which Hunter alludes, while having much in common with British Conservatism, was nonetheless clearly Scottish (and Highland) in its objectives. Initially, Unionists had campaigned for Scottish-Irish union; by the early twentieth century they were arguing for Anglo-Scottish union and were opposed to Irish Catholic demands for Irish unity and independence.[22]

In 1886, after the Liberal party's defeat, Scottish Liberal-Unionists split from the Gladstonian Liberals. In 1897, the Conservatives (many of them Scottish Liberal-Unionists) formed the government. One of the new government's first actions was to establish the Highlands Congested Districts Board, whose task it was to enlarge crofters' holdings and establish new Highland settlements to relieve the most overpopulated areas.[23] The final chapter in the story of land reform for Highlanders who stayed at home began at the end of the nineteenth century, and continues in fact today.[24]

The Napier Commission and the Crofters Holding Act of 1886 launched land reform in the Highlands. They fuelled the debate about public health as well. That debate revealed differences in class no less glaring than had the battle over land ownership.

Notes

1. Aristotle, *Politics*, Bk. 4., 1296a, 1–3.

2. *Report of Her Majesty's Commissioners of Inquiry into the Conditions of the Crofters and Cottars in the Highlands and Islands of Scotland*, 1884, B.P.P., XXXII–XXXVI. (Hereafter *Report*), v–vii.

3. Alexander Mackenzie, 'The Crofter Royal Commission', *The Celtic Magazine*, Inverness, A. & W. Mackenzie, Vol. VIII, 1882–83, 317–8.

4. *Report*, 1884, 2–3.

5. *Evidence* taken by the Royal Commission, 4 Vols., I, Examination of Revd Alexander Davidson, Free Church Minister, Harris, 837–816.

6. *Report*, Op cit., 43–4.

7. Ibid., 99–101.

8. Ibid., 24.

9. Ibid., 48–50.

10. Ibid., 81.

11. Ibid., 83.

12. Ibid., 50–3.

13. Ibid., 96.

14. Ibid., 96.

15. Statement regarding Deer Forests in the Highlands, by Revd Roderick Morison, Ibid., App. XCIV, 434–438:

    > Further, it is well known that the life these men lead is demoralising in the extreme, and soon renders the majority of them useless for any except that for which they are trained, so that when thrown out of employment they become simply an incubus on society.
    >
    > Removed, as most of them are, from all the influences of religion, education, and social and family life, it is difficult to foretell what they may become. They are not unlikely to prove, in course of time, a very troublesome and difficult element in the social fabric. 435.

    This grievance, made by a post-Disruption Established Church minister and addressed specifically by the Commission, represented the embodiment of Highland religion, by now a powerful force in Highland life. We observed in previous chapters the concern in the post-Culloden centuries with the effects that acculturation had on the morals of young people as attested by the writings of pre-Disruption Established Church ministers in the *Statistical Accounts*, in the ministries of the evangelical preachers and Free Churchmen. The discussion here is not one of theological dogma but rather of the

cultural identity of a rural people whose lifestyle followed patterns proven
and sanctioned by custom and 'designed to conform to the will of God',
patterns now threatened with extinction. Any sudden change in these
temporal or spiritual patterns would be physically traumatic and
emotionally frustrating.

By way of response to this complaint, the Commissioners ruled that

> When the employer is at the same time the proprietor, or when he
> belongs to the high class of permanent occupiers frequently found on
> sporting estates in the Highlands, safeguards are secured which may, and
> no doubt generally do, effectually control the conduct of the subordinate.
> When on the other hand, the connection between the sporting tenant
> and the locality is transitory, or when his personal disposition renders
> him careless of the morals of his servants, or a bad example to them, the
> result might be very different. It must be remembered, however, that
> temptations to dissipation are not tendered to the youth of the Highlands
> by sporting employments only. They may be found with equal facility
> and less qualified by wholesome influences in connection with the
> existence of a sea-faring man, a fisherman, or a casual labourer in the
> Lowlands, – in fact, in all the other walks of labour and gain to which
> the Highlanders betake themselves, and *betake themselves with confidence
> and success* [italics are mine].

16. Ibid., 97.

Here the Commission was obviously referring to the views of the
'Highland Problem' made by Nicolls in the 1850s:

> If the occupancy of land were to be made the sole means of subsistence
> for the population, as the crofting system implies, and if it were possible
> to furnish every crofter with the necessary capital for this purpose, the
> plan advocated by some persons of giving to each family land sufficient
> to maintain them and pay the rent, would still be found impracticable.
> For instance, in the case of Skye, with its 3,431 families — To provide
> each of these with even as much land as is now let in Skye for 10£.,
> would require more land than both the islands of Skye and Lewis could
> furnish, and would require everyone paying a rent above 10£, to be
> removed [Land with a rental value of 10£ was regarded as the minimum
> required for a croft.]; so that even if the requisite capital could be
> procured for establishing each family on its own croft, the division of
> land into crofts of a size sufficient to supply the families with food
> throughout the year, would necessitate the removal of the larger part of
> the present population, including all those who employ labour, or possess
> the means of giving employment. This shows the great disproportion
> existing between the population and the ordinary means of subsistence,
> not only in Skye but in the western districts generally, the inhabitants of
> which are said to 'have neither capital enough to cultivate the extent of

land necessary to maintain them if it could be provided, nor have they land enough were the capital supplied them.' Under these circumstances, the only remedy seems to emigration.

Sir George Nicholls, *A History of the Scotch Poor Law* (1856), Reprints of Economic Classics, Augustus M. Kelley Pubs., New York, 1967, 255–6.

17. Ibid., 99–102.

18. Ibid., 107–8.

19. J.C. Beckett, *The Making Of Modern Ireland 1603 – 1923*, 2nd edn., London, Faber Paperbacks, 1981, 390.

20. *Royal Commission (Highlands and Islands 1892), Report and Minutes of Evidence*, B.P.P., 1895, XXXVIII – XXXIX.

21. James Hunter, *The Making of the Crofting Community*, Edinburgh, John Donald, 1976, 182–3.

22. In 1912, Scottish Unionists had espoused the name 'Scottish Unionist Party'. Only in 1965 was this name changed to the Scottish Conservative and Unionist Party.

23. For fuller details on the politics of this formative period of crofting history consult:

    Hunter, (1976) Ibid.

    I.M.M. MacPhail, *The Crofters' War*, Stornoway Isle of Lewis, Acair Ltd., 1989.

24. The *Napier Report* brought the social conditions of the Highland poor to the forefront of British politics. But in the post–Gladstone decades, Highland landowners dealt with Highlanders as British statesmen had dealt with potentially rebellious minorities throughout the Empire: first acculturate, then institute 'self-government'. In the Highlands, acculturation all but complete, all that remained was to fashion a system of self government. In the crofting counties of the Highlands and Islands, the natives would be regarded as an endangered species, too valuable for the nation to lose. Thus crofters would be subsidised and educated, some thereby assisted to join the ranks of the Establishment. The 'lad of parts', the pride of the Scottish Establishment, would be moulded in their own image. This 'lad' came from the lower classes, agricultural or industrial, and by hard work and sacrifice of self and parents, could raise himself to any height he cared to aim for. Many did just that, but in the case of the crofting counties, the country was, and still is, deprived of this home-bred talent. For a discussion on this aspect of Scottish education see:

    R. A. Houston, 'Scottish Education and Literacy, 1600–1800: An International Perspective', in *Improvement and Enlightenment: Proceedings of the Scottish Historical Studies Seminar*, University of Strathclyde, 1987–88, 43–61.

T.C.Smout, *A Century of the Scottish People* 1830–1950, London, Fontana Press, 1987, 217–8.

This loss of talent, observed even in the normal emigration of today's Highland scholars, had not gone unnoticed, hence the feeling of urgency in the West Highlands and Islands for an escape from the final confinement imposed by the status of crofter and the restrictive legislation that encloses croft land. This situation is now so critical that in many areas young 'white settlers' with desirable skills and talent, irrespective of their race, creed, colour or gender, who show a genuine wish to remain in the Highlands and Islands and help with development are welcomed by the 'natives.'

Government subsidies would, however, be limited to *bona fide* crofters, thus, as in North America, the crofting counties would become native *reservations*, and Highlanders living in them would be classified as status or *non-status*; that is, crofter or non-crofter. Those legally designated crofters could, with subsidy, raise a family on small crofts. *Yet crofting alone, even though subsidised, would not sustain a family.* Only those who inherited additional land, or obtained it by amalgamation of other crofts, could subsist by crofting alone. Most crofters remain tied to small lots of inferior land to which their forefathers had been resettled. Land now 'surrounded by legislation'. Those Highlanders and Islanders not legally designated crofters were forced, like the scallags before them, to find work and shelter wherever they could. Little had changed: the need to leave the Highlands and Islands to find employment was as pressing as ever.

The administration of those *croft reservations* would ensure the kind of *self-government* which the Highland and British Establishments had in mind: government, quasi-government and academic departments and agencies proliferated. Together, they employed a corps of 'keepers', not all crofters and many not even Scots who now comprised a large and viable 'Highland' industry. By such means, from the late nineteenth century to the present, the natural and normal development of the crofter and cottar was arrested.

Only very recently, by the purchase in 1993 of the North Lochinver estate by the crofters of Assynt, has that diversionary and retarding form of *self-government* been challenged. The Assynt estate will, its crofter-pioneers believe, permit crofters and scallags on it to croft viably or to engage there in some self-sustaining ventures.

On March 1997, *The Transfer of Crofting Estates (Scotland) Bill* received Royal Assent.

11

Legislated Health Care In the Highlands and Islands

> But this knowledge remains mere intellectual exercise because social and economic factors interfere with its application.[1]

JUST AS LAND REFORM had met fierce opposition from landlords, so too did health reform measures. Reform came, but slowly, protested and stalled at every turn by Scottish and English Establishments since, 'before 1889 County Administration was in Scotland, as in England, in the hands of the local landed gentry.'[2] In 1848, Chadwick's *Report on the Sanitary Conditions of the Labouring Population of Great Britain* (1842) had prompted enactment of the Public Health Act of England. The next year, a Public Health (Scotland) Bill was introduced to the House of Commons. On April 12, 1850, that Bill died after first reading. Nonetheless, in 1862, a Medical Officer of Health for Edinburgh was appointed, the first in Scotland. A year later, Glasgow had a medical officer as well. It was not until 1867, however, that the Public Health (Scotland) Act was passed, giving a Board of Supervision general supervisory powers for Public Health in Scotland, and giving Parochial Boards authority for local sanitation.

One reason for that seventeen-year delay was the Scottish medical profession's refusal to submit to the legislative control of the only general health authority extant during those years – the London-based Central Board of Health, established during the cholera epidemic of 1832.

More formidable opposition to the legislation came from those who were to bear the cost of its enactment, the rate-paying property owners and industrialists. More than a decade earlier, the Scottish Poor Law Amendment Act of 1845 had made them responsible for subsidising the poor of Scotland.[3] The Public Health Act gave the newly-established Health Boards a sweeping mandate which would increase rates dramatically. The new Boards were charged with eliminating infectious diseases and improving sanitation in the houses of crofters and cottars. Indeed, by the last decade of the century, the District Committee in Scotland had responsibility for all facets of public health:

On them are placed the duties of suppressing nuisances, the control of offensive trades, of the general prevention and mitigation of disease. They may provide and maintain hospitals and reception houses . . . They may make by-laws for securing the sanitary condition of, and for preventing overcrowding in public conveyances . . . acquire or provide a water supply, . . . make and cleanse sewers and drains, and provide and maintain sewage utilisation works. They . . . provide for the cleansing and disinfection of verminous persons.[4]

Ratepayers' opposition remained vociferous for decades. In 1885, one writer observed that for years 'In the Highlands and Islands this Act remained practically a dead letter',[5] and the inspector for the North Highland District noted in his report that

The Public Health Act, which was passed nearly eighteen years ago, can hardly be said to be in operation except in a few places, and I can only repeat what I have formerly said, that local authorities in rural districts are really indifferent on the subject of sanitary matters.[6]

To do the job set it, eliminate infectious disease and improve sanitation, the Board had two immediate tasks: to improve housing in the Highlands and to extend medical treatment there. However, from its founding in 1847 to the end of the century, the Board achieved little success in either task.[7] In 1884, Lord Napier's Commission had cautioned that public authority was powerless to order a high standard of housing for the Highland poor. Eight years later, having considered the Commission's recommendations, the Board of Supervision agreed: they concluded that Highlanders could not be persuaded to leave their huts, however unsanitary they might be:

Many of these dwellings throughout extensive districts would, no doubt, be regarded by modern scientific sanitarians as utterly unfit for human habitation . . . On the other hand the Board feel that any attempt to secure the sanitary improvement of these dwellings is attended with quite exceptional difficulties. The people, as a rule, it is believed, are satisfied with, and even attached to, their miserable hovels, and it is impossible to change in a day the confirmed habits of a whole people . . . The Islanders in general are a hardy race, and epidemic disease cannot be said to be more generally present in the Islands than in other parts of the country . . . In these circumstances any proposal involving sudden or sweeping change would almost certainly tend to excite popular resentment and defeat the objects which the Board have in view.[8]

Ironically, when landlords had evicted Highlanders several decades earlier, they gave no consideration to how 'attached to their miserable hovels' the people were. Rather, they had effected the very 'sudden and sweeping change' that the Board advised against. In fact, a consideration far more compelling than concern for Highlanders' attachment to their dwellings was at work in the Board's stand against reform of lodgings or sanitation; the Board was loath to recommend any reform that would further burden ratepayers:

> Moreover, the local assessments are already so oppressive in many of these districts that the imposition of further burdens even for the most excellent object is to be deprecated. The Board, therefore, are not prepared to advise the local authorities of the Western Isles to take measures in the meantime for the radical reconstruction of the dwellings of the labouring population.[9]

Proprietors, owners of the most 'miserable hovels' to which evicted Highlanders had been relocated, regarded the cost of improvements in housing to be prohibitive:

> The obligation to provide a water supply rests under the Public Health Act with the owner of the dwelling, but on the majority of crofting estates it would be beyond the proprietor's resources to supply water to crofting tenants.[10]

Many health inspectors, like those sent to assess sanitation in the Lews even decades later, appeared to concur:

> The cost of providing a gravitation supply by forming Special Water Supply Districts in the Lews would be prohibitive – the rent being so low. The rates are already very high and the bulk of the population in many townships is on the verge of pauperism.[11]

Certainly, no Highland parish could, out of its own rates, upgrade its standard of sanitation to meet national standards. Further, local authorities 'had no statutory right to apply their funds towards the improvement of dwelling houses.'[12] In their appeal to the local Government Board for grants from Imperial funds to improve the houses in the districts under their supervision, the Lews District Committee provided a succinct overview of the basic sanitary problem confronting post-Clearances housing:

> [Cottages are] planted in mossy flats, peat-banks, water-logged hollows, and rocky crevices, and packed and imbedded in one another, joined not only linearly but in closely adjacent layers alongside of one another with no interspace whatever,[13]

The national health authority, responsible as it was for 'general sanitation and the stamping out of infectious diseases', could, however, seek Government aid to improve sanitation and housing in any parish.[14] And it did. But the Board's appeal for financial assistance failed.[15]

In 1895, the Board of Supervision was replaced by the new Local Government Board for Scotland, whose Second Report noted that local authorities in Harris, North Uist, and Lewis had again begged the new central authority to 'approach the Government for a grant-in-aid to enable them to rebuild their cottages.'[16] Their requests, too, were stalled.

Unwilling to increase rates to pay for rebuilding or replacing crofters' and cottars' houses and unable to persuade government to subsidize new housing, health authorities ruled that Highlanders themselves could at least improve sanitation in their houses by sheltering their animals in separate buildings. It outlawed the custom of combining byre and home, and it was prepared to compel people to clean up around their houses:

> In the first instance, take proceedings in each township against those most able to bear the expense of erecting byres for their cattle. In the second place, strict measures should be taken to see that the surroundings of their houses are kept in a comparatively clean condition, and an example should be made of those who continue to deposit filth of all kinds immediately around their doors.[17]

In 1895, four test cases were brought before the Sheriff by the District committees of Lewis and Harris. At first, the campaign was less than successful:

> These test cases roused the people in the vicinity of the convicted parties to commence building operations, but only in a few cases was the work completed, often because the people, after having built the walls, could not obtain wood for the rafters [which was not obtainable locally].[18]

And in fact, in remote areas like the southern part of the Long Island, the custom endured for many years. In 1896, for example, South Uist still had 295 dwelling houses containing 569 cattle, 204 sheep and 9 pigs.[19] In the towns, however, a few more years and a few more prosecutions brought a dramatic decline in the practice.

In 1896, a census showed that 167 dwelling-houses in Harris contained 431 animals, 397 of them cattle, 30 sheep, and 4 horses. But by 1898, Harris was almost clear of dwellings that combined byre and home:

Number of Houses in Harris Where
Cattle were Housed in the Dwelling[20]

Jan.1, 1896	167	houses containing	431	animals
Jan.1, 1897	25	houses containing	71	animals
Jan.1, 1898	13	houses containing	23	animals

The Board had some success, too, in forcing another group to improve sanitation in its buildings:

> Meanwhile the attack on insanitary buildings was being pushed against a more accessible foe. It was admittedly difficult to devise any satisfactory means of forcing impoverished crofters to undertake expensive improvements; it was less

difficult to get the school boards to move. Many of the schools were in a very bad condition: one, for example, with 200 children in attendance had no water within a quarter of a mile.[21]

Yet even in areas where sanitation improved, living conditions generally remained unchanged. Overcrowding in towns and other sites to which Highlanders had been resettled had not been ameliorated; inadequate housing had not been upgraded. Indeed, in 1895, the health inspector for the fishing villages of Caithness reported that 'In almost all the towns from Banff to Thurso, the quarters occupied by the population are in an extremely unsanitary condition.'[22] Those conditions persisted into the present century. In 1917, a Royal Commission noted that

> There are at least 5000 defective houses in the Outer Islands, of which many are in Lewis . . .There were 467 black houses in North Uist as against 247 white ones . . . In Harris the public Health officials agreed that it was hopeless to do anything with the greater part of the black houses in the parish, and these are apparently 60 or 70 per cent of the whole.

In the same year, the Medical Officer of Health for the County further testified that

> the death rate from phthisis is more than double what it was forty years ago, while in the county [Inverness] generally it has gone down about 40 per cent. While not neglecting virgin soil, I am convinced that the housing conditions are the main factor in causing the annual toll of fifty deaths from consumption.[23]

III

Progress was painfully slow too in the Board's second mission, the provision of adequate medical treatment in the Highlands and Islands. Here also impediment and opposition came from landowners and other ratepayers.[24] Certainly, there was no question that Highlanders were served by very few physicians, nor that the Highlands could not afford to pay medical fees themselves:

> For in the scattered communities of the crofting areas private practice is far from being remunerative, and in the poorer districts the fees from private patients are negligible; if the district is to have a medical attendant at all, he must be supported by the parish rates with the aid of this grant. Thus the parochial authority, ostensibly providing medical services for the paupers, in reality provides it for the community at large.[25]

Nor could it be denied that Highlanders had been among the hardest hit
by successive epidemics, so much so that during some epidemics, like that
of 1897 in Eriskay and South Uist, 'the people, panic stricken, fled from
the infected and left them to the care of a few devoted men led by the
doctor and the priest.'[26] Circumstances like those made the need for trained
practitioners urgent.

Yet there were no hospitals or any other treatment facilities in the West
Highlands and Islands, and providing them was deemed too costly. The
Medical Officer of Health for Inverness-shire threw up his hands at the
notion of providing hospitals in the Outer Isles. Thousands of pounds might
be spent on creating hospitals, he conjectured, and then the question would
be, 'On which of the forty-nine inhabited islands are hospitals to be
erected?'[27] As it turned out, the Local Government Board, after inquiry,
dismissed the local inspector and called on the District Committee to
provide, furnish and maintain a hospital for infectious diseases. Eventually,
two buildings, one for Benbecula and one for South Uist, were secured
and converted into modest hospitals, and nurses to staff them were obtained
from Edinburgh.[28]

IV

But general medical services remained spotty and under-financed for
decades in the Highlands. At its founding in 1847, the Board of Supervision
had received from Parliament an annual grant of £10,000 to be distributed
to the Parochial Boards. The grant was intended to extend medical
treatment:

> This grant was used not so much as a means of alleviating the burden of cost as
> of improving the quality of the service. The Board of Supervision fixed a
> minimum expenditure for each parish, and it was made a condition of
> participation that no grant should be paid unless the minimum was reached,
> and unless the parish authority appointed a medical officer at a fixed salary
> which could not be altered with out the consent of the board. It is not too
> much to say that the entire population – paupers and non-paupers – of the
> Highlands and Islands owe their medical service to this grant.[29]

By 1911, £13,000 was being made available for medical relief in Scotland,
but less than £3000 found its way into the Highlands and Islands. To
supplement so woefully inadequate a subsidy, parish rates were raised.
Paupers could not, however, pay the higher rates, thus medical service was
not improved and the promise of health reform went unfulfilled. In fact,
that promise remained unfulfilled into this century:

The passage of the Insurance Act in 1911 made it impossible for the State to acquiesce any longer in the existence of such conditions. This Act made insurance on a partly contributory basis compulsory for the less wealthy employed workers of the community, and the State undertook to provide various benefits such as medical services, sanatoria, payment during sickness or disability, etc . . . it may be said that this Act was quite unsuited to the Highlands and Islands. The crofting population was outwith the compulsory provisions of the Act, and no scheme of voluntary insurance, such as was provided by other sections of the Act, has any likelihood of success, considering the economic conditions of the Highlands. Yet for the handful of Highlanders who came under the Act, the State was pledged to secure the promised benefits, and it became obvious that such could not be secured under the existing medical service.[30]

In 1912, the Government appointed the Highlands and Islands Medical Services Committee to investigate the inadequacy of medical services in the crofting counties. Their recommendations were far reaching: subsidise doctors, expand nursing service, appoint consultant specialists and improve existing hospitals. In 1948, a century after the first promise of health reform had been made, the National Health Service was inaugurated and five Regional Hospital Boards were set up. Yet even in the second half of the twentieth century, the state of the nation's health still haunts the British Establishment. The *Black Report*, a report of a 'Working Group to investigate the Inequalities in Health', found that as recently as 1980,

Inequalities in health are of concern to the whole nation and represent one of the biggest possible challenges to the conduct of government policy . . . There were those like Sir John Brotherston, the Chief Medical Officer of Scotland, who in 1976 voiced the concern of many working in the health services and who had called the nation's attention to the social gulf in health which still existed and were calling for action.[31]

V

The crux of the health problem in the Highlands was poverty and overcrowding. Establishment landowners and businessmen were in the main indifferent to that problem and vehemently opposed to being taxed to relieve it. Establishment politicians often acted to protect those commercial interests at the expense of public health. In short, the health problem was created by the same class that blocked the remedy – a conclusion drawn not just by reformers and their socialist leaders, but by a much less likely critic, Nassau William Senior, Oxford economist and champion of Victorian capitalism:

What other result can be expected, when any man who can purchase or hire a plot of ground is allowed to cover it with such buildings as he may think fit, where there is no power to enforce drainage or sewage, or to regulate the width of streets, or to prevent houses from being packed back-to-back, . . . *With all our reverence for the principle of non-interference, we cannot doubt that in this matter it has been pushed too far* [italics are mine]. We believe that both the ground landlord and the speculative builder ought to be compelled by law . . . to take measures which shall prevent the towns which they create from being the centres of disease. That they have not been so forced, probably arises from the circumstances that the evils which we have described are not felt, or even known to exist, by those who principally influence our legislation — the higher and middle classes.[32]

Notes

1. René Dubos, *Man Adapting*, enlarged edn., New Haven, Yale Univ. Press, 1980, 383.

2. J.P. Day, *Public Administration in the Highlands and Islands of Scotland*, London, Univ. of London Press Ltd., 1918, 48.

3. J.H.F. Brotherston, *Observations on the Early Public Health Movement in Scotland*, London, H.K. Lewis & Co. Ltd., 1952, 100.
   For more detailed discussion of the Scottish resistance to the English Public Health Act of 1848 and Poor Law reform see:
   Brotherston, 67–96.
   T. Ferguson, *The Dawn of Scottish Social Welfare*, London, Thomas Nelson and Sons Ltd., 1848, 6–8, 194–221.

4. Day, Op cit., 52, 311.

5. Brotherston, Op cit., 42–3.

6. *Fortieth Report of the Board of Supervision 1884–5*, App. A. I, 26.

7. In 1846, Dr Coll MacDonald had complained to the Board of Supervision about the lamentable conditions of the people in Western Inverness and Ross from the want of medicines and medical attendance. He also deplored the fact that there were no doctors in the parishes of Small Isles or Glenelg or Barra:
   and those who reside in parishes as proprietors, factors, or tacksmen, seldom are much use, as the calls for medicine and advice are so frequent, that they find it expensive and troublesome to meet them. Again where some half educated medical man practises among the people they are so poor and have bad habits, and have no means to keep medicines or instruments. They visit the people and prescribe simples where active treatment is necessary.

Letter from Dr Coll Macdonald, to the Secretary of the Board of Supervision, dated March 16 1846. *First Annual Report of the Board of Supervision for the Poor in Scotland,* 1847, Appendix (D), No., 4(c), 55.

It is of interest to note Dr Macdonald's remarks regarding the traditional role of the proprietors, factors and tacksmen in the care of their people. This duty also fell to the 'Lady of the Big House.' See: Osgood Mackenzie, *A Hundred Years in the Highlands,* Edinburgh, The National Trust for Scotland, 1988, 42.

8. *The Forty-Seventh Report of the Board of Supervision,* 1891–2, App. A, 14.

9. Ibid., 14.

10. Day, 307.
    Paradoxically, one of the reasons why cholera never became established in the West Highlands and Islands, other than their relative isolation, was the lack of a public water supply.

11. *Report to the Local Government Board for Scotland on the Sanitary Condition of the Lews,* Op cit., 10–11.

12. *Second Report of the Local Government Board for Scotland,* 1895–6, xxxiii.

13. *Report by the Crofters Commission on the Social Condition of the People of Lewis in 1901, as Compared with Twenty Years Ago.* 1902, B.P.P. LXXXIII, App. M. (3), 39.

14. Day, Op cit., 289. 29, 48, 52–3.

15. Ibid., 298.

16. *Second Report of the Local Government Board for Scotland,* 1895–6, xxxiii.

17. *Report to the Local Government Board for Scotland on the Sanitary Condition of the Lews,* Op cit., 10–11.

18. *First Report of the Local Government Board,* 1894–5, App.A. 24.

19. Day, Op cit., 300.

20. Ibid., 300.

21. Ibid., 298.

22. *First Report of the Local Government Board for Scotland,* 1894–5, App.A, 18,

23. *Report of the Royal Commission on Housing,* 1917, 211, 212.

24. In the second half of the twentieth century, Dubos, writing about the underprivileged of the world, noted:
    In other words the scientific aspects of the medical problems that are most important in poor countries have been delineated and the remedial steps to be taken are obvious. But this knowledge remains mere intellectual exercise because social and economic factors interfere with its application. These factors range all the way from lack of facilities and trained personnel for the delivery of medical services to the shortage of

suitable farmland and agricultural equipment, and to traditions and taboos that prevent the needed changes in the ancestral ways of life. Dubos, Op cit., 383.

25. Day, Op cit., 128.

26. *Fourth Report of Local Government Board for Scotland*, 1897–8. App. A. 33.

27. *Fourth Report*, Op Cit., App. A. 33.

28. Ibid., xlvi.
    For details of the mandates issued to the Local Government Board and the District Committees see:
    Day, Op cit., 52–3, 310–311.

29. Day, Op cit., 128.

30. Ibid., 129–130.

31. Peter Townsend and Nick Davidson, Eds., *The Black Report,* and Margaret Whitehead, *The Health Divide,* published as one volume, *Inequalities in Health,* London, Penguin Books, 1990, Introduction to Inequalities in Health, 1.

32. *Report of the Commissioners on the Conditions of the Hand-Loom Weavers,* B.P.P. 1841, X, 73.

12

The 'Thing' at Home

There is nothing more agreeable in life than to make peace with the Establishment – and nothing more corrupting.[1]

THE STRUGGLES FOR LAND and health reform were clear signals of the growing class struggle in nineteenth-century Britain. In many ways the Napier Commission's work brought that class conflict to a head. On one hand were the Establishment forces in politics, medicine and religion; on the other the radicals and the disenfranchised, demanding ever more sweeping change. Conservatives versus Liberals, Oligarchy versus Democracy, Capitalism versus Socialism. Radicals pressed for redress of old grievances and the Liberal government lent its ear and its legislation to their cause. Landowners and businessmen felt besieged, their customary right to do as they saw fit to advance their interests at risk from the mob and the mob's political sympathisers. The democratic-socialist mob, emboldened by the spirit of revolution abroad and by their own success at home, forced the struggle:

> Such is the disposition of the people to repair the ruin of their rulers – of life to have an heir – of matter to be organized.[2]

Such was the political climate in the latter part of the nineteenth century.

The Establishment embraced as rationale for its entrenchment the century's new theory of evolution, in particular, that theory's two fundamental tenets, the twin drives for self-preservation and the preservation of the species. To save his species, man must protect its fittest members. And among man, Highland or otherwise, education, financial security and social standing represented fitness. Ergo, that class in possession of those traits merited protection – for the good of all. The survival and development of the whole depended on the continuance of that elite, thus it warranted protection, even at the sacrifice of inferior sub-groups. In *Aristocracy and Evolution*, W. H. Mallock, a social philosopher of the time, argued that 'evolution tended to improve the elite strata in society whose achievements are required to advance human welfare.'[3]

The Scottish and English Establishments found further theoretical underpinning for their self-protectionism in writers like Thomas Malthus. Malthus's *An Essay On Population* argued the urgency of controlling population growth. Amid the burgeoning population of Highland poor, the unfittest of society's sub-groups, Establishmentarians hailed Malthus and evolutionists as saviours.

Yet the ruling Liberal government courted the unfittest, commissioning aristocrats to hear their complaints and enacting legislation that extended their rights, while it circumscribed the rights of their social betters. Establishmentarians railed against that trend to government intervention:

> With growing alarm, Whigs and Tories observed the adoption of measures which served to circumscribe the rights of contract and property. Moreover, the extension of the franchise begun in 1867 slowly transferred effective control of Parliament from aristocratic and commercial hands into those of the middle and working classes.[4]

The Liberal party, and in particular its leader, Gladstone, were blamed for the excesses of interventionist policies. Herbert Spencer's scathing criticism was typical:

> Were it needful to dwell on indirect evidence, which might be made of that furnished by the behaviour of the so-called Liberal party – a party which, relinquishing the original conception of a leader as a mouthpiece for a known and accepted policy, thinks itself bound to accept a policy which its leader springs upon it without consent or warning – a party so utterly without the feeling and idea implied by liberalism, as not to resent this trampling on the right of private judgment which constitutes the root of liberalism – nay, a party which vilifies as renegade liberals, those of its members who refuse to surrender their independence! But without occupying space with indirect proofs that the mass of men have not the natures required to check the development of tyrannical officialdom . . . Instead of the selfishness of the employing classes and the selfishness of competition, we are to have the unselfishness of a mutually-aiding system. How far is this unselfishness now shown in the behaviour of working men to one another?[5]

Finding no adequate champion in government, the Establishment rallied its own members. In 1871, J.H.Levy founded the Personal Rights Defense Association – to oppose the contagious Disease Act. Six years later, Auberon William Edward Molyneux Herbert (the 'Crusader for Liberty'), youngest son of the third Earl of Carnarvon, created a second organisation, The Personal Rights and Self-Help Association, whose objectives were

> To protect and enlarge personal liberty and personal rights, [and] to oppose the multiplication of laws and the tendency to control and direct, through Parliament, the affairs of the people.[6]

By 1882, those groups amalgamated as the Liberty and Property Defence League to oppose 'The Impracticality of Socialism':

> Freedom is the most valuable of all human possessions, next after life itself. It is more valuable, in a manner, *than even health* [italics are mine]; but good laws, justly administered, can and do secure freedom.[7]

For one of its supporters, Wordsworth Donisthrope, author of *Overlegislation, Individualism, and Law in a Free State*, the League was a perfectly natural mechanism for self-protection, and in a time when government intervention was on the increase, a necessary one:

> We have societies banded together to do battle against rivals on the principle of 'Union is strength'. These clubs are defensive or aggressive. The latter class includes all trading associations, the object of which is to make profits by out-manoeuvering competitors. The former or defensive class includes all the political societies formed for the purpose of resisting the State – the most aggressive club in existence. Over one hundred of these 'protection societies' of one sort and another are now federated under the hegemony of the Liberty and Property Defence League.[8]

For a later commentator, the League was

> a natural response of fear to the challenge of democracy and the threat of socialism by forces which formerly, in most cases, had been beneficent, progressive, and enlightened. Increasingly between 1867–1882, many property owners, industrialists, and members of the old ruling oligarchy became aware that they occupied a vulnerable position — democracy might seize leadership as well as power and by gradual legislation lead the nation into a system of totalitarian socialism. As defenders of the status quo, in a nation without a written constitution, there seemed no end to the legalized plunder.[9]

The League's membership list was a roll-call of the moneyed and privileged. It included commercial associations like the Iron Trades Employers' Association, the General Shipowners' Society, the Bradford Property Owners' Association and the Licensed Victuallers' Protection Society. Its founder and Chair until his death in 1914 was a Scottish peer, Colonel Francis Wemyss-Charteris-Douglas, tenth Earl of Wemyss, Oxford-educated, a landowner and a Conservative Member of Parliament.

The League's *raison d'être* was to 'engage in parliamentary lobbying, educational pamphleteering and debating'.[10] And lobby it did – against, for example, the range of public policy measures that Napier and other liberals brought to the political agenda of the day. Against the Napier Commission's call for state-subsidised education of Highlanders:

But we need not go back through the centuries to trace transformations sufficiently great and unexpected. On the day when £30,000 a year in aid of education was voted as an experiment, the name of an idiot would have been given to an opponent who prophesied that in fifty years the sum spent through imperial taxes and local rates would amount to £10,000,000, or who said that the aid to education would be followed by aids to feeding and clothing, or who said that parents and children, alike deprived of all option, would, even if starved, be compelled by fine or imprisonment to conform, and receive that which, with papal assumption, the State calls education. No one, I say, would have dreamt that out of so innocent-looking a germ would have so quickly evolved this tyrannical system, tamely submitted to by people who fancy themselves free.[11]

And against the movement for preventive medicine and public health reform generally:

Here is a Vigilance Association sending out detectives for the purpose of discovering and lynching the unsocial wretches who knowingly travel in public conveyances with infectious diseases on them . . . and lynching persons who travel about in public places with smallpox and scarlatina [scarlet fever], what rules will they make for their guidance? Suppose they dub every unvaccinated person a 'focus of infection', shall we witness the establishment of a Vigilance Society to punch the heads of the detectives who punch the heads of 'foci of infection'? Remember we have both those societies in full working order today. One is called the State, and the other is the Anti-Vaccination Society.[12]

Nor was the League above supporting commoners' resistance to legislated improvements in sanitation and hygiene, when that support served its own purposes:

Meanwhile, it is to be observed that, wherever the working classes are brought into contact with legislative socialism as an actual fact, they invariably rebel. The greater part of the socialistic legislative statutes of recent times are simply hateful to the people whom they were intended to benefit. The enforcement of cleanliness, of sanitary regulations and such matters, is attended with the greatest difficulty as the promoters of 'model dwellings' have found to their cost, because there are no people in this world more sensitive than the working-classes of this country to encroachments, real or fancied, upon their liberty . . . He [the Englishman] loathes the inspector and the official, but the inspector and the official are the inseparable accidents of the socialist community . . . Yet the people who are dispatched upon these errands are universally detested; indeed, it is not more unpleasant to be a tax-collector than an inspector of nuisances. It is only after socialist measures become law, or when they threaten the interest of an intelligent class, that those whom they affect realise the position.[13]

Perhaps the most cynical of the Establishment's tactics to stall reform and preserve the *status quo* was its creation and cultivation of Highland myth-history. Ever a powerful tool in the hands of a ruling elite, myth-making is self-interested distortion of historical events. Myth-history was never so effectively used as in the tartan extravaganza which accompanied the State visit to Scotland in August 1822 of the British monarch, George IV. The pageant marked the introduction to the world of a mythical tartan, in which heavily-armed Highlanders were attired. The cast was made up of estate-domesticated Highlanders and stand-ins hastily recruited to swell thinned clan ranks. It was conceived and orchestrated by that master of romantic writing and member of the Scottish Establishment, Sir Walter Scott. The State visit marked the climax of months of feverish activity, improvisation, and rehearsal: Highland Chiefs frantically researched their genealogy for their clans' places 'in the order of battle', for their tartan (mainly in vain), and for the proper dress code for Highland chiefs and gentlemen. What was not known was invented. For Highland and Lowland Scotland alike, the State visit produced lucrative new industries – Gaeldom, the Highlands and the Military Tattoo. Moreover, when the young Queen Victoria was crowned in 1837, her lifelong love affair with the Highlands ensured publicity for the myth. Establishment landowners and other entrepreneurs were quick to exploit it. In 1822, Highlanders were portrayed as well-fed noble savages: strong, healthy, heavily-armed and dressed in warm, multicoloured fabrics. All this at a time when authentic Highlanders could barely feed or clothe themselves.[14]

By the time of the Napier Commission and Gladstone's liberal reforms, fifty years after the tartan burlesque, authentic Highlanders had felt the winds of revolution blowing across Europe. Their leaders, the new radicals, met conservatism head on. Class met class, capitalism met socialism, in uprisings designated in Lowland Scotland as the 'Radical War' and later in the Highlands as the 'Land Wars.' During the first clashes, violence erupted: in England with the Peterloo massacre of 1819; in Scotland a year later with insurrection which ended in a series of convictions for sedition and treason. Working men of vision, invariably self-educated and inspired by the social revolution in Europe, began to question the right of a few to control the destiny of so many. They were classically proletarian:

> A distinct social stratum characterized by (a) consciousness of its existence as a social body; (b) ability to agitate for concessions on threat of creating social unrest; (c) social status as free but insecure propertyless people who form the 'mass' base above which the 'class' hierarchy towers. That social layer without social esteem or social honor but not lacking in political influence, real or potential, through mass action, formalized or spontaneous.[15]

Their demands 'seldom went beyond the purely political, but invariably raised the spectre of social levelling.'[16] Nothing less than social levelling would do for the radical socialists of the nineteenth century. And they demanded that equality be reflected in practical reforms. When Frederick Denison Maurice and Charles Kingsley formed the Christian Socialist movement within the Anglican Church (that event itself a sign of the infectious power of the new radicalism), they published a penny weekly entitled *Politics for the People* in which to argue their case. Their case, as it appeared in the first issue on 6 May, 1848, was a demand for immediate change in a spectrum of policies:

> It is proposed in this Paper to consider the questions which are most occupying our countrymen at the present moment, such as the Extension of the Suffrage, the relation of the Capitalist to the Labourer, what a Government can or cannot do, to find work or pay for the Poor.[17]

Nor did they omit health reform from their platform:

> Man without health is a world without sun . . . let us look closely into this great matter; . . . what claims it has upon that mighty aggregate of thought, feeling, and action – the PEOPLE . . . Health is the only property of nine-tenths — ay, of ninety-nine hundredths of the human race . . . They are as much a property to them [the Government] as houses, lands, or merchandise . . . This too, the Government feels; and it is but justice to them to state that they are more anxious to confer on the people the boon of health than the people are to receive it. This is because the people do not understand the health question. They may soon do so, however, if they will bring their own strong sense to bear on it. Substitute the words artisan and labourer for sailor or prisoner, house for ship or prison, and typhus fever for gaol fever, and they are not far from understanding enough of the health-question and the merits of Sanitary Reform to stir them up to exertion in its behalf.[18]

Ironically, in their demand for overhaul of the iniquitous *status quo*, socialists found a theoretical home in the same theory of evolutionary change that their Establishment opponents had tried to appropriate. While evolutionary theory did indeed proclaim that the most fundamental drive in any species is to ensure self-survival, the tenet that Establishmentarians had laid claim to, evolutionary theory went on to argue that natural selection pushed mutations; that is, that radical changes in the *status quo* launch protective adaptation, the elementary mechanism of evolution. Highlanders' demands for reform were in this sense, the radicals argued, part of the most fundamental drive for self-preservation.

Survival, cultural and physical, was at stake for Highlanders in the nineteenth century. They had demonstrated early in the century that they would resort to violence to win the rights that their survival depended on. Though many in the Scottish and English Establishments dismissed the likelihood that Highlanders would actually revolt, others did not. Lord Brabazon, President and Chairman of the National Association for Promoting State-directed Emigration and Colonization, warned that revolution might well be imminent:

> Starving men are not to be argued with, nor are they likely to acquiesce quietly in Lord Derby's fatalistic theory, that their condition is the inevitable result of economic conditions which are to be deplored but cannot be altered.

Reformers, among them H.M. Hyndman, a wealthy, Cambridge-educated socialist leader, sounded the same alarm:

> But I, too, look with sadness to the immediate future. For when a man like Lord Brabazon, who obviously feels for the needy and sympathises with the oppressed, can look at our anarchial society only from the point of view of his own class interests, and is led astray by the fallacies of huckster economy, I despair of a peaceful solution to the inevitable class struggle even in England; and I fear that we must pass through the fiery furnace of 'some fatal national catastrophe' to the goal of full economical freedom and organised work for all.[19]

And in 1883, the Highland Land Law Reform Association counselled Highland crofters, in Gaelic, that their welfare would be secured only by their own vigilance and agitation:

> The appointment of a Royal Commission to inquire into your grievances is a tardy, though hopeful, acknowledgement on the part of the Government that the condition of the Highlands is not satisfactory. But, however you may justify your complaints and prove your case, the history of all great reforms should teach you that changes necessary to promote your welfare will not be conceded without earnest effort and a well directed agitation on your part . . . Your cause has many influential well-wishers. The Association, for instance, includes among its adherents a goodly number of Members of Parliament, private gentlemen, clergymen, doctors of medicine, barristers, professors, and others, who will earnestly support your efforts: but on your own unity and determination success will chiefly depend; for, in the words of the old proverb, 'God helps them that help themselves.'[20]

As we have seen, agitation was effective. Socialist reformers made significant gains in land and health reforms. The political Establishment began to acknowledge the plight of the Highland poor and to relieve it, even if that relief was often motivated less by humanitarianism than by fear of insurrection. But as we have seen also, the might of those with vested interests was sufficient that they were able to block the most sweeping changes reformers sought, and to delay and otherwise impede many of those advances which were legislated.

If Highlanders who stayed at home felt the weight of Establishment interests even during an era of reform and revolution, so too did those who left: whether they were able to go, when and where they went, how safely they travelled, all were determined by commercial and political interests at home. And on board the emigrant ships, as ashore in Cape Breton and elsewhere, they were subject to similar control and similar hardship.

Notes

1. A.J.P. Taylor, *New Statesman*, 8 Aug. 1953, XLVI, 236–7.

   Taylor, a social historian, writes of how 'the Thing' was woven into the very fabric of British life:

   The Establishment is enlightened, tolerant, even well-meaning. It has never been exclusive, rather drawing in recruits from outside, as soon as they are ready to conform to its standards and become respectable. There is nothing more agreeable in life than to make peace with the Establishment – and nothing more corrupting.

2. George Ensor, *An Inquiry Concerning the Population of Nations, Containing a Refutation of Mr Malthus's Essay on Population* (1818), New York, Reprints of Economic Classics, Augustus M. Kelley Pubs., 1967, 490.

3. Jeffrey Paul, in *A Plea for Liberty, An Argument Against Socialism and Socialistic Legislation*, (1891), Ed., Thomas Mackay, New York, Liberty Classics reprint, D Appleton & Co.,1981, Foreword xiv.

4. Paul, Op cit., Foreword vii.

5. Ibid., Herbert Spencer, 'From Freedom to Bondage', 25–6.

6. S. Hutchinson Harris, *Auberon Herbert: Crusader for Liberty,* London, Williams & Norgate Ltd., 1943, 189.

   This biography provides a detailed account of the personal life of a member of the Victorian Establishment.

7. Edward Stanley Robertson, 'The Impracticability of Socialism', in *A Plea for Liberty*, Op cit., 75.

8. Wordsworth Donisthrope, 'The Limits of Liberty', in *A Plea for Liberty*, Op cit., 79–8.

9. Norbert C. Soldon, *Laissez-Faire on the Defensive: The Story of the Liberty and Property Defence League, 1882–1914,* University of Delaware, unpublished PhD thesis, 1969, Preface iv–v.

10. Paul, Op cit., xii.

11. Herbert Spencer, in *A Plea for Liberty*, Op cit., 20.

12. Wordsworth Donisthrope, in *A Plea for Liberty*, Op cit., 123–4.

13. Edmund Vincent, 'The Discontent of the Working-Classes' in *A Plea for Liberty*, Op cit., 273–4.

14. For further information on the State visit and the 'Highland' concept see: John Prebble, *The King's Jaunt*, London, Harper Collins, 1991.

    Hugh Trevor-Roper, 'The Invention of Tradition: The Highland Tradition of Scotland', in *The Invention of Tradition*, Eds., Eric Hobsbawm and Terence Ranger, Cambridge, Univ. Press, 1983, 15–41.

    John Telfer Dunbar, *Highland Costume*, Edinburgh, William Blackwood, 1977.

15. *Dictionary of Sociology*, Ed., Henry Pratt Fairchild, Totowa, New Jersey, Rowman & Allanheld, 1970.

16. Bruce Lenman, *Integration, Enlightenment, and Industrialization, Scotland 1746–1832*, London, Edward Arnold, 1981, 103.

17. *Politics for the People*, London, John Parker, 1848, 1–16.

18. Ibid., Sanitary Reform – No. 1.

19. H.M. Hyndman, 'Something better than Emigration. A Reply', *The Nineteenth Century*, XVI, No. 99, 1884, 998.

20. From documents issued by the Highland Land Law Reform Association of London reprinted in *The Celtic Magazine*, Inverness, A & W Mackenzie, Vol. IX, 1883–4, 175–6

Appendix A

'The Dietaries of Scotch Agricultural Labourers', 1869

Caithness-shire

Parish of Reay

Shepherds. — J.R. Family above ten years, 2 ; below, 3. Takes meals at home. Rent free. Yearly wages, £20 in money, 7 bolls meal, 30–60 chains potatoes, keep for 8 ewes and cow, 3 tons coals or 25 loads peat, and 3 pints sweet milk daily. Wages of family, one at 9d. and one at 1s. per day. When a cow is kept £2 a-year is deducted from wages ; no pigs or poultry allowed.

Breakfast, brose at 5 a.m. before turning out, porridge and milk at 11 a.m. with tea or coffee afterwards ; of family, porridge and milk or treacle at 9 a.m. *Dinner* with family at 6 p.m., potatoes and dried herrings, or potatoes and fresh fish, or sometimes pork and meat. *Tea,* wife takes tea and oatcake at 4 p.m., *Supper,* with family at 9 p.m., brose, and bread with butter, or porridge and milk or treacle. Health extremely good.

Remarks. — In this district farms on the sea coast are often supplied with a boat, by which means the men supply themselves with fish from June to end of October. Where no boat is supplied, they fish on the lochs. Where sheep are extensively kept, a few die during winter and spring, and these, though not fit for the market, are wholesome for use, and the ploughmen and work-people buy the mutton at 2d. to 3d. per lb. The shepherds are well paid, getting from £15 to £20 per annum, and the perquisites named. They are a very intelligent class, and remain long in the same situation.

Parish of Reay

Ploughmen, — G.C. Family above ten years, 4 ; below, none. Takes meals at home. Rent free. Yearly wages, £10 in money, 8 bolls meal, 60 chains potatoes, 3 tons coals, and 3 pints sweet milk daily. Wages of family, three at 1s. per day each. No cow, pig, or poultry allowed.

Breakfast, brose at 5 a.m. before starting to work, porridge and treacle at 11 a.m. ; of family, porridge and milk or treacle. *Dinner* with family, potatoes and milk, or fish and potatoes, or potatoes and pork. *Tea,* none. *Supper* with family, brose or porridge and milk. Health very good.

Remarks. — Ploughmen with large young families are unable to buy beef or pork, and they frequently run into debt to the small country shopkeepers, leaving the debt unpaid. When in need of a few shillings, they are in the habit of taking meal to the shopkeepers, getting from 60 to 70 per cent of its value ; and when they buy groceries it is quite common to pay for them in meal. They are a very sober class.

Parish of Reay

Female Farm Workers. — J.W. Unmarried. Takes meals at home. Rent free, and fire provided. Yearly wages, £6 in money, 4_ bolls meal or porridge with milk or treacle. *Dinner,* potatoes and fish or brose and milk. *Supper,* porridge and milk, or tea and bread, or bread and milk. Health very good.

Remarks. — This case is the usual diet of outworkers (female) on large arable farms in this district. They are chiefly accommodated in bothies, which require the master's supervision.

Sutherlandshire

Parish of Golspie

Shepherds, — J.S. Family above 10 years, 1 ; below, 2. Takes meals at home. Rent free, worth £4, 5s. per annum. Yearly wages, £19 in money, 6½ bolls meal, 1½ boll potatoes, and quart of sweet milk daily. Keeps a pig and poultry.

Breakfast, porridge and milk ; of family, porridge and milk. *Dinner,* with family, tea, with oat bread and fish, or oat dread and crowdie, or oat bread and eggs ; and on Sundays, broth made of fresh meat, or salt pork and potatoes. *Supper,* with family, porridge and milk, or potatoes and fish (salt herring), with milk or tea. Health very good.

Remarks. — When milk is scarce the children get treacle and water to their porridge, but it is observed that under this diet they soon lose flesh and are not nearly so lively, nor do they seem to thrive.

Inverness-shire

Parish of Bracadale (Skye)

Hind. — A. M'A. Family above ten years, 3 ; below, 1. Takes meals at home. Rent free, worth £1,10s. per annum. Yearly wages, £12, Keeps cow and poultry.

Breakfast, oatmeal porridge and milk, or potatoes and fish; of family, oatmeal porridge and milk, or potatoes and fish. *Dinner* with family, oatmeal and potatoes with milk or coffee. *Supper* with family, oatcake, butter, and tea, or potatoes and milk. Health excellent.

Remarks. — This is a case of a hind in regular employment, and is a fair specimen of this class in this part of the Island of Skye.

Parish of Bracadale (Skye)

Labourer. — A. McP. Family above ten years of age, 4; Below, 2. Takes meals at home in winter only, from home from spring till end of harvest. Rent £1. Weekly wages 15s. ; idle in winter. Wages of family, 2s. 6d. per week all year. Keeps poultry only.

Breakfast, porridge and milk, when away — at home, potatoes and fish ; of family, potatoes and fish. *Dinner*, bread and coffee, or bread and cheese and piece of bacon, when away — at home, potatoes ; of family, potatoes. *Supper*, tea and bread when away — at home, potatoes or meal-brose, sometimes potatoes and fish. Health fair.

Remarks. — This case represents the poorest class here. The labourer leaves his home for the south of Scotland in spring, where he is employed from the end of April till end of harvest at any work he can find, generally on railway contracts and at harvest work. He returns about the end of October. Several of his family are out at service.

Parish of Bracadale (Skye)

Labourer. — K. C. Family over 10 years, 2 ; below, 4. Takes supper only at home ; on Sundays, takes all his meals at home. Rent, £1, 10s. Weekly wages, 12s. Wages of family, 3s. per week. Keeps pigs and poultry.

Breakfast, potatoes beat, and oatcake or oatmeal brose; of family, potatoes. *Dinner,* oatmeal brose, or potatoes and oatcake ; of family, potatoes and fish. *Supper* with family, tea and oatmeal cake, or coffee and fish. Health — man, scrofulous ; family subject to cutaneous eruptions.

Remarks. — This is the case of a dyker and drainer; he earns as much as any of his class and occupation, and he lives at home all the year.

Appendix B

Highlands and Islands Commission Report: Minutes of Evidence [Vol I]

Obe, Harris, Thursday, May 31. 1883.

Present:
Lord Napier and Ettrick, K.T., Chairman.
Sir Kenneth S. Mackenzie, Bart.
C. Fraser-Mackintosh, Esq., M.P.
Sheriff Nicolson, LL.D.
Professor Mackinnon, M.A.

Revd Alexander Davidson, Free Church Minister, Harris (70) –
examined.

12992. *The Chairman.-* Will you kindly make your statement to us?
– The crofters and cottars of South Harris of this generation have no charge of oppression or injustice to bring against their proprietor or his officials. The proprietor – the Earl of Dunmore – seeks in every competent way to promote the welfare of his people, and the Dowager Countess of Dunmore is greatly esteemed in Harris for her long-continued endeavours to advance the social comfort of the people. Some painful evictions there may have been, whose sting still rankles in the bosom of a few survivors to this day; and there were also frequent removals, which were most detrimental to the subject in loss of time and substance. The discontinuance of the kelp manufacture has been a great loss to the crofters of South Harris. The crofters, when engaged in kelp-making, got meal to support their families for three or four months in the year, and they earned money to pay their rates. This kept them from falling in arrears with the estate. There is now no work on the estate that will enable them to pay their rent by labour. Last winter the proprietor did provide some work, which proved a great help to many of the people. Generally the crofters have no capital, and when the season proves unfavourable in regard to crops and fishing, they have nothing to keep them except any little stock they may possess, and if they are forced to part with it, they are wholly destitute. For instance, if a man at such a time has to sell a cow, perhaps he may not be able to buy

another cow in his lifetime. Overcrowding has a tendency to impoverish; for instance, where three sons, with their families, share the croft that their father occupied alone. Huddling the people together in some particular localities, mossy bogs, as they are in Ardvee of Finnisbay, while other large areas of the country are almost without an inhabitant, is most injurious. Fishing is a most precarious source of industry in Harris, especially the herring fishing. The people buy materials and waste their time about it, and often gain nothing by it. They can earn something by the lobster fishing. Through the complete failure of the herring fishing for the last few years, and of the crops, – especially last year – many of them have fallen considerably into arrears, as they were obliged to lay out all their earnings in meal for their families. This year many of them could not have put down their crop, but for the aid that they received from friends in the south. That aid was most seasonable. *Quis cito dat, bis dat.* [He who gives quickly gives twice.] I would suggest that the people should get a competent portion of the earth to cultivate. The want of a road through the East Bays of Harris, and bridges on the rivers, is an unspeakable grievance and hardship. All the crofters pay road money. This is not a country for the squatting system of farming, where there are men to cultivate the soil. It is most unnatural that man should be chased away to make room for sheep and deer; that the land should lie uncultivated when men are perishing for lack of food. It is very unnatural that old and young should not be allowed to cast a hook into a standing lake or stream to catch a trout without being persuaded by an officer of the law. This Royal Commission is a most sacred – I had almost said divine – duty entrusted to them. The state of the Highlands and Islands of Scotland for many generations to come will be influenced either for good or evil by their report. 'The heaven even the heavens are the Lord's, but the earth has He given to the children of men.' Man's original charter was – 'God blessed them', the parents of the human family; 'and God said unto them, Be fruitful, and multiply, and replenish the earth, and subdue it; and have dominion over the fish of the sea, and over the fowl of the air, and over every living thing that moveth upon the earth.' May I add a few words? With regards to this crowding, the most of the people are driven to the East Bays. There are about 700 people about the bays between Rodel and Loch Stockinish, within an extent of seven or eight miles. There are a great many cottars, and this kind of crowding has a great tendency to impoverish the people – where there are so many, for instance, three families on one lot. And at Finsbay – the place I mentioned formerly, there are three families on a plot of ground that pays 15s. of rent. The only other particulars that I could wish very especially to bring before the Commission is the want of roads in this part. We have no road, I may say, from Rodel to the place where the bays pass with the main road that goes round the west side to Rodel. There is a distance of some fifteen or sixteen miles, and there are eight large streams. We often call them burns, but large rivers is the proper term, as they are quite impassable during a flood; and life has been lost there, and very narrow escapes with life frequently I may say. The people have been paying road money for many generations, All the crofters pay road money, and before my time I believe all the adult male population were made to pay road money. I heard it said that every young man, whether he had lands or not, had to pay 5s. in the year for road money. Another thing in regard to Stroan here – the south end. We had a conversation with the people there last night, and they think that their land is rather too highly rented, and the reason for that is, that the rent was put on the land when they had this kelp making in connection with the land – that the rent was put on the land very much in proportion to the convenience and facilities they had for kelp-making. Now the kelp-making has ceased; it is gone, but what they consider its burden still remains on the land. I shall be glad to answer, if I can, any questions that may be put to me. At Finsbay there were only two crofters in times past, and now there are seven or eight, besides a number of cottars.

12993. You have stated that the painful evictions, as you have justly termed them, are a thing of the past. Do you speak of removals from one place to another? – Yes.

12994. How long is it since any removals of that kind took place? – Well, there have not been any particular removals of late.

12995. Have there been any within the last twenty years? – I don't know. It is exactly within twenty years that the people were removed from the south end of Bernera, and when they were removed from the island of Pabbay.

12996. Where were they brought to? – A good many of them were sent to the island of Scalpa, down in Loch Tarbert, and other parts through the country.

12997. And when they were removed were they crowded upon existing crofts, or were additional lands brought in to accommodate them? – The places they would get in the island of Scalpa would be required to be taken in. I believe there was no cultivation there before. A great many were sent there, and they would be sent perhaps where there was a person occupying a lot, and one of these people would be sent in on that lot.

12998. And when they were removed to those places, was that to benefit the condition of the people who were removed or left behind, or was it for the convenience of the people who took large farms? – Well, there were no crofters left behind.

12999. The loss of the kelp must, of course, have been a great loss to the people? – A great loss.

13000. But has not been in some measure compensated by the increase in the price of the stock they have to sell? – Well, I don't think that one made up for the other at all, because the stock is a very poor stock generally, and there was no change, I would say, in the price of stock or in the increase of stock that would make up for that loss.

13001. How long have you been in this island? – Since the year 1848.

13002. Are you a native of the island? – No, I am a native of near Inverness.

13003. But your memory extends back here for more than thirty years? – Yes.

13004. What change in the condition of the people do you remark? Do you think generally, with reference to their physical condition, that they are better or worse? – Well, I think that they are nothing better whatever. They were suffering very much when I came here from the failure of the potato crop in 1846 and 1847. They were in a very depressed state at that time, but I don't think that there was any improvement since that time.

13005. Is there any marked deterioration? Do you think that they are decidedly getting worse? – I cannot say that it is very apparent that they are getting worse, but I don't think they are getting better at all, for when they are crowded together in that way it is a very great discomfort to them, and diminishes the supply of everything.

13006. Do you think that when they were removed and when they were re-settled they were taken from the best lands and put on the worst lands? – Certainly. There is no place in Harris, I believe, for grain and crop like the island of Pabbay; and the south end of Bernera too, I think, is good for crop.

13007. Is there any number of persons of either class or any age who are unable to go to church or go to school on account of want of clothes? – Yes, a good many. The school board are endeavouring to compel the children to attend, but still they suffer from want of food and clothing.

13008. They are inclined to go regularly to divine service if they can? – Well, generally. There are some who remain back, but generally they don't.

13009. Is there any reason to complain of intemperance? – There is very little intemperance in this end. There are no shebeens as far as I know, and we are most thankful that there is no public house at Obe. Strong drink is not sold at this end.

13010. You mean on this part of the island? – Yes, in south Harris.

13011. *Sheriff Nicolson.* – I thought there was a public house at Obe? – Not now; it is discontinued, and we are very thankful for it.

13012. *The Chairman.* – Then you don't think that the people who are so poor owe any of their poverty to dissipation or extravagance? – No.

13013. Do many of the people go away south during the summer to labour? – Not to the south, but they go to the herring fishing in every part – to the Moray coast, and Caithness, and everywhere.

13014. Within your recollection there has been no considerable emigration? – There was. I think two or three batches left this country for Australia.

13015. How long ago? – I can't exactly mention the date, but the last batch, I think left, left in 1858.

13016. Is there any inclination on the part of the people to emigrate? – They are not very desirous to emigrate at all. There was a sort of a move among them here in spring to go to Queensland, but they heard such bad reports of the place, in their estimation, they just gave up the idea of going.

13017. *Sir Kenneth Mackenzie.* – Do they get good crops on the west side of the country? – Yes, I think they get good crops.

13018. Is the climate very much against cropping? Is it not very wet and windy? – Not on the west side. Sometimes it is windy. It is a good deal exposed to the gales from the Atlantic, but still the land is dry, and I think in favourable seasons would produce a very safe and sure crop.

13019. There were people there when you first came? – Yes.

13020. Did they get good crops? – I cannot very well say whether they did or not. They were not there very long; they were there a year or two. The place was put under crofters in my recollection, but I think they were behind in arrears, and were removed without delay. There is no question that the place is good for crop.

13021. Do the sheep farmers have large crops? Do they cultivate their land? – Yes, Mr. Kenneth Macdonald has good crops.

13022. But the crofters on that side, though with good land, fell into arrears. What was the cause of their falling into arrears? – Well the crops were not good for some time, and they did not succeed at all at the herring fishing for some time back, and they did not even get their wages at the herring fishing for some time back, which was a great drawback to them. There were several causes which concurred in throwing them into arrears at that time.

13023. *Mr. Fraser-Mackintosh.* – I suppose you are well acquainted with your own district, and have travelled over most of it? – I have.

13024. Is there a good deal of land out of cultivation, in consequence of removal of the people you have been referring to since you came here first? – A great deal. The west side of Harris here is out of cultivation, so far as the crofting system is concerned. I may say that from Tarbert to within sight of us here, was a place at one time filled with crofters.

13025. And they cultivated the land? – Yes, and there is no crofter population there now.

13026. And I presume the farmers only cultivate a small portion of arable land? – Not much, compared to the extent of the arable land.

13027. And in consequence the production of corn in Harris is very much diminished? – Very much diminished.

13028. Will you mention the names of the larger tacks in the island here, beginning with Rodel? – There is the home farm; and then Mr. Roderick Macdonald, Caolas, has another farm; Mr. Donald Macdonald, Scarista-veg; then Scarista-vore; and then the farm of Luscantire, which is a very extensive farm, and extends to Tarbert.

13029. The proprietor has Luscantire in his own hands at present? – Yes. These are all the large farms; and there are the islands of Ensay and Pabbay. These places, especially Pabbay, were filled with a crofter population.

13030. The places you have mentioned are on the main land. How many families are resident upon these farms, beginning with Rodel and ending with Scarista-vore? – I cannot state the number, but there are not very many.

13031. They bear not the shadow of the number they could bear? – No, it bears no comparison.

13032. Or that are upon the crofter lands? – No.

13033. And I presume these lands comprise a very considerably larger proportion of acreage than the crofter population possesses? – I would say that there was more of the land under these lands – under the large farms – than we have under the crofter population in the bays.

13034. Is it within the recollection of men now living when this system of making large farms was begun? – I think that there may be some in this house who would be eye-witness of that.

13035. Of the system of making large farms at the expense of the small crofters? – Yes.

13036. And the small crofters were either crowded down to the seashore or were obliged to emigrate? – The one or the other.

13037. Is the population increasing or decreasing since your time? – I think it is about stationary.

13038. We shall come to the island of Pabbay. You mentioned it as a rich green island, which contained at one time a considerable population, and there are none on it now? – None, unless a shepherd or two.

13039. Have you an idea how many used to be there? – No, but there was a very considerable crofter population.

13040. Would there have been 100 souls? – I should say that there would have been about 100 souls.

13041. To whom does Pabbay belong? – To Mr. Stewart, Ensay. He also possesses some smaller islands in the Sound of Harris.

13042. But these were never inhabited? – No.

13043. Is there an old man now living in this neighbourhood, upwards of eighty years of age, who was very ill used at the time of some of the evictions that took place many years ago? – There is such a man, and he had some intention of coming forward to be present here, but I think he did not come forward.

13044. What is the name? – Donald Matheson.

13045. Where does he reside? – Ardvee, Finisbay.

13046. Have you heard him relate the circumstances? – Yes.

13047. Can you mention them very briefly? What is the import of his complaint? – This is a part of the subject I do not wish to enter into, as I was not an eye-witness. I know there are present here, about this house, those who were in Harris at the time, and who could give an account of these things.

13048. You mentioned in the paper something to the effect that people were prevented from fishing in the lakes or lochs? – I don't mean that they are altogether prevented, but it is the rule they are not allowed to fish.

13049. Is that one of the conditions of the estate? – Yes. A person would be afraid to go out to any of these lochs or streams to fish.

13050. Those that are connected with the sea, where the sea comes in? – No, the mountain lakes – in the burns and streams.

13051. They are not prohibited from fishing in any waters with which the sea is connected? – In some of them. At Obe, I think there is a place where they are not allowed to fish. I think that seems to be a part of the fishing connected with the estate.

13052. You mentioned that this district received certain amounts of money that were subscribed by charitable people. How was that brought about, because we find in Benbecula that the people never heard that there was such money collected? – We were in the way of reading the papers. The Sheriff went up to Edinburgh and Glasgow, and told the state of the people at these places – and then there was a move to make a collection on their behalf, and we thought we were as much entitled to it as any one else.

13053. Then, when you saw in the newspapers that there was a movement you very properly went forward yourselves? – Yes.

13054. And you got some money from the Mansion House Fund? – Yes, and a good sum.

13055. And that has been very beneficial? – Most useful. It enabled the people to put down a crop, and I hope that with the favourable season we expect they will have a more favourable crop.

13056. And I dare say you want to express to the public your thankfulness? – We are most thankful to every person who put his hand to that work.

13057. And you believe it has been beneficial? – Most beneficial and useful. There is no question it was, both in the way of seed and food.

13058. Are there any deer in south Harris? – A few. There are tame deer about the mansion house of Rodel, but very few on the hill.

13059. Is there any complaint against them? – Not much. There used to be a few, and they used to come down sometimes, but there was nothing to speak of.

13060. And there is no complaint on that score just now? – Not that I am aware of. I never heard that any damage was done here.

13061. In answer to his Lordship in the chair, you stated, after being a little pressed by him as to the condition of the people, that you came at a bad time – immediately after 1848 – and you would not say anything more in the way of contrasting their present condition with their condition at that time, than that they were not getting better? – I won't venture to say anything more. I don't think they are much better off.

13062. Is it consistent with your observation that the constant cropping which the crofters are obliged to do, in consequence of the smallness of their arable land, is rather wasting and deteriorating their land? – There is no doubt it is. The land is quite exhausted; it has no heart.

13063. Can you state, from your own observation, there is much more meal imported into Harris than when you first came? – I think there is a great deal more.

13064. You see that from your own observation? – Yes. They import almost every grain of meal they consume. They make very little meal in the bays of Harris.

13065. Is there a mill? – Yes. There is a mill at Obe. It is in working trim just now. Sometimes it is, and sometimes not. There is a mill at Loch Tarbert, but it is far away from here.

13066. What work may the proprietor, Lord Dunmore, have had for the benefit of the people, say since October last, when things began to look serious? – They drained a good deal of land. They improved the roads. They built dykes, and cut down some plantations.

13067. Do you know what rate of wages was given to those employed? – I think he was given about 2s. and 2s. 4d.

13068. Were these works convenient for the people to go to – I mean not beyond a reasonable distance from their homes? – Well, they could not go and come to their own houses every day. They had to lodge at Rodel during the week, and they went to their own homes on the Sunday. It was out of reach of many of them.

13069. So far as you are aware, were they paid in money for the work then done, or was it placed to account of any arrears they might have? – It was placed to account of arrears, and they were getting money and meal too.

13070. Then it was not a sharp payment of arrears? – No, I think he was giving them meal and money.

13071. Was that of material consequence at the time? – Very great consequence to the people that could avail themselves of it.

13072. *Sheriff Nicolson.* – Is there local fishing going on? – Sometimes there is, but not last winter.

13073. The Harris men are good boatmen? –Yes, they are good boatmen.

13074. I suppose the young men go regularly to the east coast and other deep sea fishings? –Yes; and I may mention a good many go to the militia, and they attend the naval reserve training.

13075. Have you any ideas of the numbers in the militia? – I cannot exactly state the number.

13076. Are there scores? – There may be twenty or thirty through the whole country.

13077. And in the naval reserve? – Perhaps twenty.

13078. I suppose it is good for these young men to get the training they get in the militia? –Yes, they consider it very useful at the time.

13079. How long does it take them away from home? – About a month in summer. They are away till the beginning of August.

13080. After the east coast fishing is over? – No, they go away to the east coast fishing just from the militia training, and to the Caithness fishing too.

13081. Do many of the young men go south? – Not many.

13082. Have they never been in the habit of going much from Harris? – No, they never went.

13083. A good many of the women on this island get employment in knitting and in spinning cloth? – Yes, kelt making. That is their principal employment, and of late years it has been very useful to them.

13084. Who set that agoing? – Well, the Countess of Dunmore takes some interest in it, as well as other parties. I see they get very much into the way of dealing with the local merchants in order to get meal.

13085. Are most of the women in the parish employed in that way? – Well, generally.

13086. I mean every family? – Perhaps not every family, but very generally they are.

13087. They knit a great many stockings and hose? –Yes.

13088. What price do they get for socks? – Not very much – perhaps about 1s., but I can hardly say whether that is the fixed price.

13089. And they manufacture a peculiarly coloured native cloth? – Almost every kind of cloth.

13090. Native dyes? – Yes, they use native dyes.

13091. Is there a want of harbours on the east coast, or of piers? – They have generally some landing place for their boats. There is no regular harbour in any place from Tarbert till we come to Rodel, where there is a sort of quay.

13092. Would it be a great advantage to the people of that coast to have one or two piers, with a breakwater, where they could come in any weather? – I don't think they complain very much. They are well acquainted with the shore, and they know where these landing places are.

13093. I suppose the boats they use are old fashioned skiffs? – Yes, small boats.

13094. Have they any of the big east coast boats? – Yes; young men through the country bring a good many of them. I cannot mention the number, but there are a good many of them throughout Harris.

13095. Worked by themselves? – Yes, they get them from the fish-curers and bind themselves to pay for their boats by fishing.

13096. Do they go to the east coast fishing themselves with these boats, and to the Barra fishing? – Yes and to the Caithness fishing. I don't think that there are any in this country intended for the Moray fishing.

13097. I suppose all the men would use such boats as these if they could afford to buy them? – Yes, no doubt. They would be safer and better adapted for the work than these small boats. They cannot go any distance from the shore with these small boats.

13098. Is there any cod or ling fishing round about here? – Occasionally they catch a good many cod and ling, but I don't think that is any great source of industry for them. They do sometimes earn a little in that way.

13099. *The Chairman.* – Is there any large common ground here to which the people take their flocks in summer for summer shielings? – Well, there is. They don't go now. There was such a place, and they used to go in summer from these bays, but they have given it up.

13100. But do they send their cattle to the hill? – Yes, they send their cattle to the hill.

13101. And do their cattle graze over the same area which was occupied by summer shielings? – Every day.

13102. But they don't send women to dwell in bothies and cottages? – No, they don't.

13103. Is there any land on the sandy shore and elsewhere which is held on the run-rig system? – Very little in Harris.

13104. But you think there is some? – I am not aware. As far as I am aware, there is not a bit where they go on the run-rig system.

13105. Do you think that there is not a bit of land held in common which is redivided from year to year? – There may be a croft where there are two parties occupying one croft, and they go on the run-rig system – just rig about.

13106. But you don't think that there is any large extent of ground held by one township in that way? – No, there is not a township, so far as I am aware, of that kind in Harris.

13107. Do you remember that when you were first here? – Well, I saw a little of it – one or two lots, as it were, together, in my neighbourhood, at one time, but it has been given up.

13108. When the land was redivided for the year, or at the end of two or three years, by whom was the redivision made? – Well, it would generally be made by the ground officer and by the people themselves.

13109. Had they an officer called the maor? – That is the popular name in Gaelic for the ground officer.

13110. Did you ever hear the people had a ceremony or recited any kind of rhyme or service connected with the division of the land? – I never heard of that.

13111. Or when the people were starting from the shielings? – There might be some such thing, but I never heard of it.

13112. Do you think that such a thing may exist and be concealed from the clergyman? – Well, I don't think it existed at all. I saw nothing of it in this part in my time. A great many things were put down in this country before I came.

13113. *Mr. Fraser-Mackintosh.* I forgot to follow out a question which I put about the lands. Taking South Harris as a whole, is there not enough land to support in comfort even more than the present population, if the land were distributed among the people. – I think it is quite capable of bearing all the people in comfort.

Appendix C

Highlands and Islands Commission: Report by the Commissioners

Conclusion.

IN CONCLUDING THIS REPORT, it is desirable to anticipate an objection to our recommendations, based upon general principles of public policy, which might be urged on the part of that school of economists, who, in dealing with social distresses, prefer to contemplate the operation of natural causes and tendencies, rather than the action of artificial remedies. It may be asked, on what grounds do we justify a complex system of interference on behalf of a class in the community which is not numerous, which does not contribute a preponderant share to the aggregate sum of national wealth, and which does, after all that has been said, possess, in ordinary times, conditions of welfare and happiness unknown to some other orders of the people, for instance, to the poorer sort of day labourers in England, or to those who depend on casual employment in great cities? If the Highland crofter, and it may be said, can maintain his footing under the laws affecting landed property, common to the whole country, and against the forces which contemporary science and commerce bring to bear upon his situation, let him do so, if not, do not prop up his position by curious expedients, which may merely prolong his decay, and prevent the timely transfer of his powers to more congenial scenes and means of labour and subsistence. The small tenancies of the Highlands would not be the only interest abandoned to irresistible innovations. The hand–loom of the cottage, the sailing craft along the shore, the yeoman's freehold, are gone or doomed to disappear. It is perhaps in the same order of necessity that the crofter should be extinguished.

To these objections we would thus reply:

The crofter and cottars with whom we are here concerned are, in truth, of no great significance in respect to mere numbers. All told, they probably do not comprise more than 40,000 families or 200,000 souls, the population of a single manufacturing town of the first class. They do, however, possess in their occupations and capabilities certain distinctive features which, in the opinion of many, entitle them to such exceptional

attention and protection as has been granted to other special interests. These
people take a considerable part in the fishing industry, a branch of national
production, not of the first magnitude, but still of material value, and which
should not be allowed to pass into other hands. This industry has hitherto
depended more on the hardy breeding, hereditary aptitudes, and
spontaneous association of the common people acting with the help of
local traders, and less on the direction and support of the large capitalist,
than any other department of labour and traffic in the country. It is
susceptible of more perfect organisation and of immense extension, but
these developments must be the result of time, study, intelligent direction,
and financial aid. Meanwhile, the dispersion of the fishing population, the
indispensable instruments of the craft, would be a loss that could scarcely
be repaired. It would be difficult to replace them by a race of equal ability
and worth.

It is not only with regard to fishing that the crofting and cottar
population have a peculiar value. They constitute a natural basis for the
defence of the country, a sort of defence which cannot be extemporised,
and the value of which, in possible emergencies, can hardly be overrated.
The seafaring people of the Highlands and Islands contribute at this
moment 4431 men to the Royal Naval Reserve, a number equivalent to
the crews of seven armoured war steamers of the first class, and which with
commensurate inducements could be greatly increased. It may be added,
that most of the men incorporated in the corps of militia and volunteers
would be able to serve ashore and afloat with equal efficiency.

The severance of the labouring classes from the benefits and enjoyments
of property (certainly one of the elements of civilisation, morality, and
public order), and their precarious and dangerous condition as dependents
on capital and mere recipients of wages, is a question which engages the
reflections of those who reason and of those who govern. There is a general
desire that the labouring man in every sphere of activity should be invested
with a greater share of substantial possession, and be attached by deeper
and more durable ties to the soil of his country. This great object is being
partly realised in Scotland among the élite of these workmen who are
engaged in urban industries by the regulated purchase of their habitations,
but the mass of dwellers and labourers in the country have still no
permanent interest in the land either as occupiers or owners. It is in the
Highlands and Islands that a partial exception to this rule is chiefly found,
in respect to occupancy; and it is here that occupancy may perhaps most
readily be converted into property. The connection between the crofter
and his holding is indeed of an unsubstantial character, but the kindly
custom of the country in many cases gives a practical security of tenure,

while the cultivator is endowed with some of the simpler objects and adjuncts of possession; furniture, such as it is; live stock; boats; the implements of two pursuits, husbandry and fishing; some knowledge of pastoral and agricultural processes; habits of trade, the practice of purchase and of sale. Men thus equipped are, in some degree, prepared to become substantial occupiers of small holdings under lease, or to be the managers of land belonging to themselves. While the people are in this way apt for a change in condition, there are, in the present division of agricultural areas in the north, greater facilities for bringing this to pass than exist in other quarters. To suffer the crofting class to be obliterated, or to leave them in their present depressed circumstance, if by any justifiable contrivance their condition can be improved, would be to cast away the agencies and opportunities for a social experiment connected with the land of no common interest.

The crofter and cottar population of the Highlands and Islands, small though it may be, is a nursery of good workers and good citizens for the whole empire. In this respect the stock is exceptionally valuable. By sound physical constitution, native intelligence, and good moral training, it is particularly fitted to recruit the people of our industrial centres, who without such help from wholesome sources in rural districts would degenerate under the influences of bad lodging, unhealthy occupations, and enervating habits. It cannot be indifferent to the whole nation, constituted as the nation now is, to possess within its borders a people, hardy, skilful, intelligent, and prolific, as an ever-flowing fountain of renovating life.

The claim of the crofter is, however, based not only on his qualities but on his necessities. The crofter is not in his average condition poor compared with the profounder poverty that exists elsewhere, but he is exposed to unusual risks and vicissitudes. A good harvest and a good haul may make him comfortable for a season. A blight, an early frost, a wet autumn, a long winter, a gale of wind, a wayward movement of the herring, may deprive him of food for his family, funds for his rent, and seed for his ground. In such emergencies he has heretofore appealed to his fellow-countrymen for relief, or others have made the appeal on his behalf. The relief has been granted, yet not always without anxiety and doubt. A transitory and humiliating assistance thus bestowed is but a poor substitute for permanent and honourable encouragements, which might eventually enable the crofter and cottar to support the strain of temporary misfortune.

The last argument which we shall adduce in support of our views on this subject, is the argument of public expediency. The Highlands and Islands have recently been at some points the scene of agitation, and even of disturbance. Acts of violence have occurred on the occasion of the delivery of legal summonses regarding the occupancy of land, and the enforcement of lawful claims on the part of the proprietors have been delayed or impeded by apprehensions of opposition. We do not palliate the dangers attached to this condition of affairs. There are circumstances under which it is the plain duty of Government to carry out the prescriptions of the law at all risks, and by every means at their disposal. But collisions between proprietary rights and popular demands are not to be deprecated, for they leave behind them lasting traces of resentment and alienation. The mere vindication of authority and repression of resistance would not establish the relations of mutual confidence between landlord and tenant, in the absence of which the country would not be truly at peace, and all our inquiries and counsels would be expended in vain.

The aspect of the present and the future, calmly considered, presents the following features: The dissatisfaction of the small tenants in regard to their present condition is of native origin, but it is fomented by external influences. The land movement in the Highlands, even if it were not spontaneously maintained by the people themselves, would be aroused to further action by other forces: it is impelled by the democratic and social aspirations prevalent among the various classes at home, and will probably enlist the sympathies of Highlanders in all parts of the world. There is a larger, richer, more active and more enthusiastic Celtic community beyond the limits of the Celtic region of Scotland than there is within it, and it is one of the results of increasing knowledge and expanding facilities of intercourse, that men who have forsaken the seats of their birth and early associations continue, communicate, and transmit the affections and passions of their race with even greater warmth than those who remain behind. Endowed by native vitality and fostered by such auxiliary powers, the land agitation of the Highlands is not likely to pass away without some adjustment of the claims of occupiers acceptable to the greater number who are not yet possessed with extravagant expectations. Only then may it be expected that the crofters, restored to tranquillity, confidence, and the exercise of their natural good sense, will fully avail themselves of the important benefits which may be extended to them in connection with the other remedial measures which we have proposed.

In submitting the opinions enunciated above, we do not mean to imply that the claims of the crofting people to legislative protection are of an exclusive character. Special legislation has been found necessary for the benefit of workers in plantations, in mines, in factories, and in ships. It may be invoked for other industries with equal justice. The case of the crofters and cottars of the Highlands and Islands is the special matter consigned to our consideration by Your Majesty's commands. In the recommendations embodied in the present report we have endeavoured to suggest appropriate provision for their satisfaction and relief, and thus, in the measure of our humble ability, to give effect to Your Majesty's gracious solicitude for a deserving class of your Scottish subjects.

All of which we humbly submit to your Majesty's consideration.

Napier and Ettrick.
Kenneth S. Mackenzie.
Donald Cameron.
C. Fraser-Mackintosh.
Alexander Nicolson.
Donald Mackinnon.

Index of Subjects

Acculturation (Assimilation) 1–2, 21, 40–42
Alcoholism 144–145

Clearances 4, 8, 11, 16, 17, 18, 57, 58, 124, 126, 128, 129, 132, 141, 150, 156, 165, 169, 175, 184, 191
Crofts and Crofting 5, 54, 55, 58, 63, 66, 67, 213, 219, 222, 223

Diseases
  Classifications
    Miasma (Miasmatists) 145, 194, 195, 196
    Contagion (Germs, Contagionists) 132, 194, 195
    Iatrogenic 163, 170
    Nosocomial 163, 169, 170
    Zoonosis 127, 133, 134, 163, 169
    Zymotic 170
  Anthrax 165–166
  Brucellosis, see Fevers
  Cholera 90, 110, 128, 130, 173–174
  Consumption 152, 154
  Croup 141, 154
  Diarrhoea 143, 170, 173, 174, 175
  Diphtheria 128, 154
  Dropsy 143–145
  Dysentery 128, 130, 133, 143
  Dyspepsia 133
  Gout 141, 150
  Industrial 153–154
  Influenza 130, 151
  Jaundice (Bilious) 145
  King's Evil, see Scrofula
  Malaria 130, 151
  Measles 126, 146
  Meningitis 130
  Mental illness 134–136, see also Health
  Mumps 130
  Palsy (Paralysis) 141, 143

Parasitic Infestations of Man:
  Intestinal Worms 166
  Myiasis 167
  Animal ticks (Lyme disease) 167
  Vermin (Mites, Lice, Fleas, Bed bugs, flies) 168
Pellagra 142
Pertussis (Whooping cough, Chincough) 130–131, 145
Pneumoconiosis 153
Pneumonia 130
Poliomyelitis 130
Rabies 130
Rheumatism 145, 149, 150
Salmonellosis 130
Scabies (the Itch) 168
Scrofula 128, 155
Sibbens (Sevens) 133, 143
Smallpox 130, 133, 145, 146, 147, 168, 171, 174
Syphilis 133, 143
Tetanus Neonatorum 166
Tuberculosis 127, 128, 129, 153, 154, 155, 156, 164, 229
Yaws 133
Doctrines
  Predestination (The Will of Providence) 199
  Predisposing Causes 194
  Replacement 154

Emigration
  General 1, 14, 16, 17, 241
  America 13, 17
  Cape Breton 242
  Ships 132, 167, 168, 242
Episcopalian Church (Anglican) 185, 240
Establishment
  General 2, 62, 79, 114, 116, 200, 201, 219, 225, 231, 235, 236, 241

Highland 98, 100, 109, 115, 116, 200,
  219, 224, 225, 231, 241, 242
Medical 79, 89, 92, 93, 171, 172, 173,
  175, 193, 200, 208, 225, 235, 236, 241
Religious 185, 188, 189, 190, 191, 193, 197
The Nineteenth Century
  Establishments Union to Oppose
  Popular Liberalism 235–238

Fevers
  General 152, 194
  Puerperal fever 150, 195
  Relapsing fever (Famine Fever) 132,
    168
  Rheumatic fever 150
  Scarlet fever 132, 144
  Typhoid fever (Enteric Fever) 130, 145
  Typhus fever 130, 132, 133, 167–168
  Undulant fever (Brucellosis) 130, 164–
    165
  Yellow fever 130, 145

Health
  Definitions 78, 79, 80, 81, 89
  Care 18, 225, 226, 231
  Mental Health 18, 134–136, 198
Health Administration
  Board of Supervision 225
  Central Board Of Health (England) 225
  Health Boards 225
  Highlands and Islands Medical Services
    Committee 231
  Highland Congested Districts Board 220
  Hospitals 85, 91, 226, 230
  Inequality (The Black Report) 231
  Insurance Act 1911 231
  Local Government Board For Scotland
    227–228
  Public Health (Scotland) Act (1867)
    225, 226
  Registrar General Of Scotland 153,
    170, 173
  Sanitation (Poor) 166, 167, 228–229

Highlands and Highlanders
  (General) 1, 5, 8, 10–16, 19, 32, 35–40,
    43–46, 49–51, 53, 106–107, 126, 149,
    165, 169, 186, 189, 200, 208

Destitution 15, 100, 134, 195
Estates:
  Argyll 15, 52–53, 55–56, 108, 189–190
  Mackenzies of Seaforth 9
  Macleod of Skye 56
  Matheson of Lochalsh 7, 10
  Sutherland (Stafford) 7, 56–58
Education 191–193
Evangelicalism 185–187
Famine 103, 108, 111, 112, 142–145
Farming 4, 14, 49, 50, 64, 67, 105
Flannel 149
French Wars 59
Fuel 62, 66, 67
Heritors, Landlords and Ratepayers 5–
  6, 8, 18, 58, 109, 196, 226, 227
Houses 48–49, 68–70, 153, 165, 166,
  226, 227–228
Ill-Health 78–79
Inoculation 146, 147–148
Kelp 49, 59, 60
Land Law Reform Association 241
Leadership 5–6
Lewis 10, 90–91, 173, 174, 227, 228,
  229
Linen 149, 150
Longevity 126
Lordship of the Isles 43–44
Middens 199
Mythology 80, 83, 84, 85, 239
Patronage Act 188
Pauperism 135, 193, 194, 229
Poor Law 101, 193, 194, 196, 197, 198,
  199
Population 61
Social Relationships 19
Society for Propagating the Gospel at
  Home 185–186
Society in Scotland for Propagating
  Christian Knowledge (SSPCK) 186
Statistical Accounts 124, 141, 146, 153,
  156, 163
Statutes of Iona 51–52
Somerled 43
Swine 105
Tacksman 54
Tiree 55, 56, 58, 61
Transhumance 63

Township 63, 108
Unemployment 10, 101
Union of the Crowns 45
Union of Parliaments 45
Uprising 184
Variolation 146, 147–148, 149
Water (Contaminated) 128
Weavers 154
'Westward Drifts' 13
Women 8, 67, 144

Infection
  Definition 127
  Agents of Infection
    Microbes (Bacteria) 127
    Spirochaetes 133
    Viruses 130
  Carriers 132, 133
  Immunity 124, 125, 126, 130, 132
  Fomites 153
  Louse, *see* Fevers, Typhus fever
  Milk (Contaminated) 164
  Mosquito 130, 151
  Periods of a Communicable Disease:
    Incubation, Prodromal Symptoms,
    Invasion, Acme, Defervescence,
    Convalescence 131–132
  Portals of Entry 129
  Portals of Exit 129, 130
  Prerequisites for Infection 129
  Reservoir of Infection 132
  Transmission of Communicable
    Diseases 131
Ireland 8, 11, 110, 111, 112, 113, 219, 220

Medicine
  General 79–92, 98, 163, 194
  Highland 91–92, 146–149, 170–171,
    229, 230
  Quacks 92

Napier Commission 18, 208, 210–211
  Members 210
  Report (See Appendix B) 211–218

Nutrition 60, 61, 67, 91, 98, 100, 102–
  110, 130, 131, 142–145, 164, 175

Political Parties
  Conservative 220
  Liberal 201, 219
  Unionist 220
  Whigs and Tories 236

Radicalism
  Christian Socialist Movement
    (Anglican) 240
  Highland Land Law Reform
    Association 241
  Land Wars (Highland) 239
  Peterloo Massacre (England) 239
  Proletariat 239
  Quakers 195
  Radical War (Scotland) 239
  Reformers 9, 195, 198, 235, 240, 241
Religion 2, 40, 41, 44, 81, 82–85, 184–191,
  193, 240
Reports
  Royal Commission (Highlands and
    Islands 1892) 220
  Report of the Commissioners on the
    Conditions of the Handloom
    Weavers 1841 232
Revolutions
  Agricultural 2, 56
  Industrial 2, 56
  French 201
Roman Catholicism
  Roman Catholics 184, 191
  Catholic Corridor 184
Small Isles 196

Index of Personal Names

Alison, W.P. 194
Argyll, 3rd Duke 55
  5th Duke 56
  8th Duke 55, 59, 189

Beatons 85, 91
Brabazon, Lord 241
Buchan, William 143, 170, 171, 172
Burt, Captain Edward 11
Burns, Robert 116, 146, 201

Cameron, Donald 210, 247–262
Chadwick, Edwin 193, 194, 199
Chalmers, Thomas 193
Coffin, E.P. 112
Cullen, William 77, 172-173

Davidson, Alexander 211
Denisthorpe, W. 237

Ferguson, M. 18
Fraser Mackintosh, Charles 210,
  247–262

Galen 87
George IV 239
Gillies, H.C. 91, 92
Gladstone, W.E. 219, 220, 236

Haldane, James 185
Haldane, Robert 185
Harvey, William 88
Hutchison, Robert 98, 101
Hyndman, H.M. 241

Jane, Duchess of Gordon 200
Jenner, Edward 147
Johnson, Samuel 144

Kelman, Sander 78
Khalduun, Ibn 84
Kingsley, Charles 240
Knox, John 184

Levy, J.H. 236
Loch, James 56, 57, 58

MacGregor, William 174
Mackenzie, Alexander 113
Mackenzie, K.S. 210, 247–262
Mackinnon, Donald 210, 247–262
Macleod, Norman 191
Malthus, Thomas 236
Martin, Martin 166
Matheson, James 7, 10
Maurice, F.D. 240
Morison, Roderick 217
Munro, Donald 7
Murdoch, John 9, 14

Napier, Lord 210, 247
Nicolson, Alexander 210, 247–262

Paracelsus 88
Pennant, Thomas 165, 166

Scott, Walter 239
Smith, Adam 114, 115, 116
Smith, Alexander 3
Smollett, Tobias 164
Spencer, Herbert 236
Stafford, Lord and Lady 57
Sutherland, John 199

Taylor, A.J.P. 235

Wemyss, 10th Earl 237